AS-Level

Biology

AS Biology is seriously tricky — no question about that.
To do well, you're going to need to revise properly and practise hard.

This book has thorough notes on all the theory you need,
and it's got practice questions... lots of them.
For every topic there are warm-up and exam-style questions.

And of course, we've done our best to make the whole thing vaguely entertaining for you.

Complete Revision and Practice

Published by CGP

Editors:
Ellen Bowness, Joe Brazier, Charlotte Burrows, Tom Cain, Katherine Craig, Andy Park,
Laurence Stamford, Jane Towle.

Contributors:
Gloria Barnett, Jessica Egan, James Foster, Barbara Green, Derek Harvey, Brigitte Hurwitt, Liz
Masters, Stephen Phillips, Claire Ruthven, Adrian Schmit, Sophie Watkins, Anna-fe Williamson.

Proofreaders:
Glenn Rogers, Sue Hocking.

This book covers: **AQA**
Edexcel
OCR

There are notes on the pages to tell you which
bits you need for your syllabus.

The whole of Section 15 is for **Edexcel** only.

ISBN: 978 1 84762 121 4

With thanks to Jan Greenway for the copyright research.

With thanks to Science Photo Library for permission to reproduce the photographs used on pages 55 and 167.

Data used to construct the graph on page 88 from National Statistics online. Reproduced under the terms of the Click-Use licence.

MMR graph on page 98 adapted from H. Honda, Y. Shimizu, M. Rutter. No effect of MMR withdrawal on the incidence of autism:
a total population study. Journal of Child Psychology and Psychiatry 2005; 46(6):572-579.

Data used to construct Herceptin graph on page 98 from M.J. Piccart-Gebhart, et al. Trastuzumab after Adjuvant Chemotherapy
in HER2-positive Breast Cancer. NEJM 2005; 353: 1659-72.

Data used to construct the Hib graph on page 99 reproduced with kind permission from the Health Protection Agency.

With thanks to Cancer Research UK for permission to reproduce the graph on page 113
Cancer Research UK, http://info.cancerr[...]ies/[...]ncidence/mortality/, January 2008.
Cancer Research UK, http://info.cancerr[...]ies/[...]various types of smoking/, January 2008.

Data used to construct asthma and sulfur [...] pages. Source: National Statistics website: www.statistics.gov.uk
Crown copyright material is reproduced with the permission of the Controller Office of Public Sector Information (OPSI).

Exam question graph on page 113: The [...]oke And Sulphur Dioxide Pollution And Deaths During The Great
London Smog, December 1952, Source: [...]

Data used to construct the graph on page 126 from [...] Sutherland.
Mortality in relation to smoking: 50 yea[...] observations on male British doctors, BMJ 2004; 328:1519.

Data used to construct the graph of pag[...] 127 from P.M. Ridker et al. Comparison of C-reactive protein and low-density
lipoprotein cholesterol levels in the prediction of first cardiovascular [...] NEJM 2002; 347: 1557-65.

Graph of breast cancer and family history on page 132 reprinted from the Lancet, Vol number 358,
Familial breast cancer: collaborative reanalysis of individual data from 52 epidemiological studies including
58209 women with breast cancer and 101986 women without the disease, 1389 -1399, Copyright 2001,
With permission from Elsevier.

Graph of breast cancer and alcohol consumption on page 132 from Hamajima, N. Hirose, K. Tajima, K. et al.
Alcohol, tobacco and breast cancer - collaborative reanalysis of individual data from 53 epidemiological studies,
including 58,515 women with breast cancer and 95,067 women without the disease. BJC 2002; 87:1234-45

Graph of skylark population on page 150 from BTO/JNCC Breeding Birds of the Wider Countryside.

Graph of rainforest diversity on page 151 from Schulze et al. Biodiversity Indicator Groups of Tropical Land-Use Systems:
Comparing Plants, Birds and Insects. Ecological Applications 2004; 14(5) Ecological Society of America.

Exam question graph on page 151 from Defra. Reproduced under the terms of the Click-Use licence.

Groovy website: www.cgpbooks.co.uk
Jolly bits of clipart from CorelDRAW®
Printed by Elanders Ltd, Newcastle upon Tyne.

Based on the classic CGP style created by Richard Parsons.

Photocopying — it's dull, grey and sometimes a bit naughty. Luckily, it's dead cheap, easy and
quick to order more copies of this book from CGP — just call us on 0870 750 1242. Phew!

Contents

The Scientific Process

_'How Science Works' is all about the scientific process — how we develop and test scientific ideas.
It's what scientists do all day, every day (well, except at coffee time — never come between a scientist and their coffee)._

Scientists Come Up with **Theories** — Then **Test Them**...

Science tries to explain **how** and **why** things happen — it **answers questions**. It's all about seeking and gaining **knowledge** about the world around us. Scientists do this by **asking** questions and **suggesting** answers and then **testing** them, to see if they're correct — this is the **scientific process**.

1) **Ask** a question — make an **observation** and ask **why or how** it happens. E.g. why is trypsin (an enzyme) found in the small intestine but not in the stomach?

2) **Suggest** an answer, or part of an answer, by forming a **theory** (a possible **explanation** of the observations) e.g. pH affects the activity of enzymes. (Scientists also sometimes form a **model** too — a **simplified picture** of what's physically going on.)

3) Make a **prediction** or **hypothesis** — a **specific testable statement**, based on the theory, about what will happen in a test situation. E.g. trypsin will be active at pH 8 (the pH of the small intestine) but inactive at pH 2 (the pH of the stomach).

4) Carry out a **test** — to provide **evidence** that will support the prediction (or help to disprove it). E.g. measure the rate of reaction of trypsin at various pH levels.

The evidence supported Quentin's Theory of Flammable Burps.

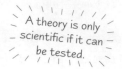

A theory is only scientific if it can be tested.

...Then They **Tell** Everyone About Their **Results**...

The results are **published** — scientists need to let others know about their work. Scientists publish their results in **scientific journals**. These are just like normal magazines, only they contain **scientific reports** (called papers) instead of the latest celebrity gossip.

1) Scientific reports are similar to the **lab write-ups** you do in school. And just as a lab write-up is **reviewed** (marked) by your teacher, reports in scientific journals undergo **peer review** before they're published.

2) The report is sent out to **peers** — other scientists that are experts in the **same area**. They examine the data and results, and if they think that the conclusion is reasonable it's **published**. This makes sure that work published in scientific journals is of a **good standard**.

3) But peer review **can't guarantee** the science is **correct** — other scientists still need to **reproduce** it.

4) Sometimes **mistakes** are made and bad work is published. Peer review **isn't perfect** but it's probably the best way for scientists to self-regulate their work and to publish **quality reports**.

...Then **Other Scientists** Will **Test** the Theory Too

Other scientists read the published theories and results, and try to **test the theory** themselves. This involves:

- Repeating the **exact same experiments**.
- Using the theory to make **new predictions** and then testing them with **new experiments**.

If the **Evidence** Supports a Theory, It's **Accepted** — for Now

1) If all the experiments in all the world provide good evidence to back it up, the theory is thought of as **scientific 'fact'** (for now).

2) But it will never become **totally indisputable** fact. Scientific **breakthroughs or advances** could provide new ways to question and test the theory, which could lead to **new evidence** that **conflicts** with the current evidence. Then the testing starts all over again...

And this, my friend, is the **tentative nature of scientific knowledge** — it's always **changing** and **evolving**.

Water

Water's *Polarity* Also Makes it a *Good Solvent*

1) A lot of important substances in biological reactions are **ionic** (like **salt**, for example). This means they're made from **one positively charged** atom or molecule and **one negatively charged** atom or molecule (e.g. salt is made from a positive sodium ion and a negative chloride ion).

2) Because water is polar, the **positive end** of a water molecule will be attracted to the **negative ion**, and the **negative end** of a water molecule will be attracted to the **positive ion**.

3) This means the ions will get **totally surrounded** by water molecules — in other words, they'll **dissolve**.

4) So water's **polarity** makes it useful as a **solvent** for other polar molecules.

Remember — a molecule is polar if it has a negatively charged bit and a positively charged bit.

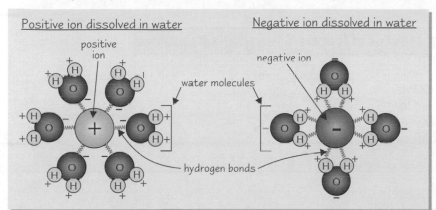

Positive ion dissolved in water

Negative ion dissolved in water

positive ion

negative ion

water molecules

hydrogen bonds

The polar nature of bears sometimes results in unexpected attraction.

Hydrogen Bonds Give Water a High Specific Heat Capacity   *OCR only*

1) Specific heat capacity is the **energy** needed to **raise the temperature** of 1 gram of a substance by 1 °C.

2) The **hydrogen bonds** between water molecules can **absorb** a lot of energy.

3) So water has a **high** specific heat capacity — it takes a lot of energy to heat it up.

4) This is useful for living organisms because it **stops rapid temperature changes**, allowing them to keep their temperature **fairly stable**.

Hydrogen Bonds Also Give Water a High Latent Heat of Evaporation   *OCR only*

1) It takes a lot of **energy** (**heat**) to **break** the hydrogen bonds between water molecules.

2) So water has a **high latent heat of evaporation** — a lot of energy is used up when water **evaporates**.

3) This is useful for living organisms because it means water's great for **cooling** things.

Practice Questions

Q1 State four functions of water in living organisms.

Q2 Briefly describe the structure of a water molecule.

Q3 Briefly describe what is meant by a polar molecule.

Q4 Why is water's high specific heat capacity useful for living organisms?

Exam Question

Q1 Relate the structure of water to its ability to transport substances. [6 marks]

Pssssssssssssssssssssssssssssssssssssssssssss — need the loo yet?

Water is pretty darn useful really. It looks so, well, dull — but in fact it's scientifically amazing. It's essential for all kinds of jobs — enabling reactions, transporting things, keeping cool etc. You need to learn its properties and functions, and be able to say how they relate to its structure. Right, I'm off — when you gotta go, you gotta go.

Proteins

These pages are for AQA Unit 1, Edexcel Unit 1 and OCR Unit 2.

There are millions of different proteins. They're the most abundant molecules in cells, making up 50% or more of a cell's dry mass — now that's just plain greedy.

Proteins are Made from Long Chains of Amino Acids

1) A **dipeptide** is formed when **two** amino acids join together.
2) A **polypeptide** is formed when **more than two** amino acids join together.
3) **Proteins are made up of one or more polypeptides.**

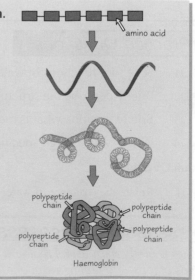

Grant's cries of "die peptide, die" could be heard for miles around. He'd never forgiven it for sleeping with his wife.

Different Amino Acids Have Different Variable Groups

All amino acids have the same general structure — a **carboxyl group** (-COOH) and an **amino group** (-NH$_2$) attached to a **carbon** atom. The **difference** between different amino acids is the **variable** group (**R** on diagram) they contain.

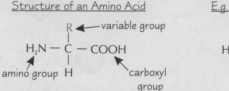

Structure of an Amino Acid

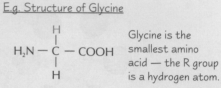

E.g. Structure of Glycine

Glycine is the smallest amino acid — the R group is a hydrogen atom.

Amino Acids are Joined Together by Peptide Bonds

Amino acids are linked together by **peptide bonds** to form dipeptides and polypeptides. It's a **condensation reaction**, which means a molecule of **water** is **released** during the reaction. The **reverse** of this reaction **adds** a molecule of water to **break** the peptide bond. This is called a **hydrolysis** reaction.

Condensation reactions are also called 'synthesis' reactions.

amino acid 1   amino acid 2   dipeptide

condensation ⇌ hydrolysis

H_2O — a molecule of water is formed during synthesis.

peptide bond

Proteins Have Four Structural Levels

Proteins are **big**, **complicated** molecules. They're much easier to explain if you describe their structure in four 'levels'. These levels are a protein's **primary**, **secondary**, **tertiary** and **quaternary** structures.

<u>Primary Structure</u> — this is the **sequence** of **amino acids** in the **polypeptide chain**.

<u>Secondary Structure</u> — the polypeptide chain doesn't remain flat and straight. **Hydrogen bonds** form between the amino acids in the chain. This makes it automatically **coil** into an **alpha (α) helix** or **fold** into a **beta (β) pleated sheet** — this is the secondary structure.

<u>Tertiary Structure</u> — the coiled or folded chain of amino acids is often **coiled** and **folded further**. **More bonds** form between different parts of the polypeptide chain. For proteins made from a **single** polypeptide chain, the tertiary structure forms their **final 3D structure**.

<u>Quaternary Structure</u> — some proteins are made of **several different polypeptide chains** held together by **bonds**. The **quaternary structure** is the way these polypeptide chains are assembled together. E.g. **haemoglobin** is made of **four** polypeptide chains, bonded together. For proteins made from **more than one** polypeptide chain, the quaternary structure is the protein's **final 3D structure**.

amino acid

polypeptide chain

polypeptide chain

polypeptide chain

polypeptide chain

Haemoglobin

Proteins

Different Bonds Hold Different Structural Levels Together — *Edexcel and OCR only*

The four structural levels of a protein are held together by **different kinds** of **bonds**:

1) **Primary structure** — held together by the **peptide bonds** between amino acids.

2) **Secondary structure** — held together by **hydrogen bonds** that form between nearby amino acids. These bonds create **α-helix chains** or **β-pleated sheets**.

Hydrogen bonds are weak bonds between a positive hydrogen atom in one molecule and a negative atom or group in another molecule (see p. 4).

3) **Tertiary structure** — this is affected by a few different kinds of bonds:
   - **Ionic interactions**. These are **weak attractions** between **negative** and **positive** charges on different parts of the molecule.
   - **Disulfide bonds**. Whenever two molecules of the amino acid **cysteine** come close together, the **sulfur atom** in one cysteine bonds to the sulfur in the other cysteine, forming a disulfide bond.
   - **Hydrophobic** and **hydrophilic interactions**. When **hydrophobic** (water-repelling) groups are close together in the protein, they tend to **clump together**. This means that **hydrophilic** (water-attracting) groups are more likely to be pushed to the **outside**, which affects how the protein **folds up** into its final structure.
   - **Hydrogen bonds**.

4) **Quaternary structure** — this tends to be determined by the **tertiary structure** of the individual polypeptide chains being bonded together. Because of this, it can be influenced by **all the bonds** mentioned above.

A Protein's Primary Structure Determines its 3D Structure — *Edexcel only*

The **amino acid sequence** of a protein determines what **bonds** will form and how the protein will **fold up** into its 3D structure. E.g. if there are many cysteines, these will form **disulfide bonds** with each other, so the protein folds up in a certain way.

A Protein's 3D Structure Allows it to Carry Out Its Function — *AQA and Edexcel only*

A protein's **shape** is closely related to its **function**. E.g. **insulin**'s function is to make cells take up glucose from the blood. It's a **compact** protein, which makes it **easy to transport** around the body in the blood, so it can carry out its function.

Proteins can be Fibrous or Globular — *Edexcel and OCR only*

GLOBULAR
1) Globular proteins are **round, compact** proteins made up of **multiple polypeptide chains**.
2) The chains are **coiled up** so that **hydrophilic** (water-attracting) parts of chains are on the **outside** of the molecule and **hydrophobic** (water-repelling) parts of chains face **inwards**.
3) This makes the proteins **soluble**, so they're **easily transported** in fluids.
4) E.g. **haemoglobin** is a globular protein made of **four** polypeptide chains. It **carries oxygen** around the body in the blood. It's **soluble**, so it can be easily transported in the blood. It also has iron-containing **haem groups** that **bind** to oxygen.

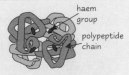
haem group
polypeptide chain

FIBROUS
1) Fibrous proteins are made up of **long, insoluble polypeptide chains** that are **tightly coiled** round each other to form a **rope shape**.
2) The chains are held together by **lots of bonds** (e.g. disulfide and hydrogen bonds), which make the proteins **strong**.
3) Because they're strong, fibrous proteins are often found in **supportive tissue**.
4) E.g. **collagen** is a **strong, fibrous protein** that forms supportive tissue in **animals**. It's made of **three polypeptide chains** that are **tightly coiled** into a **triple helix**. The chains are interlinked by strong **covalent bonds**. **Minerals** can bind to the triple helix to **increase its rigidity**.

Proteins

This page is for AQA only. If you're doing Edexcel or OCR, you can skip straight to the questions.

Proteins have a **Variety** of **Functions**

There are **loads** of different **proteins** found in **living organisms**. They've all got **different structures** and **shapes**, which makes them **specialised** to carry out particular **jobs**. For example:

ENZYMES

1) Enzymes are usually roughly **spherical** in shape due to the **tight folding** of the polypeptide chains.

2) They're **soluble** and often have roles in **metabolism**, e.g. some enzymes break down large food molecules (**digestive enzymes**, see p. 78) and other enzymes help to **synthesise** (make) large molecules.

Unlike proteins, Kevin had only one function — looking darn cool.

ANTIBODIES

1) Antibodies are involved in the **immune response**.

2) They're made up of **two light** (short) polypeptide chains and **two heavy** (long) polypeptide chains bonded together.

3) Antibodies have **variable regions** (see p. 92) — the **amino acid sequences** in these regions **vary** greatly.

TRANSPORT PROTEINS

1) Transport proteins are present in **cell membranes** (p. 36).

2) They contain **hydrophobic** (water hating) and **hydrophilic** (water loving) amino acids, which cause the protein to **fold up** and form a **channel**.

3) These proteins **transport molecules** and **ions across** cell membranes.

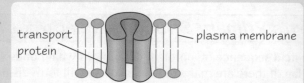

transport protein   plasma membrane

STRUCTURAL PROTEINS

1) **Structural proteins** are physically **strong**.

2) They consist of **long polypeptide chains** lying **parallel** to each other with **cross-links** between them.

3) Structural proteins include **keratin** (found in hair and nails) and **collagen** (found in connective tissue).

Practice Questions

Q1   Name the two groups found in all amino acid molecules.

Q2   Name the bond that joins amino acids together in proteins.

Q3   Name four types of bond that determine the structure of a protein.

Q4   Give three functions of proteins.

Exam Questions

Q1   Describe the structure of proteins, explaining the terms primary, secondary, tertiary and quaternary structure.   [9 marks]

Q2   Describe the structure of the collagen molecule and explain how this structure relates to its function in the body.   [6 marks]

The name's Bond — Peptide Bond...

Protein structure is hard to imagine. I think of a Slinky — the wire's the primary structure, it coils up to form the secondary structure and if you coil the Slinky round your arm that's the tertiary structure. When a few Slinkies get tangled up that's like the quaternary structure. Oh, I need to get out more. I wish I had more friends and not just this stupid Slinky for company.

Carbohydrates

These pages are for AQA Unit 1, AQA Unit 2, Edexcel Unit 1 and OCR Unit 2.

Carbohydrates are Made from Monosaccharides

1) Most carbohydrates are **large**, complex molecules composed of **long chains of monosaccharides** (e.g. starch is a large carbohydrate composed of long chains of glucose).

2) **Single** monosaccharides are also called carbohydrates though.

3) **Glucose** is a hexose sugar — a monosaccharide with **six carbon** atoms in each molecule.

4) There are **two forms** of glucose — **alpha (α)** and **beta (β)**:

The structure of β-glucose is for AQA Unit 2 and OCR only.

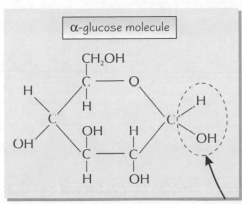

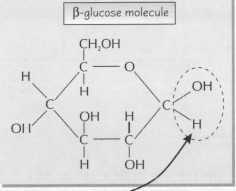

Remember, beta-glucose has the H on the bottom as you look at the structural diagram.

The two types of glucose have these groups reversed.

Glucose's **structure** is related to its **function** as the main **energy source** in animals and plants. Its structure makes it **soluble** so it can be **easily transported**. Its chemical bonds contain **lots of energy**.

Disaccharides are Two Monosaccharides Joined Together

1) Monosaccharides are **joined together** by **glycosidic bonds** in a **condensation reaction**.

2) A **hydrogen** on one monosaccharide bonds to a **hydroxyl (OH)** group on the other, **releasing** a molecule of **water**.

3) The **reverse** of this is a **hydrolysis reaction** — a molecule of water reacts with the glycosidic bond, **breaking it apart**.

4) When **two monosaccharides** join together, they form a **disaccharide**:

Two α-glucose molecules are joined together by a glycosidic bond to form **maltose**:

glucose H_2O is removed   glucose   condensation ⇌ hydrolysis   glycosidic bond   maltose $+ H_2O$

5) If you're doing **Edexcel**, you need to know a bit more about glycosidic bonds:

Glycosidic bonds can form in **different places** in different molecules. So you can describe **where** the bonds have formed, the **carbon atoms** in the rings of glucose are **numbered 1 to 6**. E.g. in **maltose**, the glycosidic bonds form between **carbon 1** of the first monosaccharide and **carbon 4** of the second, so it's a **1-4 glycosidic bond**.

1-4 glycosidic bond

6) For **AQA** and **Edexcel**, you also need to know about the two disaccharides in the table to the right. (But you only need to learn the bond numbers if you're doing **Edexcel**.)

Disaccharide	Monosaccharides	Glycosidic bonds
Lactose	β–glucose + galactose	1-4
Sucrose	α–glucose + fructose	1-2

Carbohydrates

Polysaccharides are Chains of More Than Two Monosaccharides

1) A **polysaccharide** is formed when **more than two monosaccharides** join together.

2) Polysaccharides form in exactly the **same way** as disaccharides — monosaccharides join together in a **condensation reaction**, releasing a molecule of **water**.

Lots of α-**glucose** molecules are joined together by **glycosidic bonds** to form **amylose**:

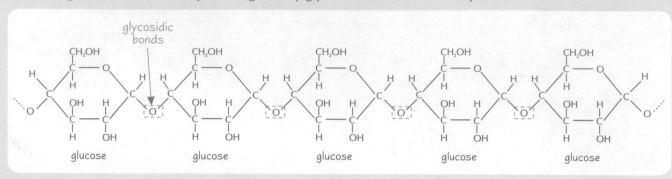

If you're doing AQA Unit 1 you can skip to the questions now — the rest is for AQA Unit 2, Edexcel and OCR.

You Need to Learn About Three Polysaccharides

You need to know about the relationship between the **structure** and **function** of three polysaccharides:

1 **Starch** — the main **energy storage material** in **plants**

1) Cells get **energy** from **glucose**. Plants **store** excess glucose as **starch** (when a plant **needs more glucose** for energy it **breaks down** starch to release the glucose).

2) Starch is a mixture of **two** polysaccharides of **alpha-glucose** — **amylose** and **amylopectin**:

Amylose

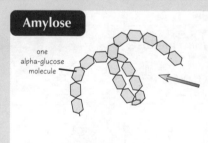

one alpha-glucose molecule

A long, **unbranched chain** of α-glucose. The angles of the glycosidic bonds give it a **coiled structure**, almost like a cylinder. This makes it **compact**, so it's really **good for storage** because you can **fit more in** to a small space.

Amylopectin

A long, **branched chain** of α–glucose. Its **side branches** allow the **enzymes** that break down the molecule to get at the **glycosidic bonds easily**. This means that the glucose can be **released quickly**.

3) Starch is **insoluble** in water, so it **doesn't** cause water to enter cells by **osmosis** (which would make them swell). This makes it good for **storage**.

Edexcel only

Amylose is held together by **1-4 glycosidic bonds**. **Amylopectin** is the **same**, except it also has a few **1-6 glycosidic bonds**, which cause **branching**.

Carbohydrates

(2) **Glycogen** — the main **energy storage material** in **animals**

1) Animal cells get **energy** from **glucose** too. But animals **store** excess glucose as **glycogen** — another polysaccharide of **alpha-glucose**.

2) Its structure is very similar to amylopectin, except that it has **loads** more **side branches** coming off it. Loads of branches means that stored glucose can be **released quickly**, which is **important for energy release** in animals.

3) It's also a very **compact** molecule, so it's good for storage.

4) Like starch, glycogen's also **insoluble** in water, so it doesn't bloat cells by osmosis.

5) It's a **large molecule**, so it can store **lots of energy**.

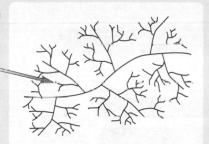

Edexcel only

Glycogen has **1-4 glycosidic bonds** and a few **1-6 glycosidic bonds**, which cause **branching**.

AQA and OCR only

(3) **Cellulose** — the major component of **cell walls** in **plants**

1) Cellulose is made of **long, unbranched** chains of **beta-glucose**.

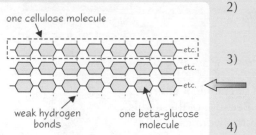

one cellulose molecule

etc.
etc.
etc.

weak hydrogen bonds

one beta-glucose molecule

2) The **bonds** between the sugars are **straight**, so the cellulose chains are straight.

3) The cellulose chains are linked together by **hydrogen bonds** to form strong fibres called **microfibrils**.

4) The strong fibres mean cellulose provides **structural support** for cells (e.g. in plant cell walls).

(4) **Booze** — the major component of **Keith**

Practice Questions

Q1 Draw the structure of an α–glucose molecule.

Q2 What is a disaccharide?

Q3 Name the two monosaccharides that join together to form lactose.

Q4 What is the function of glycogen?

Q5 What is a cellulose microfibril?

Exam Questions

Q1 Describe, with the aid of a diagram, how glycosidic bonds are formed and broken in living organisms. [7 marks]

Q2 Describe how the structure of starch makes it suited to its function. [6 marks]

Mmmmm, starch... Tasty, tasty chips and beans... *dribble*. Ahem, sorry.

Remember that condensation and hydrolysis reactions are the reverse of each other. You need to learn how disaccharides and polysaccharides are formed and broken down by these reactions. And don't forget that starch is composed of two different polysaccharides... and that glucose exists in two forms... so many reminders, so little space...

Lipids

These pages are for AQA Unit 1, Edexcel Unit 1 and OCR Unit 2.

Right, that's proteins and carbohydrates dealt with. There's only really one more important kind of molecule in biology, and that's lipids, or 'fatty oily things' to you and me...

Triglycerides are a Kind of Lipid

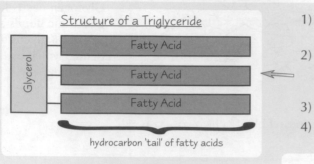

Structure of a Triglyceride

Glycerol

Fatty Acid

Fatty Acid

Fatty Acid

hydrocarbon 'tail' of fatty acids

1) A triglyceride is made of **one** molecule of **glycerol** with **three fatty acids** attached to it.

2) Fatty acid molecules have long tails made of **hydrocarbons** (carbon chains with hydrogen atoms branching off).

3) The tails are **hydrophobic** (water-repelling).

4) These tails make lipids **insoluble** in water.

5) All **fatty acids** consist of the same basic structure, but the **hydrocarbon tail varies**. The tail is shown in the diagram with the letter **R**.

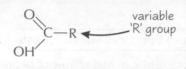

variable 'R' group

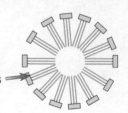

Contrary to popular belief, cows aren't hydrophobic.

If you're doing **OCR**, you need to know how the **structure** of triglycerides relates to their **function**:

Triglycerides are mainly used as **energy storage molecules**. They're good for this because:

1) The **long hydrocarbon tails** of the fatty acids contain lots of **chemical energy** — a load of energy is **released** when they're **broken down**. Because of these tails, lipids contain about **twice** as much energy per gram as carbohydrates.

2) They're **insoluble**, so they don't cause water to enter the cells by **osmosis** (which would make them swell). The triglycerides bundle together as **insoluble droplets** in cells because the fatty acid tails are **hydrophobic** (water-repelling) — the tails **face inwards**, shielding themselves from water with their glycerol heads.

Triglycerides are Formed by Condensation Reactions *AQA and Edexcel only*

1) Like carbohydrates, triglycerides are formed by **condensation reactions** and broken up by **hydrolysis reactions**.

2) Three **fatty acids** and a single **glycerol molecule** are joined together by **ester bonds**.

3) A **hydrogen** atom on the glycerol molecule bonds to a **hydroxyl** (OH) group on the fatty acid, **releasing** a molecule of **water**.

4) The **reverse** happens in **hydrolysis** — a molecule of water is added to **each ester bond** to break it apart, and the triglyceride **splits up** into three fatty acids and one glycerol molecule.

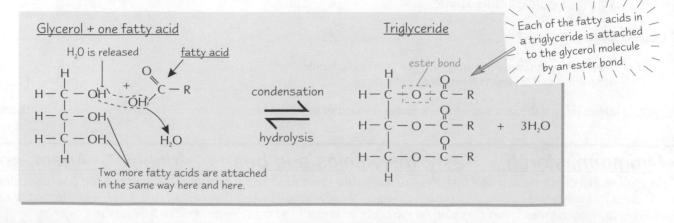

Glycerol + one fatty acid

H_2O is released   fatty acid

condensation ⇌ hydrolysis

Triglyceride   ester bond

$+ 3H_2O$

Two more fatty acids are attached in the same way here and here.

Each of the fatty acids in a triglyceride is attached to the glycerol molecule by an ester bond.

Lipids

Lipids can be Saturated or Unsaturated   *AQA and Edexcel only*

1) There are two kinds of lipids — **saturated** lipids and **unsaturated** lipids.

2) **Saturated** lipids are mainly found in **animal fats** (e.g. butter) and **unsaturated** lipids are found mostly in **plants** (e.g. olive oil).

3) Unsaturated lipids **melt at lower temperatures** than saturated ones.

4) The difference between these two types of lipids is the **hydrocarbon tails** of the **fatty acids**.

Saturated

Saturated fatty acids **don't** have any **double bonds** between their **carbon atoms** — every carbon is attached to at least two **hydrogen** atoms.

hydrocarbon tail

Unsaturated

Unsaturated fatty acids **do** have **double bonds** between **carbon atoms**, which cause the chain to kink.

hydrocarbon tail

double bond between carbon atoms in the hydrocarbon tail causes a <u>kink</u> in the tail

Phospholipids are Similar to Triglycerides   *AQA and OCR only*

1) The lipids found in **cell membranes** are **phospholipids**.

2) Phospholipids are pretty similar to triglycerides except one of the fatty acid molecules is replaced by a **phosphate group**.

3) The phosphate group is **hydrophilic** (attracts water). The fatty acid tails are **hydrophobic** (repel water). This is important in the **cell membrane** (see p. 31 to find out why).

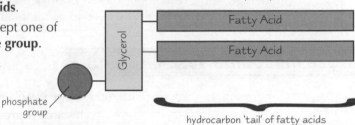

Structure of a Phospholipid

phosphate group

hydrocarbon 'tail' of fatty acids

Cholesterol has a Hydrocarbon Ring Structure   *OCR only*

1) Cholesterol is a type of lipid often found in **cell membranes**. It's also used to make other things like **steroids**.

2) It has a **hydrocarbon ring** structure attached to a **hydrocarbon tail**.

3) The hydrocarbon ring has a **polar hydroxyl group** attached to it, which makes cholesterol **soluble** in water. However, it's insoluble in blood, so is carried around the body by proteins called lipoproteins.

hydroxyl group → HO — hydrocarbon rings — hydrocarbon tail

Practice Questions

Q1 Briefly describe the structure of a triglyceride.

Q2 What type of bonds join fatty acids to glycerol in a triglyceride?

Exam Questions

Q1	Explain how the structure of a triglyceride is related to its function in living things.	[4 marks]
Q2	Explain the difference between a saturated fatty acid and an unsaturated fatty acid.	[2 marks]
Q3	Describe the structure of a phospholipid.	[3 marks]

<u>Hydrocarbon tails, unsaturated lipids... Whatever happened to plain old lard?</u>

You don't get far in life without extensive lard knowledge, so learn all the details on this page good and proper. Lipids pop up in other sections, so make sure you know the basics. Right, all this lipids talk is making me hungry — chips time...

Biochemical Tests for Molecules

This page is for AQA Unit 1 and OCR Unit 2.

Use the **Benedict's Test** for Sugars

Sugar is a general term for **monosaccharides** and **disaccharides**. All sugars can be classified as **reducing** or **non-reducing**. To **test** for sugars you use the **Benedict's test**. The test **differs** depending on the **type** of sugar you are testing for.

REDUCING SUGARS

1) Reducing sugars include **all monosaccharides** (e.g. glucose) and **some disaccharides** (e.g. maltose).

2) You add **Benedict's reagent** (which is **blue**) to a sample and **heat it**. Make sure the solution **doesn't boil**. If the test's **positive** it will form a **coloured precipitate** (solid particles suspended in the solution).

> The colour of the precipitate changes from:
> **blue** → **green** → yellow → **orange** → **brick red**

Always use an excess of Benedict's solution — this makes sure that all the sugar reacts.

3) The higher the concentration of reducing sugar, the further the colour change goes — you can use this to **compare** the amount of reducing sugar in different solutions. A more accurate way of doing this is to **filter** the solution and **weigh the precipitate**.

NON-REDUCING SUGARS

1) To test for **non-reducing sugars**, like sucrose, first you have to break them down into monosaccharides.

2) You do this by **boiling** the test solution with **dilute hydrochloric acid** and then **neutralising** it with **sodium hydrogencarbonate**. Then just carry out the Benedict's test as you would for a reducing sugar.

3) Annoyingly, if the result of this test is **positive** the sugar could be reducing **or** non-reducing. To **check** it's non-reducing you need to do the **reducing sugar test** too (to rule out it being a reducing sugar).

Use the **Iodine Test** for Starch

Make sure you always talk about iodine in potassium iodide solution, not just iodine.

Just add **iodine dissolved in potassium iodide solution** to the test sample.

- If starch **is present**, the sample changes from **browny-orange** to a dark, **blue-black** colour.
- If there's **no starch**, it stays browny-orange.

Use the **Biuret Test** for Proteins

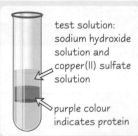

test solution: sodium hydroxide solution and copper(II) sulfate solution

purple colour indicates protein

There are **two stages** to this test.

1) The test solution needs to be **alkaline**, so first you add a few drops of **sodium hydroxide solution**.

2) Then you add some **copper(II) sulfate solution**.

- If protein **is present** a **purple layer** forms.
- If there's **no protein**, the solution will **stay blue**. The colours are pale, so you need to look carefully.

Carbohydrates are polar molecules. No wait, lipids are polar molecules. No wait, I know this, I know this...

Humphrey's revision for his starch test wasn't going so well.

Use the **Emulsion Test** for Lipids

The emulsion test is for OCR only.

Shake the test substance with **ethanol** for about a minute, then **pour** the solution into **water**.

- If lipid **is present**, the solution will turn **milky**.
- The **more lipid** there is, the **more noticeable** the milky colour will be.
- If there's **no lipid**, the solution will **stay clear**.

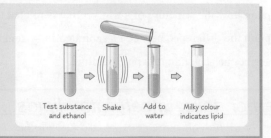

Test substance and ethanol — Shake — Add to water — Milky colour indicates lipid

Biochemical Tests for Molecules

This page is for OCR Unit 2 only. If you're doing AQA, you can skip straight to the questions.

Colorimetry is Used to Determine the Concentration of a Glucose Solution

1) A **quantitative** version of the **Benedict's test** allows you to estimate **how much** glucose (or other **reducing sugar**) there is in a solution.

2) It uses a **colorimeter** — a device that measures the **strength** of a **coloured solution** by seeing how much **light** passes through it.

3) A colorimeter measures **absorbance** (the amount of light absorbed by the solution). The **more concentrated** the **colour** of the solution, the **higher** the **absorbance** is.

4) It's pretty difficult to measure the concentration of the coloured precipitate formed in the Benedict's test, so when you're estimating glucose concentration you measure the **concentration** of the **blue Benedict's solution** that's **left** after the test (the **paler** the solution left, the **more glucose** there was). So, the **higher** the glucose concentration, the **lower** the absorbance of the solution.

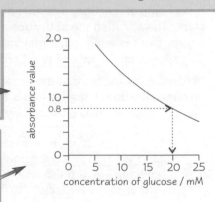

Here's how you do it:

First you need to make a **calibration curve**. To do this you need to:

1) Make up several glucose solutions of **different, known concentrations**, e.g. 10 mM, 20 mM and 30 mM. There should be the **same volume** of each.

2) Do a **Benedict's test** on each solution. Use the **same amount** of Benedict's solution in each case — it has to be a **large** enough volume to react with **all** the sugar in the strongest solution and still have some reagent **left over**.

3) **Remove** any **precipitate** from the solutions — either leave the test tubes for **24 hours** (so that the precipitate **settles out**) or **centrifuge** them.

4) Use a **colorimeter** to measure the **absorbance** of the Benedict's solution **remaining** in each tube.

5) Use the results to make the **calibration curve**, showing absorbance against glucose concentration.

Then you can test the **unknown solution** in the same way as the known concentrations and use the calibration curve to find its concentration.

E.g. an **unknown solution** gives an absorbance value of **0.80**. Reading across the calibration graph from an absorbance value of 0.8 shows that the concentration of glucose in the unknown solution is **20 mM**.

Practice Questions

Q1 Describe how you would test a solution for starch. What result would you expect if:
a) starch was present;   b) starch was not present?

Q2 Describe how you would test for lipids in a solution.

Exam Questions

Q1 Describe how you would use the Benedict's test to identify a non-reducing sugar. Include the result you would expect to see if the test was positive.   **[8 marks]**

Q2 Equal volumes of three different sugar solutions (A, B and C) were each tested with the same large volume of Benedict's solution. Later, the concentrations of Benedict's solution in each test tube were compared, using a colorimeter. The table shows the absorbance of each solution.

solution	absorbance
A	1.22
B	0.68
C	0.37

a) Which original solution contained the highest concentration of reducing sugar?   **[1 mark]**

b) Explain why a large volume of Benedict's solution had to be used.   **[1 mark]**

c) Suggest two factors that should be kept constant when carrying out this test.   **[2 marks]**

The Anger Test — annoy the test subject. If it goes red, anger is present...

A double page of biochemical tests... I literally can't think of anything worse. Well, maybe being slowly dissolved in a vat of vinegar would be worse, but it's a close one. Oh well, that's the end of this section, so good times must be on their way...

Enzyme Action

These pages are for AQA Unit 1, Edexcel Unit 1 and OCR Unit 2.

*Enzymes crop up loads in biology — they're really useful 'cos they make reactions work more quickly. So, whether you feel the need for some speed or not, read on — because you **really** need to know this basic stuff about enzymes.*

Enzymes are Biological Catalysts

Enzymes **speed up chemical reactions** by acting as **biological catalysts**.

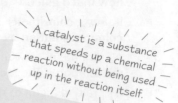
A catalyst is a substance that speeds up a chemical reaction without being used up in the reaction itself.

1) They catalyse **metabolic reactions** in your body, e.g. digestion and respiration. Even your **phenotype** (physical appearance) is due to enzymes that catalyse the reactions that cause growth and development (see p. 42).

2) Enzyme action can be **intracellular** — **within** cells, or **extracellular** — **outside** cells (e.g. in places like the blood and digestive system).

3) Enzymes are **globular proteins** (see p. 7).

4) Enzymes have an **active site**, which has a **specific shape**. The active site is the part of the enzyme where the **substrate** molecules (the substance that the enzyme interacts with) **bind to**.

5) Enzymes are **highly specific** due to their tertiary structure (see next page).

Enzymes Lower the Activation Energy of a Reaction

In a chemical reaction, a certain amount of **energy** needs to be supplied to the chemicals before the reaction will **start**. This is called the **activation energy** — it's often provided as **heat**. Enzymes **lower** the amount of activation energy that's needed, often making reactions happen at a **lower temperature** than they could without an enzyme. This **speeds up** the **rate of reaction**.

When a substrate fits into the enzyme's active site it forms an **enzyme-substrate complex** — it's this that lowers the activation energy. Here are two reasons why:

1) If two substrate molecules need to be **joined**, being attached to the enzyme holds them **close together**, **reducing** any **repulsion** between the molecules so they can bond more easily.

2) If the enzyme is catalysing a **breakdown reaction**, fitting into the active site puts a **strain** on bonds in the substrate, so the substrate molecule **breaks up** more easily.

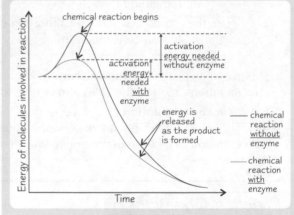

The 'Lock and Key' Model is a Good Start...

Enzymes are a bit picky — they only work with substrates that fit their active site. Early scientists studying the action of enzymes came up with the '**lock and key**' model. This is where the **substrate fits** into the **enzyme** in the same way that a **key fits** into a **lock**.

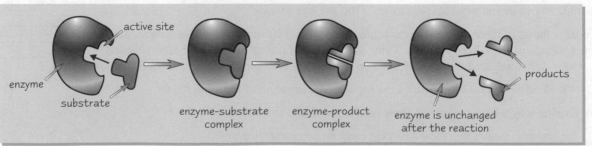

Scientists soon realised that the lock and key model didn't give the full story. The enzyme and substrate do have to fit together in the first place, but new evidence showed that the **enzyme-substrate complex changed shape** slightly to complete the fit. This **locks** the substrate even more tightly to the enzyme. Scientists modified the old lock and key model and came up with the '**induced fit**' model.

Enzyme Action

...but the 'Induced Fit' Model is a **Better Theory**

The '**induced fit**' model helps to explain why enzymes are so **specific** and only bond to one particular substrate. The substrate doesn't only have to be the right shape to fit the active site, it has to make the active site **change shape** in the right way as well. This is a prime example of how a widely accepted theory can **change** when **new evidence** comes along. The 'induced fit' model is still widely accepted — for now, anyway.

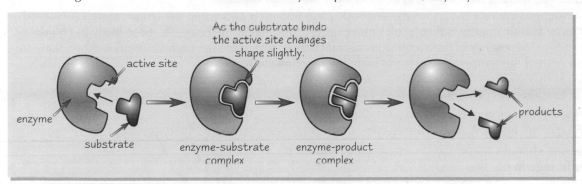

The 'Luminous Tights' model was popular in the 1980s but has since been found to be grossly inappropriate.

Enzyme **Properties** relate to their **Tertiary Structure**

1) Enzymes are **very specific** — they usually only catalyse **one** reaction, e.g. maltase only breaks down maltose, sucrase only breaks down sucrose.

2) This is because **only one substrate will fit** into the active site.

3) The active site's **shape** is determined by the enzyme's **tertiary structure** (which is determined by the enzyme's **primary structure**).

4) Each **different enzyme** has a **different tertiary structure** and so a **different shaped active site**. If the substrate shape doesn't match the active site, the reaction won't be catalysed.

5) If the tertiary structure of a protein is **altered** in any way, the **shape** of the active site will **change**. This means the **substrate won't fit** into the active site and the enzyme will no longer be able to carry out its function.

6) The tertiary structure of an enzyme may be **altered** by changes in **pH** or **temperature** (see next page).

7) The **primary structure** (amino acid sequence) of a protein is determined by a **gene**. If a mutation occurs in that gene (see p. 42), it could change the tertiary structure of the enzyme **produced**.

Practice Questions

Q1 What is an enzyme?

Q2 What is the name given to the amount of energy needed to start a reaction?

Q3 What is an enzyme-substrate complex?

Q4 Explain why enzymes are specific.

Exam Question

Q1 Describe the 'lock and key' model of enzyme action and explain how the 'induced fit' model is different. [7 marks]

But why is the enzyme-substrate complex?

So enzymes lower the activation energy of a reaction. I like to think of it as an assault course (bear with me). Suppose the assault course starts with a massive wall — enzymes are like the person who gives you a leg up over the wall (see?). Without it you'd need lots of energy to get over the wall yourself and complete the rest of the course. Unlikely.

Factors Affecting Enzyme Activity

This page is for AQA Unit 1, Edexcel Unit 1 and OCR Unit 2.

Now you know what enzymes are, let's have a look at a few things that affect their activity — enzymes get slowed down or speeded up by lots of things. Personally, I get speeded up as the concentration of wolverines chasing me increases.

Temperature *has a* Big Influence *on Enzyme Activity*   AQA and OCR only

Like any chemical reaction, the **rate** of an enzyme-controlled reaction **increases** when the **temperature's increased**. More heat means **more kinetic energy**, so molecules **move faster**. This makes the enzymes **more likely** to **collide** with the substrate molecules. The **energy** of these collisions also **increases**, which means each collision is more likely to **result** in a **reaction**. But, if the temperature gets too high, the **reaction stops**.

1) The rise in temperature makes the enzyme's molecules **vibrate more**.

2) If the temperature goes above a certain level, this vibration **breaks** some of the **bonds** that hold the enzyme in shape.

3) The **active site changes shape** and the enzyme and substrate **no longer fit together**.

4) At this point, the enzyme is **denatured** — it no longer functions as a catalyst.

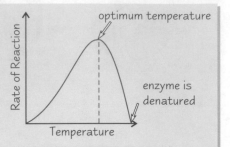

pH *Also Affects Enzyme Activity*   AQA and OCR only

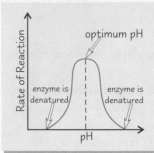

All enzymes have an **optimum pH value**. Most human enzymes work best at pH 7 (neutral), but there are exceptions. **Pepsin**, for example, works best at acidic pH 2, which is useful because it's found in the stomach. Above and below the optimum pH, the H^+ and OH^- ions found in acids and alkalis can mess up the **ionic bonds** and **hydrogen bonds** that hold the enzyme's tertiary structure in place. This makes the active site change shape, so the enzyme is **denatured**.

Substrate Concentration *Affects the Rate of Reaction* Up to a Point   AQA and OCR only

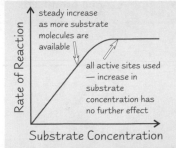

The **higher** the substrate concentration, the **faster** the reaction — more substrate molecules means a **collision** between substrate and enzyme is **more likely** and so more active sites will be used. This is only true up until a 'saturation' point though. After that, there are so many substrate molecules that the enzymes have about as much as they can cope with (all the **active sites are full**), and adding more **makes no difference**.

Enzyme Concentration *Affects the Rate of Reaction*   Edexcel and OCR only

1) The **more enzyme molecules** there are in a solution, the more likely a substrate molecule is to **collide** with one and form an **enzyme-substrate complex**. So increasing the concentration of the enzyme **increases** the **rate of reaction**.

2) But, if the amount of **substrate** is **limited**, there comes a point when there's more than enough enzyme molecules to deal with all the available substrate, so adding more enzyme has **no further effect**.

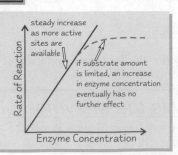

Factors Affecting Enzyme Activity

This page is for Edexcel and OCR. If you're doing AQA you can go straight to the questions.

You can **Measure** the **Rate** of an **Enzyme-Controlled** Reaction

You need to be able to **describe** how the effects of pH, temperature, enzyme concentration and substrate concentration can be investigated **experimentally**. Here are two ways of measuring the **rate** of an enzyme-controlled reaction:

Example 1

You can measure **how fast** the **product of** the reaction **appears**. The diagram on the right shows how to measure this with the enzyme **catalase**. Catalase catalyses the **breakdown** of **hydrogen peroxide** into **water** and **oxygen**. It's easy to collect the oxygen produced and measure **how fast** it's given off.

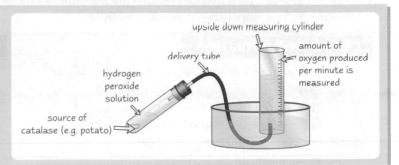

Example 2

You can also measure the **disappearance** of the **substrate** rather than the appearance of the product and use this to **compare the rate** of reaction under different conditions. For example, the enzyme **amylase** catalyses the breakdown of **starch** to **maltose**. It's easy to detect starch using a solution of potassium iodide and iodine. You can **time** how long it takes for the starch to disappear by **regularly sampling** the starch solution, and use the times to compare rates between different tests.

Time when iodine solution no longer turns blue-black is noted — starch has then been broken down.

Here are some general tips on what to include when describing an experiment:

1) Describe the **method** and the **apparatus** you'd use.
2) Say **what** you're **measuring** (the dependent variable), e.g. the volume of gas produced per minute.
3) Describe how you'd **vary** the **independent variable**, e.g. if your independent variable is **enzyme concentration** you might test **five different concentrations** of enzyme.
4) Describe what **variables** you're **keeping constant**, e.g. temperature, pH, volume of solution, substrate concentration etc.
5) Say that you need to **repeat** the experiment at least twice, to make the results **more reliable**.
6) Say that you need a **control**, e.g. a test tube containing the substrate solution but no enzyme.

See pages 175-176 for more on variables.

Practice Questions

Q1 What does it mean if an enzyme is denatured?

Q2 Explain the effect of increasing substrate concentration on the rate of an enzyme-catalysed reaction.

Exam Questions

Q1 When doing an experiment on enzymes, explain why it is necessary to control the temperature and pH of the solutions involved. [8 marks]

Q2 An experiment was carried out to find out the effect of increasing the enzyme concentration on the rate of a reaction. Using your knowledge, predict the outcome of the experiment and explain your answer. [4 marks]

This enzyme's not working very fast — he's out of shape...

Crikey, enzymes are all 'I want, I want, I want, me, me, me' — they'll only work best when they're nice and comfortable with all the right conditions. Learn them all well, then next time an enzyme comes to stay, they'll be right at home.

Factors Affecting Enzyme Activity

These pages are for AQA Unit 1 and OCR Unit 2.

Enzyme inhibitors, yep you guessed it, inhibit enzyme action — they can be competitive or non-competitive.

Enzyme **Activity** can be **Inhibited**

Enzyme activity can be prevented by **enzyme inhibitors** — molecules that **bind to the enzyme** that they inhibit. Inhibition can be **competitive** or **non-competitive**.

COMPETITIVE INHIBITION

1) **Competitive inhibitor** molecules have a **similar shape** to that of **substrate** molecules.

2) They **compete** with the substrate molecules to **bind** to the **active site**, but **no reaction** takes place.

3) Instead they **block** the active site, so **no substrate** molecules can **fit** in it.

4) How much the enzyme is inhibited depends on the **relative concentrations** of the inhibitor and substrate.

5) If there's a **high concentration** of the **inhibitor**, it'll take up nearly **all the active sites** and hardly any of the substrate will get to the enzyme.

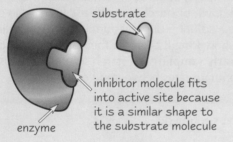

substrate

inhibitor molecule fits into active site because it is a similar shape to the substrate molecule

enzyme

NON-COMPETITIVE INHIBITION

1) **Non-competitive inhibitor** molecules bind to the enzyme **away from its active site**.

2) This causes the active site to **change shape** so the substrate molecules can no longer bind to it.

3) They **don't** 'compete' with the substrate molecules to bind to the active site because they are a **different shape**.

4) **Increasing** the concentration of **substrate won't** make any difference — enzyme activity will still be inhibited.

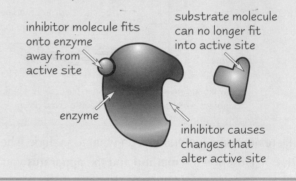

inhibitor molecule fits onto enzyme away from active site

substrate molecule can no longer fit into active site

enzyme

inhibitor causes changes that alter active site

If you're doing AQA, you can skip straight to the questions — the rest is for OCR only.

Inhibitors can be **reversible** or **non-reversible**.
Which one they are depends on the **strength of the bonds** between the enzyme and the inhibitor.

1) If they're **strong, covalent bonds**, the inhibitor can't be removed easily and the inhibition is **irreversible**.

2) If they're **weaker hydrogen bonds** or weak **ionic bonds**, the inhibitor can be removed and the inhibition is **reversible**.

Some **Metabolic Poisons** are **Enzyme Inhibitors**

Metabolic **poisons interfere** with **metabolic reactions** (the reactions that occur in cells), causing **damage**, **illness** or **death** — they're often **enzyme inhibitors**.
In the **exam** you might be asked to **describe the action** of one **named poison**, for example:

1) **Cyanide** is an **irreversible** inhibitor of **cytochrome c oxidase**, an enzyme that catalyses **respiration** reactions. Cells that can't respire **die**.

2) **Malonate** inhibits **succinate dehydrogenase** (which also catalyses respiration reactions).

3) **Arsenic** inhibits the action of **pyruvate dehydrogenase**, yet another enzyme that catalyses **respiration** reactions.

Gillian didn't think Hugo would find it quite so funny when he realised she'd spiked his food with an irreversible enzyme inhibitor. Mwah ha ha ha.

Factors Affecting Enzyme Activity

This page is for OCR. If you're doing AQA you can go straight to the questions.

Some **Drugs** Work by **Inhibiting Enzymes**

Some **medicinal drugs** are **enzyme inhibitors**, for example:

1) Some **antiviral** drugs (drugs that stop **viruses** like **HIV**) — e.g. **reverse transcriptase inhibitors** inhibit the enzyme **reverse transcriptase**, which catalyses the **replication** of **viral DNA**. This **prevents** the virus from **replicating**.

2) Some **antibiotics** — e.g. **penicillin** inhibits the enzyme **transpeptidase**, which **catalyses** the **formation** of **proteins** in bacterial cell walls. This **weakens the cell wall** and prevents the bacterium from regulating its osmotic pressure. As a result the cell **bursts** and the bacterium is **killed**.

Cofactors and **Coenzymes** are **Essential** for Enzymes to **Work**

Some enzymes will only work if there is another **non-protein** substance bound to them.
These non-protein substances are called **cofactors**.

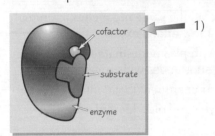

1) Some cofactors are **inorganic** molecules. They work by helping the enzyme and substrate to **bind together**. They don't directly participate in the reaction so aren't **used up** or **changed** in any way. For example, **manganese ions** are cofactors found in hydrolase enzymes (enzymes that catalyse the hydrolysis of chemical bonds).

2) Some cofactors are **organic** molecules — these are called **coenzymes**. They participate in the reaction and are **changed** by it (they're just like a second substrate, but they're not called that). They often act as **carriers**, moving **chemical groups** between different enzymes. They're **continually recycled** during this process.

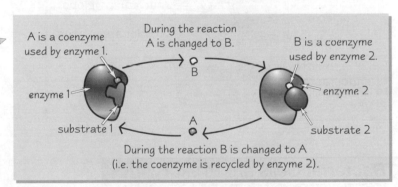

Practice Questions

Q1 What are metabolic poisons?

Q2 Describe one medicinal use of enzyme inhibitors.

Q3 What are cofactors and coenzymes?

Exam Question

Q1 Inhibitors prevent enzymes from working properly. They can be competitive or non-competitive.

a) Explain how a competitive inhibitor works. [3 marks]

b) Explain how a non-competitive inhibitor works. [2 marks]

Activity — mine is usually inhibited by pizza and a movie...

Competitive inhibition is like your grandma sitting in your grandad's favourite chair — if she's in it, he can't occupy it. Non-competitive inhibition is like your grandma leaving the TV remote under your grandad's favourite cushion — it's now the wrong shape, so he can't get comfy any more. Grandparents don't exactly speed up any reactions though.

Cells and Organelles

These pages are for AQA Unit 1, OCR Unit 1 and Edexcel Unit 2. If you're doing AQA Unit 2 you need to learn the differences between plant and animal cells, the structure of the cell wall and chloroplasts, and all the stuff on page 25.
There are two types of cell — prokaryotic and eukaryotic. Both types contain organelles (all the tiny bits and bobs that you can only see in detail with a fancy microscope), and you need to know about all of them...

Organisms can be **Prokaryotes** or **Eukaryotes**

1)   Prokaryotic organisms are **prokaryotic cells** (i.e. they're single-celled organisms) and eukaryotic organisms are made up of **eukaryotic cells**.

2)   Both types of cells contain **organelles**. Organelles are **parts** of cells — each one has a **specific function**.

1)   Eukaryotic cells are **complex** and include all **animal** and **plant cells**.

2)   Prokaryotic cells are **smaller** and **simpler**, e.g. bacteria.

Plant and **Animal** Cells are Both **Eukaryotic**

Eukaryotic cells are generally a **bit more complicated** than prokaryotic cells. You've probably been looking at **animal** and **plant cell** diagrams for years, so hopefully you'll be familiar with some of the bits and pieces...

Animal Cell

cell membrane
rough endoplasmic reticulum
nucleolus
nucleus
smooth endoplasmic reticulum

lysosome
ribosome
nuclear envelope
Golgi apparatus
cytoplasm
mitochondrion

Plant Cell

Plant cells have all the **same organelles** as animal cells, but with a few **added extras**:

• a **cell wall** with **plasmodesmata** ('holes' for exchanging substances with adjacent cells),
• a **vacuole** (compartment that contains cell sap),
• and of course good old **chloroplasts**.

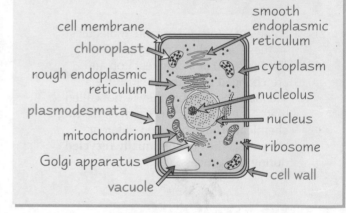

cell membrane
chloroplast
rough endoplasmic reticulum
plasmodesmata
mitochondrion
Golgi apparatus
vacuole

smooth endoplasmic reticulum
cytoplasm
nucleolus
nucleus
ribosome
cell wall

Bacterial Cells are **Prokaryotic**

You need to know the **structure** of a prokaryotic cell, as well as the **differences** between prokaryotic cells and eukaryotic cells:

• Prokaryotic cells are **a lot smaller** than eukaryotic cells.

• Prokaryotic cells **don't have a nucleus** — their DNA **floats free** in the cytoplasm. Their DNA is **circular** (the DNA in eukaryotic cells in linear).

• Prokaryotic cells have **fewer organelles** than eukaryotic cells (e.g. they **don't** have **mitochondria**).

• Prokaryotic cells have **smaller ribosomes** than eukaryotic cells.

Bacterial Cell

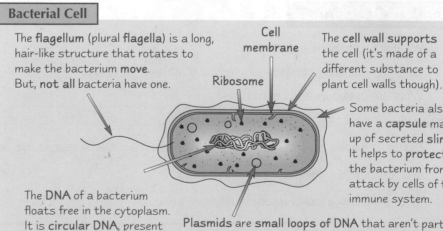

The **flagellum** (plural **flagella**) is a long, hair-like structure that rotates to make the bacterium **move**. But, **not all** bacteria have one.

Cell membrane

Ribosome

The **cell wall supports** the cell (it's made of a different substance to plant cell walls though).

Some bacteria also have a **capsule** made up of secreted **slime**. It helps to **protect** the bacterium from attack by cells of the immune system.

The DNA of a bacterium floats free in the cytoplasm. It is **circular** DNA, present as one long coiled-up strand.

Plasmids are **small loops of DNA** that aren't part of the chromosome. Plasmids contain genes for things like antibiotic resistance, and can be passed between bacteria. Plasmids are **not always** present in bacteria.

Cells and Organelles

Different Organelles have Different Functions

This giant table contains a big list of organelles — you need to know the **structure** and **function** of them all. Sorry. Most organelles are surrounded by **membranes**, which sometimes causes confusion — don't make the mistake of thinking that a diagram of an organelle is a diagram of a whole cell. They're not cells   they're **parts of** cells.

ORGANELLE	DIAGRAM	DESCRIPTION	FUNCTION
Cell surface (plasma) membrane	cell membrane / cytoplasm	The membrane found on the surface of **animal cells** and just inside the cell wall of **plant cells** and **prokaryotic cells** . It's made mainly of **lipids** and **protein**.	**Regulates the movement** of substances into and out of the cell. It also has **receptor molecules** on it, which allow it to respond to chemicals like hormones.
Microvilli *Microvilli are for AQA only.*	microvilli / cell membrane	These are **folds** in the cell membrane.	They're found on cells involved in processes like absorption, such as epithelial cells in the small intestine (see p. 25). They **increase** the **surface area** of the cell membrane.
Nucleus	nuclear envelope / nucleolus / nuclear pore / chromatin	A large organelle surrounded by a **nuclear envelope** (double membrane), which contains many **pores**. The nucleus contains **chromatin** and often a structure called the **nucleolus**.	**Chromatin** is made from proteins and DNA (DNA **controls the cell's activities**). The pores allow substances (e.g. RNA) to move between the nucleus and the cytoplasm. The **nucleolus** makes **ribosomes** (see below).
Lysosome		A **round organelle** surrounded by a **membrane**, with no clear internal structure.	Contains **digestive enzymes**. These are kept separate from the cytoplasm by the surrounding membrane, and can be used to **digest invading cells** or to **break down** worn out components of the cell.
Ribosome	small subunit / large subunit	A **very small organelle** that floats free in the cytoplasm or is attached to the rough endoplasmic reticulum.	The **site** where **proteins** are **made**.
Endoplasmic Reticulum (ER)	a) / b) ribosome / fluid	There are two types of endoplasmic reticulum: the **smooth endoplasmic reticulum** (diagram **a**) is a system of membranes enclosing a fluid-filled space. The **rough endoplasmic reticulum** (diagram **b**) is similar, but is **covered in ribosomes**.	The **smooth endoplasmic reticulum synthesises** and **processes lipids**. The **rough endoplasmic reticulum folds** and **processes proteins** that have been made in the ribosomes.
Golgi Apparatus		A group of fluid-filled **flattened sacs**.	It **processes** and **packages** new lipids and proteins. It also **makes lysosomes**.
Mitochondrion	outer membrane / inner membrane / crista / matrix	They're usually oval-shaped. They have a **double membrane** — the inner one is folded to form structures called **cristae**. Inside is the **matrix**, which contains enzymes involved in respiration.	The **site of aerobic respiration**. They're found in large numbers in cells that are very **active** and require a lot of **energy**.

Cells and Organelles

ORGANELLE	DIAGRAM	DESCRIPTION	FUNCTION
Vesicle	cell's surface membrane — vesicle	A small **fluid-filled sac** in the cytoplasm, surrounded by a membrane.	**Transports substances** in and out of the cell (via the cell surface membrane) and between organelles. Some are formed by the Golgi apparatus or the endoplasmic reticulum, while others are formed at the cell surface.
Cell wall	cell membrane — cell wall — cytoplasm	A rigid structure that surrounds **plant cells**. It's made mainly of the carbohydrate **cellulose**.	**Supports** plant cells.
Chloroplast	stroma — two membranes — granum (plural = grana) — lamella (plural = lamellae)	A small, **flattened** structure found in **plant cells**. It's surrounded by a **double membrane**, and also has membranes inside called **thylakoid membranes**. These membranes are stacked up in some parts of the chloroplast to form **grana**. Grana are linked together by lamellae — thin, flat pieces of thylakoid membrane.	The **site** where **photosynthesis** takes place. Some parts of photosynthesis happen in the **grana**, and other parts happen in the **stroma** (a thick fluid found in chloroplasts).
Centriole *Centrioles are for OCR and Edexcel only.*		Small, **hollow cylinders**, containing a ring of microtubules (tiny protein cylinders).	Involved with the **separation of chromosomes** during cell division (see p. 54).
Cilia *Cilia are for OCR only.*	side — cross-section	Small, **hair-like structures** found on the surface membrane of some **animal cells**. In cross-section, they have an outer membrane and a ring of nine pairs of **protein microtubules** inside, with a single pair of microtubules in the middle.	The microtubules allow the cilia to **move**. This movement is used by the cell to **move substances along the cell surface**.
Flagellum *Flagella are for OCR only.*		Flagella on eukaryotic cells are **like cilia** but **longer**. They **stick out** from the cell surface and are surrounded by the cell membrane. Inside they're like cilia too — two **microtubules** in the centre and nine pairs around the edge.	The microtubules **contract** to make the flagellum **move**. Flagella are used like **outboard motors** to propel cells forward (e.g. when a **sperm cell** swims).

The flagella on prokaryotic cells have the same function, but a different internal structure.

Cells and Organelles

This page is for AQA Unit 1 and Unit 2 only. If you're doing OCR or Edexcel you can skip straight to the questions.

Cells Have **Different Organelles** Depending on Their **Function**

In the exam, you might get a question where you need to apply your knowledge of the **organelles** in a cell to explain why it's particularly **suited** to its **function**. Here are some tips.

- Think about how the **structure** of the cell might affect its **job** — e.g. if it's part of an **exchange surface** it might have organelles that **increase** the **surface area** (e.g. microvilli). If it **carries things** it might have **lost** some of its organelles to make **more room**.
- Think about **what** the cell **needs** to do its **job** — e.g. if the cell uses a lot of **energy**, it'll need lots of **mitochondria**. If it makes a lot of **proteins** it'll need a lot of **ribosomes**.

| **Example** | **Epithelial cells** in the **small intestine** are adapted to **absorb food efficiently**. |

1) The walls of the small intestine have lots of finger-like projections called **villi** to **increase surface area**.
2) The **cells** on the surface of the villi have **microvilli** to increase surface area even more.
3) They also have **lots of mitochondria** — to provide **energy** for the transport of digested food molecules into the cell.

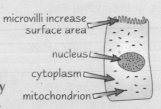

microvilli increase surface area
nucleus
cytoplasm
mitochondrion

You need to learn the structure of an epithelial cell from the small intestine for Unit 1 and learn the structure of a palisade cell for Unit 2.

| **Example** | **Palisade cells** are **adapted** for **photosynthesis**. |

1) They have rigid **cell walls** made of **cellulose**, which **support** and **strengthen** the cell.
2) Inside the cell is a **permanent vacuole** containing **cell sap** — a weak solution of sugar and salts.
3) They have **chloroplasts** — where **photosynthesis** occurs. They contain a **green** substance called **chlorophyll**.

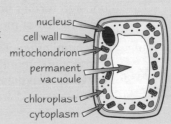

nucleus
cell wall
mitochondrion
permanent vacuole
chloroplast
cytoplasm

Practice Questions

Q1 Give two differences between prokaryotic and eukaryotic organisms.

Q2 Describe the function of vesicles.

Q3 How does the structure of rough endoplasmic reticulum differ from that of smooth endoplasmic reticulum?

Q4 What is the function of chloroplasts?

Exam Questions

Q1 Give four things commonly found in plant cells but not in animal cells. [4 marks]

Q2 a) Identify these two organelles from their descriptions as seen in an electron micrograph.

　　i) An oval-shaped organelle surrounded by a double membrane. The inner membrane is folded and projects into the inner space, which is filled with a grainy material. [1 mark]

　　ii) A collection of flattened membrane 'sacs' arranged roughly parallel to one another. Small, circular structures are seen at the edges of these 'sacs'. [1 mark]

　b) State the function of the two organelles that you have identified. [2 marks]

Q3 Cilia are hair-like structures found on lung epithelial cells. Their function is to beat and move mucus out of the lungs. Beating requires energy. Suggest how ciliated cells are adapted to their function in terms of the organelles they contain. Explain your answer. [2 marks]

That's enough talk of fluid-filled sacs for my liking. Scientists these days...

'Organelle' is a very pretty-sounding name for all those blobs. Actually, under a microscope some of them are really quite fetching — well I think so anyway, but I also find mullets quite fetching so maybe they're not... hmmm. Anyway, you need to know the names and functions of all the organelles and also what they look like.

Organelles

These pages are for AQA Unit 1, OCR Unit 1 and Edexcel Unit 2.

After that endless list of organelles, you might need a few minutes to regain consciousness... Then you can read this lovely page about how they work together to produce proteins. And there's some stuff on cytoskeletons too... Whoop!

Organelles are Involved in Protein Production — *OCR and Edexcel only*

1) Proteins are made at the **ribosomes**.

2) The ribosomes on the **rough endoplasmic reticulum (rER)** make proteins that are **excreted** or attached to the **cell membrane**. The free ribosomes in the cytoplasm make proteins that **stay in the cytoplasm**.

3) New proteins produced at the rER are **folded** and **processed** (e.g. sugar chains are added) in the rER.

4) Then they're **transported** from the ER to the **Golgi apparatus** in vesicles.

5) At the Golgi apparatus, the proteins may undergo **further processing** (e.g. sugar chains are trimmed or more are added).

6) The proteins enter more **vesicles** to be transported around the cell. E.g. **extracellular enzymes** (like digestive enzymes) move to the cell surface and are **secreted**.

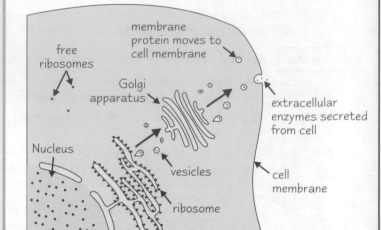

Protein Production in a Cell

The Cytoskeleton has Several Functions — *The cytoskeleton is for OCR only.*

1) The organelles in cells are surrounded by the **cytoplasm**. The cytoplasm is more than just a solution of chemicals though — it's got a **network of protein threads** running through it. These protein threads are called the **cytoskeleton**.

2) In eukaryotic cells the protein threads are arranged as **microfilaments** (small solid strands) and **microtubules** (tiny protein cylinders).

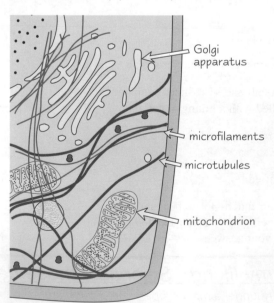

The cytoskeleton has **four main functions**:

1) The microtubules and microfilaments **support** the cell's organelles, keeping them **in position**.

2) They also help to **strengthen** the cell and **maintain its shape**.

3) As well as this, they're responsible for the **transport of materials** within the cell. For example, the movement of **chromosomes** when they separate during cell division depends on contraction of microtubules in the spindle (see page 54 for more on cell division).

4) The proteins of the cytoskeleton can also cause the cell to **move**. For example, the movement of **cilia** and **flagella** is caused by the cytoskeletal protein filaments that run through them. So in the case of single cells that have a flagellum (e.g. sperm cells), the cytoskeleton propels the **whole cell**.

Organelles

Cell Fractionation Separates Organelles *AQA only*

Suppose you wanted to look at some **organelles** under an **electron microscope**. First you'd need to **separate** them from the **rest of the cell** — you can do this by **cell fractionation**. There are **three** steps to this technique:

① Homogenisation — Breaking Up the Cells

Homogenisation can be done in several **different ways**, e.g. by vibrating the cells or by grinding the cells up in a blender. This **breaks up** the **cell surface membrane** and **releases** the **organelles** into solution.

② Filtration — Getting Rid of the Big Bits

Next, the homogenised cell solution is **filtered** through a **gauze** to separate any **large cell debris** or **tissue debris**, like connective tissue, from the organelles. The organelles are much **smaller** than the debris, so they pass through the gauze.

③ Ultracentrifugation — Separating the Organelles

After filtration, you're left with a solution containing a **mixture** of organelles.
To separate a particular organelle from all the others you use **ultracentrifugation**.

1) The cell fragments are poured into a **tube**. The tube is put into a **centrifuge** (a machine that separates material by spinning) and is spun at a **low speed**. The **heaviest organelles**, like nuclei, get flung to the **bottom** of the tube by the centrifuge. They form a **thick sediment** at the bottom — the **pellet**. The rest of the organelles stay suspended in the fluid above the sediment — the **supernatant**.

2) The supernatant is **drained off**, poured into **another tube**, and spun in the centrifuge at a **higher speed**. Again, the **heaviest organelles**, this time the mitochondria, form a pellet at the bottom of the tube. The supernatant containing the rest of the organelles is drained off and spun in the centrifuge at an **even higher speed**.

3) This process is **repeated** at higher and higher speeds, until all the organelles are **separated out**. Each time, the pellet at the bottom of the tube is made up of lighter and lighter organelles.

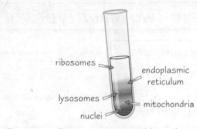

The organelles are separated in order of mass (from heaviest to lightest) — this order is usually: nuclei, then mitochondria, then lysosomes, then endoplasmic reticulum, and finally ribosomes.

Practice Questions

Q1 List the four main functions of a cell's cytoskeleton.

Exam Questions

Q1 Some cells that secrete extracellular enzymes were immersed in a solution of radioactive amino acids. Every five seconds, some of the cells were removed and their organelles were separated and analysed. The radioactivity in the different organelles was measured for each five second interval.

When answering the questions below, use organelles from this list —
Golgi apparatus, ribosomes, rough endoplasmic reticulum, vesicles.

a) In which of these organelles would you expect radioactivity to appear first? Explain your answer. [2 marks]

b) After 5 minutes, the Golgi apparatus had become radioactive.
Which other organelle(s) would be radioactive by this time? [3 marks]

Q2 Describe how you would separate organelles from a cell sample using cell fractionation. Explain why each step is done. [8 marks]

Cell fractionation — sounds more like maths to me...

All those organelles devoting their lives to making things like enzymes... Not the most exciting thing, but I guess it's better than revision. Cytoskeletons, on the other hand, make a bit more sense. No one wants floppy cells after all. Anyway, if you fancy getting up close and personal with some organelles, just remember to homogenise, filter and ultracentrifuge first.

Analysis of Cell Components

These pages are for AQA Unit 1 and OCR Unit 1.

If you were born over a century ago then you wouldn't have had to learn all this stuff about organelles because people wouldn't have known anything about them. But then better microscopes were invented and here we are. Unlucky.

Magnification *is* Size, Resolution *is* Detail

We all know that microscopes produce a **magnified image** of a sample, but **resolution** is just as important...

1) MAGNIFICATION is how much **bigger** the image is than the specimen (the sample you're looking at). It's calculated using this formula:

$$\text{magnification} = \frac{\text{length of image}}{\text{length of specimen}}$$

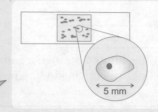

5 mm

For example:
If you have a magnified image that's 5 mm wide and your specimen is 0.05 mm wide the magnification is:
$5 \div 0.05 = \times 100$.

2) RESOLUTION is how **detailed** the image is. More specifically, it's how well a microscope **distinguishes** between **two points** that are **close together**. If a microscope lens can't separate two objects, then increasing the magnification won't help.

If you're doing OCR you need to be able to calculate magnification.

There are **Two Main Types** of Microscope — **Light** and **Electron**

Light microscopes

1) They use **light** (no surprises there).

2) They have a **lower resolution** than electron microscopes.

Electron microscopes

1) They use **electrons** instead of light to form an image.

2) They have a **higher resolution** than light microscopes so give a **more detailed image**.

Electron Microscopes *are either* 'Scanning' *or* 'Transmission'

There are **two** types of **electron microscope**:

Transmission electron microscopes (TEMs)

1) TEMs use **electromagnets** to focus a **beam of electrons**, which is then transmitted **through** the specimen.

2) **Denser** parts of the specimen absorb **more electrons**, which makes them look **darker** on the image you end up with.

3) TEMs are good because they give **high resolution images**.

4) But they can only be used on **thin specimens**.

Nancy's New Year's resolution was to get a haircut.

Scanning electron microscopes (SEMs)

1) SEMs **scan** a beam of electrons across the specimen.

2) This **knocks off** electrons from the **specimen**, which are gathered in a **cathode ray tube** to form an **image**.

3) The images you end up with show the **surface** of the specimen and they can be **3-D**.

4) SEMs are good because they can be used on **thick specimens**.

5) But they give **lower resolution images** than TEMs.

A micrometre (μm) is one millionth of a metre, or 0.001 mm.

You need to know about the **magnification** and **resolution** of light microscopes and both types of electron microscope. So I've put all the important numbers in this box 'cos I'm nice like that.

	light microscope	TEM	SEM
maximum resolution	0.2 μm	0.0001 μm	0.005 μm
maximum magnification	× 1500	more than × 1 000 000	less than × 1 000 000

Analysis of Cell Components

You Need to Stain Your Samples
Staining samples is for OCR only.

1) In light microscopes and TEMs, the beam of light (or electrons) **passes through the object** being viewed. An image is produced because some parts of the object **absorb more light** (or electrons) than others.

2) Sometimes the object being viewed is completely **transparent**. This makes the whole thing look **white** because the light rays (or electrons) just pass **straight through**.

3) To get round this, the object can be **stained**:

- For the light microscope, this means using some kind of **dye**. Common stains are **methylene blue** and **eosin**. The stain is taken up by some parts of the object more than others — the **contrast** makes the different parts show up.

- For the electron microscope, objects are dipped in a solution of **heavy metals** (like **lead**). The metal ions scatter the electrons, again creating contrast.

Either way, an image is produced because some parts of the object show up **darker** than others.

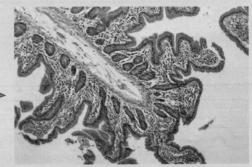

An eosin stained specimen, as seen through a light microscope.

Practice Questions

Q1 What is the formula for calculating the magnification of an image?

Q2 What is meant by a microscope's resolution?

Q3 Why is it sometimes necessary to stain an object before viewing it through a microscope?

Exam Questions

Q1 An insect is 0.5 mm long. In a book, a picture of the insect is 8 cm long.
Calculate the magnification of the image. [2 marks]

Q2 Describe the difference between SEMs and TEMs and give one limitation of each. [6 marks]

Q3 The table shows the dimensions of some different organelles found in animal cells.

organelle	diameter / μm
lysosome	0.1
mitochondrion	2
nucleus	5
ribosome	0.02
vesicle	0.05

a) Name those organelles in the table that would be visible using a good quality light microscope. Explain your answer. [3 marks]

b) Which organelles would be visible using an SEM? Explain your answer. [2 marks]

'Staining your samples' — a common problem at the start of exams...

OK, there's quite a bit of info on these pages, but the whole magnification thing isn't all that bad once you've given it a go. Make sure you can define resolution — that's a bit trickier. You also need to have a good grasp of what TEMs and SEMs are, and how the resolution of their images compare to each other and to those of light microscopes. Happy memorising...

Cell Membranes

These pages are for AQA Unit 1, Edexcel Unit 1 and OCR Unit 1.

Membranes Control What Passes Through Them

Cells, and many of the organelles inside them, are surrounded by membranes, which have a range of functions:

Membranes at the surface of cells

1) They control **which substances enter and leave** the cell. They're **partially permeable** — they let some molecules through but not others. Substances can move across the cell membrane by **diffusion**, **osmosis** or **active transport** (see pages 34-37).

2) They allow **recognition** by other cells, e.g. the cells of the **immune system** (see p. 90).

3) They allow **cells** to **communicate** with each other (see p. 33 for more).

Partially permeable membranes can be useful at sea.

Membranes within cells

1) The membranes around **organelles divide** the cell into different **compartments**. This makes different **functions more efficient**, e.g. substances needed for **respiration** (like enzymes) are kept together inside **mitochondria**.

2) The membranes of some organelles are folded, increasing their **surface area** and making **chemical reactions more efficient**. E.g. the **inner membrane** of a mitochondrion contains **enzymes** needed for **respiration**. It has a large surface area, which **increases** the **number** of enzymes present and makes respiration more efficient.

3) They can form **vesicles** to **transport** substances between different areas of the cell.

4) They control **which substances enter and leave** the organelle, e.g. RNA leaves the nucleus via the nuclear membrane. They are also **partially permeable**.

Cell Membranes have a 'Fluid Mosaic' Structure

Cell membranes are also sometimes called plasma membranes.

The **structure** of all membranes is basically the same. They're composed of **lipids** (mainly phospholipids), **proteins** and **carbohydrates** (usually attached to proteins or lipids).

1) In 1972, the **fluid mosaic model** was suggested to describe the **arrangement** of **molecules** in the membrane.

2) In the model, **phospholipid molecules** form a continuous, double layer (**bilayer**). This bilayer is 'fluid' because the phospholipids are **constantly moving**.

3) **Protein molecules** are scattered through the bilayer, like tiles in a **mosaic**. Because the bilayer is fluid, the proteins can **move around** within it.

4) Some **proteins** have a **polysaccharide** (carbohydrate) **chain** attached — these are called **glycoproteins**.

5) Some **lipids** also have a **polysaccharide chain** attached — these are called **glycolipids**.

6) **Cholesterol** (a type of lipid) is also present in the membrane.

Diagram labels: glycoprotein, glycolipid, phospholipids, protein, cholesterol, protein channel

The Fluid Mosaic Model is Based on Scientific Evidence

Edexcel only

Electron microscopes show more detail than light microscopes.

1) Before the 1970s, most scientists believed cell membranes were composed of a **phospholipid layer** between **two continuous layers of proteins**. This was because **electron microscope** (EM) **images** appeared to show **three layers** in a cell membrane.

2) In time, **improved** EM techniques showed a **bilayer** of phospholipids, and **new methods** for **analysing proteins** showed that they were **randomly distributed** in cell membranes, not in a continuous layer.

3) Scientists also carried out experiments that proved the cell membrane is **fluid** — e.g. they fused a **mouse cell** with a **human cell**, and found that the mouse and human **membrane proteins** completely **intermixed** throughout the cell membrane — the proteins could only **move** like this if the membrane was fluid.

4) All of this **new evidence** gave rise to the **fluid mosaic model**.

Cell Membranes

You can use the **Fluid Mosaic Model** to Explain **Membrane Properties**

AQA and OCR only

If you're doing **AQA** or **OCR**, you might get a question in the exam where you need to use your **knowledge** of the **fluid mosaic model** to explain why the **cell membrane** has various **properties**. You can't go far wrong if you learn these **five** points.

(1) The membrane is a good barrier against most water-soluble molecules

Phospholipids are the major component of the membrane bilayer. The molecules automatically **arrange** themselves into a **bilayer** — the **hydrophilic heads face out** towards the water on either side of the membrane, and the **hydrophobic tails** face inwards. This hydrophobic centre makes it difficult for **water-soluble** substances, such as sodium ions and glucose, to get through.

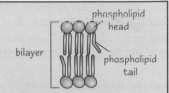

bilayer

phospholipid head

phospholipid tail

(2) The membrane controls what enters and leaves

Proteins in the membrane (e.g. **channel proteins** and **carrier proteins**) allow the passage of **large** or **charged water-soluble** substances that would otherwise find it difficult to cross the membrane (see page 36 for more). **Different cells** have **different** protein channels and carrier proteins — e.g. the membrane of a **nerve cell** has many **sodium-potassium carrier proteins** (which help to conduct nerve impulses) and **muscle cells** have **calcium protein channels** (which are needed for muscle contraction).

(3) The membrane allows cell communication

Membranes contain **receptor proteins**. These allow the cell to **detect chemicals** released from other cells. The chemicals **signal** to the cell to **respond** in some way, e.g. the hormone insulin binds to receptors in the membranes of liver cells — this tells the liver cells to absorb glucose. This cell communication is vital for the body to **function properly**. **Different cells** have **different receptors** present in their membranes.

(4) The membrane allows cell recognition

Glycoproteins and **glycolipids** tell **white blood cells** that the cell is **your own**. White blood cells only attack cells that they don't recognise as **self** (e.g. those of **microorganisms** like bacteria).

(5) The membrane is fluid

The **phospholipids** in the plasma membrane are **constantly moving** around. The more **unsaturated** fatty acids there are in the phospholipid bilayer, the **more fluid** it becomes. **Cholesterol** molecules fit in between the phospholipids of the bilayer, binding to their hydrophobic tails, causing them to pack more closely together. So the **more** cholesterol molecules there are, the **less fluid** the membrane becomes. Cholesterol is important as it makes the cell membrane more **rigid** and prevents it from **breaking up**.

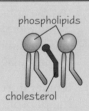

phospholipids

cholesterol

Practice Questions

Q1 Give two functions of membranes within the cell and two functions of membranes at the cell surface.

Q2 Give three molecules, other than proteins and cholesterol, that are present in animal cell membranes.

Exam Questions

Q1 Explain why the plasma membrane can be described as having a fluid-mosaic structure. [2 marks]

Q2 Use the fluid mosaic model of membrane structure to explain how the membrane controls what enters and leaves the cell. [5 marks]

Fluid Mosaic Model — think I saw one being sold at a craft fair...

It's weird to think that cells are surrounded by a layer that's 'fluid' — it's a good job it is though, 'cause if the cell membrane was rigid a cell wouldn't be able to change shape or stretch without bursting, and that wouldn't be a pretty sight. It's also a good job that the membrane's partially permeable — so that it can let oxygen and carbon dioxide in and out of the cell.

Cell Membranes

This page is for Edexcel Unit 1 and OCR Unit 1. If you're doing AQA skip to page 34.

Scientists like to heat up membranes or cover them in booze and see what happens. They're also interested in how membranes are involved in cell communication. There's no accounting for taste...

The **Permeability** of the **Cell Membrane** can be **Investigated** in the **Lab**

Edexcel only

The permeability of cell membranes is affected by **different conditions**, e.g. **temperature** and **alcohol concentration**. You can investigate how these things affect permeability by doing an experiment using **beetroot**. Beetroot cells contain a **coloured pigment** that **leaks out** — the **higher** the **permeability** of the membrane, the **more pigment** leaks out of the cell.

> Here's how you could investigate how **temperature** affects **beetroot membrane permeability**:
>
> 1) Cut five **equal sized** pieces of beetroot and **rinse** them to remove any pigment released during cutting.
>
> 2) Place the five pieces in five different **test tubes**, each with **5 cm³ of water**.
>
> 3) Place each test tube in a **water bath** at a **different temperature**, e.g. 10 °C, 20 °C, 30 °C, 40 °C, 50 °C, for the **same length of time**.
>
> 4) **Remove** the pieces of beetroot from the tubes, leaving just the **coloured liquid.**
>
> 5) Now you need to use a **colorimeter** — a machine that passes **light** through the liquid and measures how much of that light is **absorbed**. The **higher** the absorbance, the **more pigment released**, so the **higher** the permeability of the membrane.

Increasing the Temperature Increases Membrane Permeability

Membrane permeability **changes** with temperature like this:

(1) Temperatures below 0 °C
The phospholipids don't have much energy, so they can't move very much. They're **packed closely together** and the membrane is **rigid**. But **channel proteins** and **carrier proteins** in the membrane **denature**, **increasing** the **permeability** of the membrane. **Ice crystals** may form and **pierce** the membrane, making it **highly permeable** when it thaws.

(2) Temperatures between 0 and 45 °C
The phospholipids can **move** around and **aren't** packed as tightly together — the membrane is **partially permeable**. As the temperature **increases** the phospholipids **move more** because they have more energy — this **increases** the **permeability** of the membrane.

(3) Temperatures above 45 °C
The phospholipid bilayer starts to **melt** (break down) and the membrane becomes more **permeable**. **Water** inside the cell **expands**, putting pressure on the membrane. **Channel proteins** and **carrier proteins** in the membrane **denature** so they can't control what enters or leaves the cell — this increases the **permeability** of the membrane.

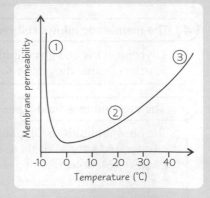

Increasing the Alcohol Concentration Increases Membrane Permeability

Edexcel only

1) You can also test the effect of **alcohol concentration** on **membrane permeability** — the graph on the right shows the results you'd expect to get.

2) As alcohol concentration **increases**, the permeability of the cell membrane **increases**.

3) This is because alcohol **dissolves** the **lipids** in the cell membrane, so the membrane **loses** its **structure**.

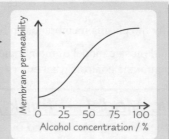

Cell Membranes

This page is for OCR Unit 1 only. If you're doing Edexcel you can skip straight to the questions.

Cell Signalling is How Cells Communicate with Each Other

Cells need to communicate with each other to **control processes** inside the body and to **respond** to **changes** in the **environment**. Cells communicate with each other using **messenger molecules**:

1) One cell **releases** a messenger molecule (e.g. a **hormone**).
2) This molecule **travels** to another cell (e.g. in the blood).
3) The messenger molecule is detected by the cell because it **binds** to a **receptor** on its **cell membrane**.

Cell Membrane Receptors Play an Important Role in Cell Signalling

1) Membrane-bound **proteins** act as **receptors** for messenger molecules.

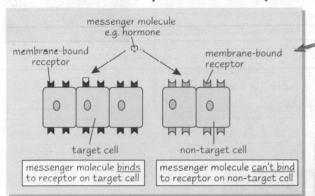

2) Receptor proteins have **specific shapes** — only **messenger molecules** with a **complimentary shape** can **bind** to them.

3) **Different cells** have **different types** of receptors — they respond to **different messenger molecules**.

4) A cell that responds to a particular messenger molecule is called a **target cell**.

Example: **Glucagon** is a **hormone** that's **released** when there **isn't enough glucose** in the **blood**. It **binds** to **receptors** on **liver cells**, causing them to **break down** stores of **glycogen** to glucose.

Drugs Also Bind to Cell Membrane Receptors

1) Many **drugs** work by **binding** to **receptors** in cell membranes.

2) They either **trigger** a **response** in the cell, or **block** the receptor and **prevent** it from **working**.

Example: **Cell damage** causes the release of **histamine**. Histamine binds to receptors on the surface of other cells and causes **inflammation**. **Antihistamines** work by **blocking histamine receptors** on cell surfaces. This **prevents** histamine from binding to the cell and **stops inflammation**.

Practice Questions

Q1 What happens to the permeability of a cell membrane as the alcohol concentration increases?

Q2 What do messenger molecules bind to?

Tube number	Temperature /°C	Absorbance
1	10	1
2	30	5
3	50	43
4	70	56

Exam Questions

Q1 Beetroot cells contain a red pigment. In an experiment, four identical cubes of beetroot were washed and placed in four different test tubes of water. Each test tube was placed in a water bath at a different temperature, for 10 minutes. The water from each test tube was then placed in a colorimeter, to measure the concentration of pigment. A large absorbance value indicates a high concentration of pigment. The results are shown in the table above.

a) Describe and explain the difference between the results for tubes 2 and 3. [4 marks]

b) The experiment was repeated, with a test tube placed in the freezer for 10 minutes. The test tube was left to thaw before the absorbance reading was taken. Suggest whether the absorbance reading would have been high or low, and explain your answer. [4 marks]

Q2 Nicotine has an effect on nerve cells, but not on other types of cell in the body. Use your knowledge of cell membrane structure to explain why. [3 marks]

Perm-eability — it's definitely decreased since the 80s...

Well that's a full double page if ever I saw one... There's lots to learn on here, so make sure you're not filling your brain with things you don't need — only learn the stuff that's relevant to your exam board, otherwise you'll be here all night...

Exchange Across Cell Membranes

This page is for AQA Unit 1, OCR Unit 1 and Edexcel Unit 1.

The beauty of cell membranes is that they're partially permeable — they'll only let certain substances enter and leave. Some substances move across the cell membrane by passive transport, which means no energy is involved in the process. Passive transport processes include diffusion, osmosis and facilitated diffusion (see p. 36).

Diffusion *is the* Passive Movement *of* Particles

1) Diffusion is the net movement of particles (molecules or ions) from an area of **higher concentration** to an area of **lower concentration**.

2) Molecules will diffuse **both ways**, but the **net movement** will be to the area of **lower concentration**. This continues until particles are **evenly distributed** throughout the liquid or gas.

3) The **concentration gradient** is the path from an area of higher concentration to an area of lower concentration. Particles diffuse **down** a concentration gradient.

4) Diffusion is a **passive process** — **no energy** is needed for it to happen.

5) Particles can diffuse **across cell membranes**, as long as they can **move freely** through the membrane. E.g. oxygen and carbon dioxide molecules are **small enough** to pass easily through spaces between phospholipids.

Diffusion — not good in a swimming pool.

The Rate of Diffusion *Depends on* Several Factors

1) The **concentration gradient** — the **higher** it is, the **faster** the rate of diffusion.

2) The **thickness** of the **exchange surface** — the **thinner** the exchange surface (i.e. the **shorter** the **distance** the particles have to travel), the **faster** the rate of diffusion.

3) The **surface area** — the **larger** the surface area (e.g. of the cell membrane), the **faster** the rate of diffusion.

Osmosis *is* Diffusion *of* Water Molecules

1) Osmosis is the **diffusion** of **water molecules** across a **partially permeable membrane**, from an area of **higher water potential** (i.e. higher concentration of water molecules) to an area of **lower water potential** (i.e. lower concentration of water molecules).

2) **Water potential** is the potential (likelihood) of water molecules to diffuse out of or into a solution.

3) **Pure water** has the **highest water potential**. All solutions have a **lower** water potential than pure water.

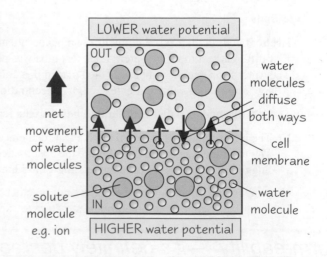

LOWER water potential

OUT

net movement of water molecules

water molecules diffuse both ways

cell membrane

solute molecule e.g. ion

IN

water molecule

HIGHER water potential

Exchange Across Cell Membranes

This page is for OCR Unit 1 only. If you're doing AQA or Edexcel you can skip straight to the questions.

Cells are Affected by the Water Potential of the Surrounding Solution

Water moves **in** or **out** of a cell by osmosis. **How much** moves in or out depends on the **water potential** of the **surrounding solution**. Animal and plant cells behave differently in different solutions.

ANIMAL CELL

Solution with a higher water potential than the cell (hypotonic solution).

Solution with the same water potential as the cell (isotonic solution).

Solution with a lower water potential than the cell (hypertonic solution).

Net movement of water molecules is into the cell. Cell bursts.

Water molecules pass into and out of the cell in equal amounts. The cell stays the same.

Net movement of water molecules is out of the cell. The cell shrinks.

PLANT CELL

Hypotonic solution

Isotonic solution

Hypertonic solution

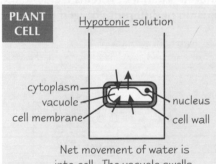

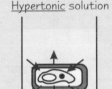

Net movement of water is into cell. The vacuole swells. The vacuole and cytoplasm push against the cell wall. The cell becomes turgid (swollen).

Water molecules move into and out of the cell in equal amounts. The cell stays the same.

Net movement of water is out of the cell. The cell becomes flaccid (limp). The cytoplasm and the membrane pull away from the cell wall. This is called plasmolysis.

Practice Questions

Q1 Diffusion is a passive transport process. What does this mean?

Q2 How does the thickness of an exchange surface affect the rate of diffusion across it?

Q3 What happens to a plant cell if it is placed in a solution with a higher water potential than the cell?

Exam Question

Q1 Pieces of potato of equal mass were put into different concentrations of sucrose solution for three days. The difference in mass for each is recorded in the table.

Concentration of sucrose / %	1	2	3	4
Mass difference / g	0.4	0.2	0	− 0.2

a) Explain why the pieces of potato in 1% and 2% sucrose solutions gained mass. [3 marks]

b) Suggest a reason why the mass of the piece of potato in 3% sucrose solution stayed the same. [1 mark]

c) What would you expect the mass difference for a potato in a 5% solution to be? Explain your answer. [4 marks]

Ginantonic solution — my gran's favourite...

Osmosis is just a fancy name for the diffusion of water molecules. But whether water moves in or out of a cell depends on the water potential of the surrounding solution. Water potential can be pretty confusing — if you can't make head nor tail of an exam question about it try replacing the word 'potential' with 'concentration' and it'll become clearer.

Exchange Across Cell Membranes

These pages are for AQA Unit 1, OCR Unit 1 and Edexcel Unit 1.

Facilitated diffusion is another passive transport process, but there's also an active transport process, which is imaginatively named 'active transport'...

Facilitated Diffusion uses Carrier Proteins and Protein Channels

1) Some **larger molecules** (e.g. amino acids, glucose) and **charged atoms** (e.g. chloride ions) **can't diffuse directly through** the phospholipid bilayer of the cell membrane.

2) Instead they diffuse through **carrier proteins** or **channel proteins** in the cell membrane — this is called **facilitated diffusion**.

3) Like diffusion, facilitated diffusion moves particles **down** a **concentration gradient**, from a higher to a lower concentration.

4) It's also a passive process — it **doesn't** use **energy**.

Andy needed all his concentration for this particular gradient...

Carrier proteins move **large molecules** into or out of the cell, down their concentration gradient. **Different carrier proteins** facilitate the diffusion of **different molecules**.

1) First, a large molecule **attaches** to a carrier protein in the membrane.

2) Then, the protein **changes shape**.

3) This **releases** the molecule on the **opposite side** of the membrane.

Channel proteins form **pores** in the membrane for **charged particles** to diffuse through (down their concentration gradient).

Different channel proteins facilitate the diffusion of **different charged particles**.

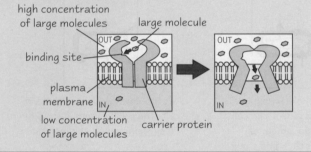

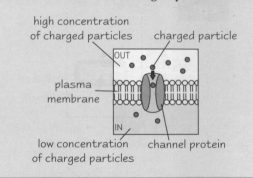

Active Transport Moves Substances Against a Concentration Gradient

Active transport uses **energy** to move **molecules** and **ions** across plasma membranes, **against** a **concentration gradient**.

Carrier proteins are also involved in active transport:

1) The process is pretty similar to facilitated diffusion — a molecule **attaches** to the carrier protein, the protein **changes shape** and this moves the molecule **across** the membrane, **releasing it** on the other side.

2) The only difference is that **energy** is used (from **ATP** — a common source of energy used in the cell), to move the solute against its concentration gradient.

The diagram shows the active transport of **calcium**.

Co-transporters are a type of **carrier protein** that you need to learn about if you're doing **AQA**.

1) They bind **two** molecules at a time.

2) The concentration gradient of one of the molecules is used to move the other molecule **against** its own concentration gradient.

The diagram shows the co-transport of **sodium ions** and **glucose**. Sodium ions move into the cell **down** their concentration gradient. This moves glucose into the cell too, **against** its concentration gradient.

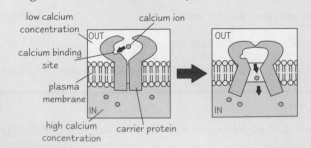

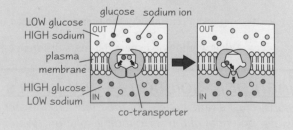

Exchange Across Cell Membranes

This page is just for Edexcel Unit 1 and OCR Unit 1. If you're doing AQA you can go straight to the questions.

OK, before you start thinking that you've reached the end of the whole substances-getting-across-the-membrane bit, feast your eyes on this lovely page. That's right — just when you thought you'd made it, along come endocytosis and exocytosis to ruin your day. On the plus side, they're a lot easier than all that carrier protein malarkey.

Cells can **Take in** Substances by **Endocytosis**

1) Some molecules are way too **large** to be taken into a cell by carrier proteins, e.g. proteins, lipids and some carbohydrates.

2) Instead a cell can **surround** a substance with a **section** of its **cell membrane**.

3) The membrane then **pinches off** to form a **vesicle** inside the cell containing the **ingested substance** — this is **endocytosis**.

4) Some cells also take in much **larger objects** by endocytosis — for example, some **white blood cells** (called phagocytes) use endocytosis to take in things like **microorganisms** and **dead cells** so that they can destroy them.

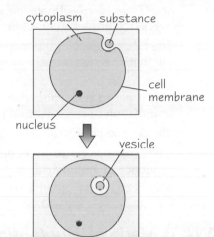

Cells can **Secrete** Substances by **Exocytosis**

1) Some substances **produced** by the cell (e.g. **digestive enzymes**, **hormones**, **lipids**) need to be **released** from the cell — this is done by **exocytosis**.

2) **Vesicles** containing these substances **pinch off** from the sacs of the **Golgi apparatus** (a structure that processes new proteins and lipids — see p. 23) and **move towards** the cell membrane.

3) The vesicles **fuse** with the **cell membrane** and **release** their contents **outside** the cell.

4) Some substances (like membrane proteins) **aren't** released outside the cell — instead they are **inserted** straight into the cell membrane.

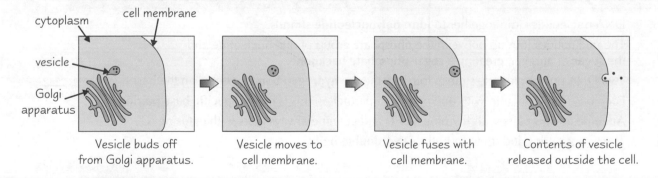

Vesicle buds off from Golgi apparatus.

Vesicle moves to cell membrane.

Vesicle fuses with cell membrane.

Contents of vesicle released outside the cell.

Practice Questions

Q1 What is active transport?

Q2 Which molecule provides the energy for active transport?

Exam Questions

Q1 Describe the role of membrane proteins in facilitated diffusion. [6 marks]

Q2 Explain the difference between endocytosis and exocytosis. [4 marks]

Revision — like working against a concentration gradient...

Wouldn't it be great if you could revise by endocytosis — you could just stick this book on your head and your brain would slowly surround it and take it in... actually when I put it like that it sounds a bit gross. Maybe just stick to good old 'closing the book and scribbling down the diagrams till you know them off by heart'.

DNA

This page is for AQA Unit 2, Edexcel Unit 1 and OCR Unit 2.
This section's all about genetic information — the instructions contained within DNA.

DNA is Used to Store Genetic Information

1) Your DNA (deoxyribonucleic acid) contains your **genetic information** — that's **all the instructions** needed to **grow and develop** from a fertilised egg to a fully grown adult.

2) The DNA molecules are really **long** and are **coiled** up very tightly, so a lot of genetic information (all that's needed to make you) can fit into a **small space** in the cell nucleus.

3) DNA molecules have a **paired structure** (see below), which makes it much easier to **copy itself**. This is called **self-replication** (see p. 52). It's important for **cell division** and for passing genetic information from **generation to generation**.

4) The double-helix structure means DNA is **very stable** in the cell.

5) DNA contains **genes** — **sections of DNA** that code (contain the instructions) for a specific **sequence of amino acids** that forms a particular **protein**. See page 40.

6) **RNA** (ribonucleic acid) is similar in structure to DNA. It's involved in making **proteins** (see p. 40).

DNA is Made of Nucleotides that Contain a Sugar, a Phosphate and a Base

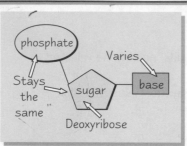

1) DNA is a **polynucleotide** — it's made up of lots of **nucleotides** joined together.

2) Each nucleotide is made from a **pentose sugar** (with 5 carbon atoms), a **phosphate** group and a **nitrogenous base**.

3) The **sugar** in DNA nucleotides is a **deoxyribose** sugar.

4) Each nucleotide has the **same sugar and phosphate**. The **base** on each nucleotide can **vary** though.

5) There are **four** possible bases — adenine (**A**), thymine (**T**), cytosine (**C**) and guanine (**G**).

Two Polynucleotide Strands Join Together to Form a Double-Helix

1) DNA nucleotides join together to form **polynucleotide strands**.

2) The nucleotides join up between the **phosphate** group of one nucleotide and the **sugar** of another, creating a **sugar-phosphate backbone**.

3) **Two** DNA polynucleotide strands join together by **hydrogen bonding** between the bases.

4) Each base can only join with one particular partner — this is called **specific base pairing**.

5) **Adenine** always pairs with **thymine** (**A - T**) and **guanine** always pairs with **cytosine** (**G - C**).

6) The two strands **wind up** to form the **DNA double-helix**.

Specific base pairing is also called complementary base pairing.

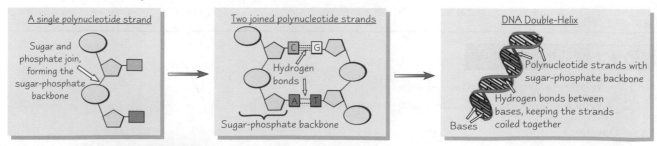

A single polynucleotide strand

Sugar and phosphate join, forming the sugar-phosphate backbone

Two joined polynucleotide strands

Hydrogen bonds

Sugar-phosphate backbone

DNA Double-Helix

Polynucleotide strands with sugar-phosphate backbone

Hydrogen bonds between bases, keeping the strands coiled together

Bases

RNA is Very Similar to DNA   *Edexcel and OCR only*

Like DNA, RNA is made of nucleotides that contain one of four different bases. The nucleotides also form a polynucleotide strand with a sugar-phosphate backbone. But RNA **differs** from DNA in three main ways:

1) The **sugar** in RNA nucleotides is a **ribose sugar** (not deoxyribose).

2) The nucleotides form a **single polynucleotide strand** (not a double one).

3) **Uracil** replaces thymine as a base. Uracil **always pairs** with **adenine** in RNA.

DNA

This page is for AQA Unit 2 only. If you're doing Edexcel or OCR you can skip straight to the questions.

DNA is **Stored Differently** in **Different Organisms**

Although the **structure** of DNA is the same in all organisms, **eukaryotic** and **prokaryotic** cells store DNA in slightly different ways. (For a recap on the differences between prokaryotic and eukaryotic cells see p. 22.)

Eukaryotic DNA is **Linear** and Associated with **Proteins**

1) Eukaryotic cells contain **linear** DNA molecules that exist as **chromosomes** — thread-like structures, each made up of **one long molecule** of DNA.

2) The DNA molecule is **really long** so it has to be **wound up** so it can **fit** into the nucleus.

3) The DNA molecule is wound around **proteins** (called **histones**).

4) Histone proteins also help to **support** the DNA.

5) The DNA (and protein) is then coiled up **very tightly** to make a **compact chromosome**.

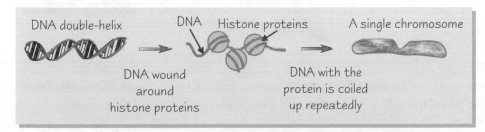

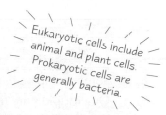

Eukaryotic cells include animal and plant cells. Prokaryotic cells are generally bacteria.

DNA Molecules are **Shorter** and **Circular** in **Prokaryotes**

1) Prokaryotes also carry DNA as **chromosomes** — but the DNA molecules are **shorter** and **circular**.

2) The DNA **isn't** wound around proteins — it condenses to fit in the cell by **supercoiling**.

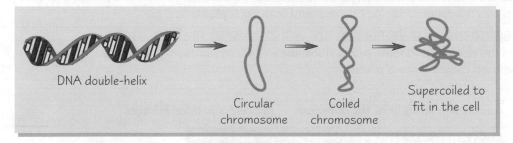

If one more person confused Clifford with supercoiled DNA, he'd have 'em.

Practice Questions

Q1 What are the three main components of nucleotides?

Q2 Name the four possible bases found in DNA.

Q3 What type of bonds join the bases together?

Exam Questions

Q1 Fill in the missing nucleotides on the diagram opposite.  [1 mark]

Q2 Describe, using diagrams where appropriate, how nucleotides are joined together in DNA and how two single polynucleotide strands of DNA are joined. [4 marks]

Give me a D, give me an N, give me an A! What do you get? — very confused...

You need to learn the structure of DNA — the polynucleotide strands, the hydrogen bonds, and don't forget the specific (complementary) base pairing. You need to learn all this before moving on, or you'll struggle later.

Genes and Protein Synthesis

These pages are for AQA Unit 2, Edexcel Unit 1 and OCR Unit 2.

Here comes some truly exciting stuff — genes, RNA and protein synthesis.

DNA Contains *Genes* Which are *Instructions* for *Proteins*

1) Genes are **sections of DNA**. They're found on **chromosomes**.

2) Genes **code** for **proteins** (polypeptides) — they contain the **instructions** to make them.

3) Proteins are made from **amino acids**.

4) Different proteins have a **different number** and **order** of amino acids.

5) It's the **order** of **nucleotide bases** in a gene that determines the **order of amino acids** in a particular **protein**.

6) Each amino acid is coded for by a sequence of **three bases** (called a **triplet** or a **codon**) in a gene.

7) Different sequences of **bases** code for different **amino acids**. For example:

Polypeptide is just another word for a protein.

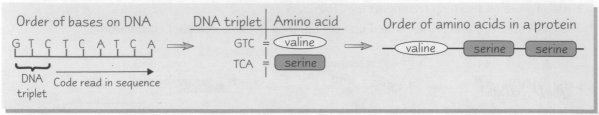

Order of bases on DNA
G T C T C A T C A
DNA triplet → Code read in sequence

DNA triplet	Amino acid
GTC	= valine
TCA	= serine

Order of amino acids in a protein
valine — serine — serine

8) Some amino acids are coded for by **more than one** triplet, e.g. CGA, CGG, CGT and CGC **all** code for arginine.

9) Other triplets are used to tell the cell when to **start** and **stop** production of the protein — these are called **start** and **stop** signals (**codons**). They are found at the beginning and end of a gene. E.g. TAG is a stop signal.

If you're doing AQA you can skip straight to the questions.

DNA is *Copied* into *RNA* for *Protein Synthesis*

1) DNA molecules are found in the **nucleus** of the cell, but the organelles for protein synthesis (**ribosomes**, see p. 23) are found in the **cytoplasm**.

2) DNA is too large to move out of the nucleus, so a section is **copied** into **RNA**.

3) The RNA **leaves** the nucleus and joins with a **ribosome** in the cytoplasm, where it can be used to synthesise a **protein**.

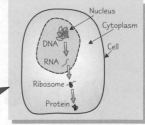

If you're doing OCR you can skip straight to the questions — the rest is just for Edexcel.

First Stage *of* Protein Synthesis — *Transcription*

During transcription an **RNA copy** of a gene is made in the **nucleus**:

1) The **hydrogen bonds** between the two DNA strands in a **gene** break, **separating** the strands, and the DNA molecule **uncoils** at that point.

2) One of the strands is then used as a **template** to make an RNA copy, called **messenger RNA** (**mRNA**). The template strand is called the **antisense** strand.

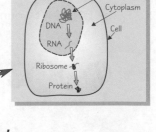

- **mRNA** is a **single polynucleotide** molecule.
- **Specific base pairing** means that the mRNA ends up being an exact **reverse copy** of the DNA template section (except the base **T** is replaced by **U** in **RNA**).

3) Free **RNA nucleotides** line up alongside the template strand. Once the RNA nucleotides have **paired up** with their **specific bases** on the DNA strand they're joined together, forming an **mRNA** molecule.

4) The **mRNA** moves **out** of the **nucleus** through a nuclear pore, and attaches to a **ribosome** in the cytoplasm, where the next stage of protein synthesis takes place (see next page).

5) When enough mRNA has been produced, the hydrogen bonds between the uncoiled strands of DNA re-form, and the strands **coil back into a double helix**.

Genes and Protein Synthesis

Second Stage of Protein Synthesis — Translation

Translation occurs at the **ribosomes** in the **cytoplasm**. During **translation**, **amino acids** are stuck together to make a polypeptide chain (protein), following the order of bases on the mRNA.

1) The **mRNA** attaches itself to a **ribosome** and **transfer RNA (tRNA)** molecules carry **amino acids** to the ribosome.

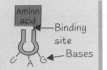

- **tRNA** is a folded molecule made of a **single polynucleotide strand**.
- Each tRNA molecule has a **binding site** at one end, where a specific **amino acid** attaches.
- Each tRNA molecule also has a specific sequence of **three bases** at one end of it.

2) A tRNA molecule, with **complementary bases** to the **first triplet of bases** (codon) on the mRNA, attaches itself to the mRNA by **specific base pairing**.

3) A second tRNA molecule attaches itself to the **next triplet of bases** on the mRNA in the **same way**.

The three bases on the tRNA molecule are called the anticodon.

4) The two amino acids attached to the tRNA molecules are **joined together** by a **peptide bond**. The first tRNA molecule **moves away**, leaving its amino acid behind.

5) A third tRNA molecule binds to the **next triplet** on the mRNA. Its amino acid **binds** to the first two and the second tRNA molecule **moves away**.

6) This process continues, producing a chain of linked amino acids (a **polypeptide chain**), until there's a **stop signal** on the mRNA molecule.

7) The polypeptide chain (protein) moves away from the ribosome and translation is complete.

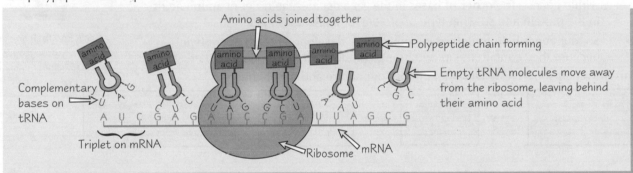

Practice Questions

Q1 What is a DNA triplet?

Q2 What determines the order of amino acids in a protein?

Q3 Why is DNA copied into RNA?

Q4 Where is messenger RNA formed?

Q5 Where does translation take place?

Amino acid	DNA triplet
Glycine	GGC
Glutamic acid	GAG
Proline	CCG
Tryptophan	TGG

Exam Questions

Q1 Use the table above to write the protein sequence coded for by the DNA sequence TGGCCGCCGGAG. [1 mark]

Q2 Describe the process of protein synthesis. [10 marks]

Genes contain instructions — wash at 40 °C...

Quite a few terms to learn here I'm afraid. And some are quite similar, which makes it even more confusing. Worse still, some mean the same thing, like three bases is a base triplet, which is also called a codon. Just copy them out over and over again until you're absolutely sure you know what every word on this page means. Genetics is such fun...

Genes and Development

These pages are for AQA Unit 2 only. If you're doing Edexcel you can skip to p. 46. OCR can go to the next section.

Genes can Exist in Different Forms Called Alleles

A gene can exist in more than one form — these forms are called **alleles**. The order of bases in each allele is slightly different, so they code for **slightly different versions** of the **same characteristic**. For example, the gene that codes for **blood group** exists as one of three alleles — one codes for group O, another for group A and the other for group B.

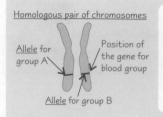

Homologous pair of chromosomes

Allele for group A

Position of the gene for blood group

Allele for group B

Our DNA is stored as **chromosomes** in the nucleus of cells. Humans have **23 pairs** of chromosomes, 46 in total — two number 1s, two number 2s, two number 3s etc. Pairs of matching chromosomes (e.g. the 1s) are called **homologous pairs**. In a homologous pair both chromosomes are the same size and have the **same genes**, although they could have **different alleles**. Alleles coding for the same characteristic are found at the **same position** (**locus**) on each chromosome in a homologous pair.

The Nature and Development of Organisms is Determined by Genes

1) **Enzymes** speed up most of our **metabolic pathways** — the chemical reactions that occur in the body. These pathways determine how we **grow and develop**.

2) Because enzymes control the metabolic pathways, they **contribute** to our **development**, and ultimately what we look like (our **phenotype**).

3) All enzymes are **proteins**, which are built using the **instructions** contained within genes. The **order of bases** in the gene decides the order of **amino acids** in the protein and so what type of protein (or enzyme) is made.

4) So, our genes help to **determine** our **nature**, **development** and **phenotype** because they contain the information to **produce** all our proteins and enzymes.

Ken's bad fashion sense was literally down to his genes. (A genes/jeans joke — classic CGP.)

This flowchart shows how **DNA** determines our **nature** and **development**:

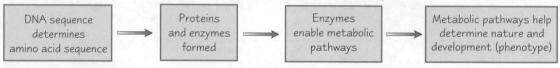

| DNA sequence determines amino acid sequence | → | Proteins and enzymes formed | → | Enzymes enable metabolic pathways | → | Metabolic pathways help determine nature and development (phenotype) |

Gene Mutations can Result in Non-functioning Proteins

1) **Mutations** are **changes** in the **base sequence** of an organism's **DNA**. So, mutations can produce **new alleles** of genes.

2) A gene codes for a particular protein, so if the sequence of bases in a gene changes, a **non-functional** or **different protein** could be produced.

3) All **enzymes** are **proteins**. If there's a mutation in a gene that codes for an enzyme, then that enzyme may not **fold up** properly. This may produce an **active site** that's the wrong shape and so a **non-functional enzyme**.

See p.16 for a recap of enzymes and active sites.

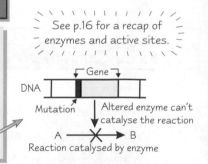

DNA

Mutation

Gene

Altered enzyme can't catalyse the reaction

A ──✗──> B

Reaction catalysed by enzyme

Not All the DNA in Eukaryotic Cells Codes for Proteins

1) Genes in eukaryotic DNA contain sections that **don't code** for amino acids.

2) These sections of DNA are called **introns** (all the bits that do code for amino acids are called **exons**).

3) Introns are **removed** during **protein synthesis**. Their purpose isn't known for sure.

4) Eukaryotic DNA also contains regions of **multiple repeats** outside of genes.

5) These are DNA sequences that **repeat** over and over.

6) These areas **don't code** for amino acids either.

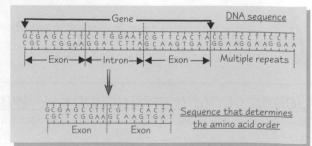

Gene

DNA sequence

GCGAGCCTTCCTGGAAT CGTTCACTACCTTCCTTCCTTCCT
CGCTCGGAAGGACCTTAG CAAGTGATGGAAGGAAGGA

Exon — Intron — Exon — Multiple repeats

GCGAGCCTTCGTTCACTA
CGCTCGGAAGCAAGTGAT

Exon — Exon

Sequence that determines the amino acid order

Genes and Development

You May Have to *Interpret Experimental Work* About *DNA*

In the exam you might have to interpret **experimental evidence** that shows the **role** and **importance** of DNA.
Here are some examples of the **early experiments** that were carried out. You **don't** need to learn them, just **understand** how the results show the role and importance of DNA and that DNA is the **genetic material**.

Evidence of hereditary molecules

An experiment with **mice** and two kinds of **pneumonia**, a **disease-causing** strain (**D**) and a **non disease-causing** strain (**N**), showed there's a **hereditary molecule** (genetic material).

1) Mice injected with **strain D died** and with **strain N survived**.

2) **Killed D** was injected into mice — they **survived**.

3) **Killed D** and **live N** were injected together — they **died**.

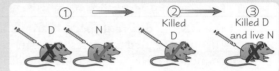

Killed D had **passed on** an inheritance molecule to the live N strain, making it **capable** of causing **disease**.

Evidence that DNA is the genetic material

Scientists were unsure if the hereditary molecule was **DNA**, **RNA** or **protein**. They investigated it by treating the killed D strain with **protease** (destroys protein), **RNase** (destroys RNA) or **DNase** (destroys DNA) and then **injecting** it along with live N strain into mice. The strains that had been treated with DNase **didn't** kill the mice, so DNA was shown to be the **hereditary molecule** (genetic material).

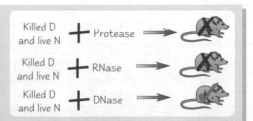

More evidence that DNA is the genetic material

When viruses infect bacteria they **inject** their genetic material into the **cell**. So whatever viral material is found **inside** the bacterial cell must be the genetic material.

1) Scientists labelled the DNA of some viruses with radioactive **phosphate**, ^{32}P (**blue**), and the **protein** of some more viruses with radioactive **sulfur**, ^{35}S (**red**).

2) They then let the viruses **infect** some bacteria.

3) When they **separated** the bacteria and viruses they found ^{32}P (**blue**) inside the bacteria and ^{35}S (**red**) on the outside, providing **evidence** that DNA was the **genetic material**.

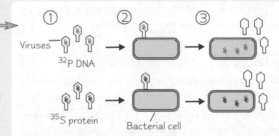

Practice Questions

Q1 What is an allele?

Q2 What is the name for the position a gene occupies on a chromosome?

Q3 What is meant by the term phenotype?

Q4 How can a mutation result in a non-functional enzyme?

Q5 What is an intron?

Exam Question

Q1 Describe how the DNA of an organism helps to determine its nature and development. [4 marks]

*What do you call an eel named Alison?**

Luckily for you, you don't need to learn those three DNA experiments off by heart. What you do need to learn is how they show that DNA is the genetic material and why it's so important, just in case it pops up in the exam.

*An allele.

Genetic Diversity

These pages are for AQA Unit 2 only.

Genetic diversity describes the variety of alleles in a species or population.

Variation in DNA can Lead to Genetic Diversity

Genetic diversity is all about **variety**. The **more variety** in a population's DNA, the **more genetically diverse** it is.

1) Genetic diversity exists **within** a species. The DNA within a species varies **very little** though. **All** the members of the species will have the **same genes** but **different alleles**. For example, approximately 99.5% of DNA is the same in all humans.

2) The DNA of **different species** varies **a lot**. Members of different species will have **different genes**. The more **related** a species is, the more DNA they **share**, e.g. around 94% of human and chimpanzee DNA is the same, and around 85% of human and mouse DNA is the same.

Genetic diversity within a species, or a **population** of a species, is caused by differences in **alleles**, but new genes **don't appear** and old genes **don't disappear**. For example, all humans have a gene for blood type, but different alleles (versions) of blood type may come and go. The **more alleles** in a population, the **more genetically diverse** it is. Genetic diversity within a population is **increased** by:

1) **Mutations** in the DNA — forming new alleles.

2) Different alleles being introduced into a population when individuals from another population **migrate into them** and reproduce. This is known as **gene flow**.

Genetic Bottlenecks Reduce Genetic Diversity

A **genetic bottleneck** is an event that causes a big **reduction** in a population, e.g. when a large number of organisms within a population **die** before reproducing. This reduces the number of **different alleles** in the gene pool and so reduces **genetic diversity**. The survivors **reproduce** and a larger population is created from a few individuals.

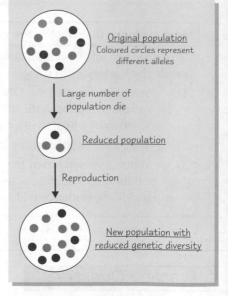

Original population
Coloured circles represent different alleles

Large number of population die

Reduced population

Reproduction

New population with reduced genetic diversity

Example — Northern Elephant Seals

Northern elephant seals were hunted by humans in the late 1800s. Their **original population** was reduced to around **50 seals** who have since produced a population of around 100 000. This new population has **very little** genetic diversity compared to the southern elephant seals who never suffered such a **reduction** in numbers.

The gene pool is the complete range of alleles in a population.

Colin's offer to introduce new alleles into the population had yet to be accepted.

The Founder Effect is a Type of Genetic Bottleneck

The **founder effect** describes what happens when just a **few** organisms from a population start a **new colony**. Only a small number of organisms have contributed their **alleles** to the **gene pool**. There's more **inbreeding** in the new population, which can lead to a **higher incidence** of genetic disease.

Example — The Amish

The **Amish population** of North America are all descended from a **small** number of Swiss who **migrated** there. The population shows **little genetic diversity**. They have remained **isolated** from the surrounding population due to their **religious beliefs**, so **few new alleles** have been introduced. The population suffers an unusually high incidence of certain **genetic disorders**.

The founder effect can occur as a result of **migration** leading to geographical **separation** or if a new colony is separated from the original population for **another reason**, such as **religion**.

Genetic Diversity

Selective Breeding Involves Choosing Which Organisms Reproduce

Changes in genetic diversity aren't just brought about by **natural events** like bottlenecks or migration.
Selective breeding of plants and animals by humans has resulted in **reduced genetic diversity** in some populations.
Selective breeding involves humans **selecting** which domesticated animals or strains of plants **reproduce** together in
order to produce **high-yielding** breeds. For example:

1) A farmer wants a strain of **corn plant** that is tall and produces lots of ears, so he **breeds** a **tall** corn strain with one that produces **multiple ears**.

2) He selects the **offspring** that are tallest and have most ears, and breeds them **together**.

3) The farmer **continues** this until he produces a **very tall** strain that produces **multiple ears** of corn.

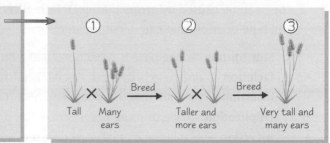

Selective breeding leads to a **reduction** in genetic diversity — once an organism with the **desired characteristics**
(e.g. tall with multiple ears) has been produced, only that type of organism will continue being **bred**. So only similar
organisms with **similar traits** and therefore **similar alleles** are bred together. It results in a type of **genetic bottleneck**
as it reduces the **number of alleles** in the gene pool.

Selective Breeding can Cause Problems for the Organisms Involved

You need to be able to discuss the **ethical issues** involved with selective breeding.

Arguments for selective breeding	Arguments against selective breeding
1) It can produce **high-yielding** animals and plants.	1) It can cause **health problems**. E.g. dairy cows are often **lame** and have a **short life expectancy** because of the extra strain making and carrying loads of milk puts on their bodies.
2) It can be used to produce animals and plants that have increased **resistance** to disease. This means farmers have to use **fewer** drugs and pesticides.	2) It **reduces genetic diversity**, which results in an increased incidence of **genetic disease** and an **increased susceptibility** to new diseases because of the lack of **alleles** in the population.
3) Animals and plants could be bred to have increased tolerance of bad conditions, e.g. **drought** or **cold**.	

Practice Questions

Q1 How does the founder effect reduce genetic diversity?

Q2 Describe the process of selective breeding.

Q3 Describe two arguments for and two arguments against selective breeding.

Exam Questions

Q1 Describe what a genetic bottleneck is and explain how it causes reduced genetic
diversity within a population. [3 marks]

Q2 Describe what selective breeding is and explain why it leads to reduced genetic diversity
within a population. [3 marks]

Sausage dogs didn't come from the wild...

*You might think that selective breeding is a relatively new thing that we've developed with our knowledge of genetics...
but you'd be wrong. We've been selectively breeding animals for yonks and yonks. All the different breeds of dog are
just selectively bred strains which came from a general wolf-type dog back in the day. Even sausage dogs. Amazing...*

Mutations and Inheritance

The rest of this section is for Edexcel Unit 1 only.

The rest of this section is all about genetic disorders — inherited disorders caused by abnormal genes or chromosomes.

Some Genetic Disorders are Caused by Mutations

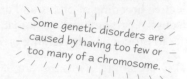
Some genetic disorders are caused by having too few or too many of a chromosome.

1) Mutations are **changes** to the **base sequence** of DNA.

2) They can be caused by **errors** during **DNA replication**.

3) The **type** of errors that can occur include:

- **Substitution** — one base is substituted with another, e.g. ATGCCT becomes ATTCCT (G is **swapped** for T).
- **Deletion** — one base is deleted, e.g. ATGCCT becomes ATCCT (G is **deleted**).
- **Insertion** — an extra base is added, e.g. ATGCCT becomes ATGACCT (an extra A is **added**)
- **Duplication** — one or more bases are repeated, e.g. ATGCCT becomes ATGCCCCT (two Cs are **duplicated**).
- **Inversion** — a sequence of bases is reversed, e.g. ATGCCT becomes ATGTCC (CCT is **reversed**).

4) The **order** of **DNA bases** in a gene determines the **order of amino acids** in a particular **protein**. If a mutation occurs in a gene, the **primary structure** (the sequence of amino acids) of the protein it codes for could be **altered**:

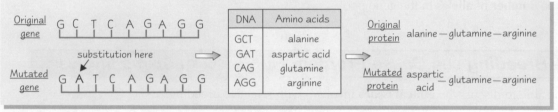

This could **change** the final **3D shape** of the protein so it **doesn't work properly**.

5) If a mutation occurs in a **gene** it can cause a **genetic disorder**, which is then **passed on**. E.g. **cystic fibrosis** (**CF**) is a genetic disorder caused by a mutation in a gene. The protein the gene codes for is important for **mucus production** (see page 48 for more details).

6) Some genetic disorders can be caused by lots of **different mutations**, e.g. over 1000 possible mutations are known to cause CF.

You Need to Know These Genetic Terms

TERM	DESCRIPTION
Gene	A sequence of bases on a DNA molecule that codes for a protein, which results in a characteristic, e.g. the gene for eye colour.
Allele	A different version of a gene. Most plants and animals, including humans, have two copies of each gene, one from each parent. The two copies can be the same or they can be different. Different versions (alleles) have slightly different base sequences, which code for different versions of the same characteristic, e.g. brown eyes and blue eyes. They're represented using letters, e.g. the allele for brown eyes (B) and the allele for blue eyes (b).
Genotype	The alleles a person has, e.g. BB, Bb or bb for eye colour.
Phenotype	The characteristics the alleles produce, e.g. brown eyes.
Dominant	An allele whose characteristic appears in the phenotype even when there's only one copy, e.g. the allele for brown eyes (B) is dominant — if a person's genotype is Bb or BB, they'll have brown eyes. Dominant alleles are shown by a capital letter.
Recessive	An allele whose characteristic only appears in the phenotype if two copies are present, e.g. the allele for blue eyes (b) is recessive — if a person's genotype is bb, they'll have blue eyes. Recessive alleles are shown by a lower case letter
Homozygote	An organism that carries two copies of the same allele, e.g. BB or bb.
Heterozygote	An organism that carries two different alleles, e.g. Bb.
Carrier	If a recessive allele can cause disease, a carrier is someone who has one dominant and one recessive allele (heterozygous). They won't have the disease but they carry a copy of the allele for the disease.

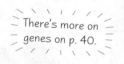
There's more on genes on p. 40.

Unfortunately, liking leotards and '80s legwarmers is a dominant characteristic.

Mutations and Inheritance

Genetic Diagrams show the Possible Alleles of Offspring

Monohybrid inheritance is the inheritance of a **single characteristic** controlled by **different** alleles. **Genetic diagrams** can be used to predict the **genotypes** and **phenotypes** of the **offspring** produced if two parents are **crossed** (**bred**). You need to be able to **interpret** genetic diagrams for characteristics like garden pea plant seed morphology and height.

Seed Morphology

1) The **shape** of garden pea seeds is controlled by a **single** gene with **two alleles**.

2) The allele for **smooth** seeds (**S**) is **dominant** over the allele for **wrinkled** seeds (**s**).

3) The diagram below shows the predicted genotypes and phenotypes of the offspring if a **homozygous** pea plant with smooth seeds (**SS**) is crossed with a **heterozygous** pea plant with smooth seeds (**Ss**).

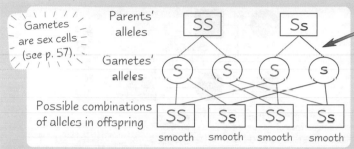

Gametes are sex cells (see p. 57).

The lines show all the possible ways the parents' alleles could combine.

Predicted genotypes and phenotypes:

- 2 in 4 (**50%**) **chance** of offspring having the **genotype SS**.
- 2 in 4 (**50%**) **chance** of offspring having the **genotype Ss**.
- **100%** chance of offspring having **smooth** seeds.

Plant Height

1) The **height** of garden pea plants is also controlled by a **single** gene with **two alleles**.

2) The allele for **tall** plants (**T**) is **dominant** over the allele for **dwarf** plants (**t**).

3) The diagram below shows the predicted genotypes and phenotypes of the offspring if **two heterozygous** pea plants (**Tt**) are crossed:

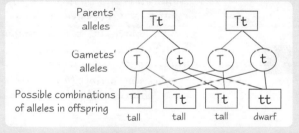

Predicted genotypes and phenotypes:

- 2 in 4 (**50%**) **chance** of offspring having the **genotype Tt** (phenotype = **tall**).
- 1 in 4 (**25%**) chance of offspring having the **genotype TT** (phenotype = **tall**).
- 1 in 4 (**25%**) chance of offspring having the **genotype tt** (phenotype = **dwarf**).

So there's a **75%** (3 in 4) chance of offspring being **tall**.

Practice Questions

Q1 What are mutations?

Q2 Explain the difference between a dominant and a recessive allele.

Q3 What is monohybrid inheritance?

Exam Question

Q1 A garden pea plant is heterozygous for seed colour. The allele for yellow colour (Y) is dominant over the allele for green colour (y).

a) Give the genotype and phenotype of the heterozygous plant. [2 marks]

b) Complete the genetic diagram above to show the possible genotypes of the offspring produced if the heterozygous plant is crossed with a homozygous plant with green seeds. [3 marks]

c) Give the predicted ratio of green seeds to yellow seeds in the offspring from the genetic cross in part b). [1 mark]

What do you get if you cross a one-legged donkey with a one-eyed donkey?*

There's quite a lot to get to grips with on these two pages — that list of genetic terms just goes on and on and on. You won't get very far in this section without learning them first though, so just grin and bear it. Oh... and learn it of course.

Inheritance of Genetic Disorders

These pages are just for Edexcel Unit 1.

Seeing as you enjoyed those genetic diagrams so much, here's another page of them — only this time they're ever so slightly different...

Genetic Pedigree Diagrams Show How Traits Run in Families

Genetic pedigree diagrams show an **inherited trait** (characteristic) in a group of **related individuals**. You need to be able to **interpret** genetic pedigree diagrams for the **genetic disorders** cystic fibrosis, albinism and thalassaemia. Here are some examples of pedigree diagrams for these genetic disorders:

Cystic fibrosis (CF)

Cystic fibrosis is an inherited disorder that mainly affects the **respiratory**, **digestive** and **reproductive systems** (see next page). It's caused by a **recessive** allele (f), so a person will only have the disorder if they're **homozygous** for the allele (ff) — they must inherit one recessive allele **from each parent**. If a person is **heterozygous** (Ff), they **won't** have CF but they'll be a **carrier**.

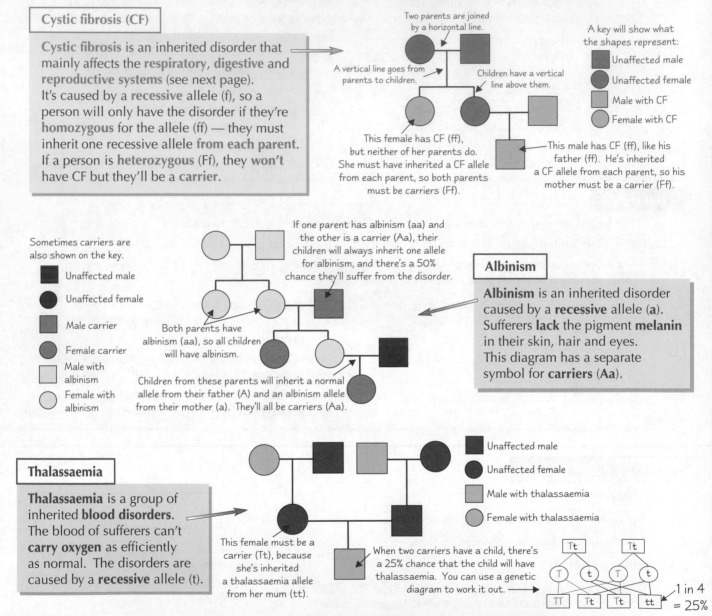

Two parents are joined by a horizontal line.

A vertical line goes from parents to children.

Children have a vertical line above them.

A key will show what the shapes represent:
- Unaffected male
- Unaffected female
- Male with CF
- Female with CF

This female has CF (ff), but neither of her parents do. She must have inherited a CF allele from each parent, so both parents must be carriers (Ff).

This male has CF (ff), like his father (ff). He's inherited a CF allele from each parent, so his mother must be a carrier (Ff).

Sometimes carriers are also shown on the key.
- Unaffected male
- Unaffected female
- Male carrier
- Female carrier
- Male with albinism
- Female with albinism

If one parent has albinism (aa) and the other is a carrier (Aa), their children will always inherit one allele for albinism, and there's a 50% chance they'll suffer from the disorder.

Both parents have albinism (aa), so all children will have albinism.

Children from these parents will inherit a normal allele from their father (A) and an albinism allele from their mother (a). They'll all be carriers (Aa).

Albinism

Albinism is an inherited disorder caused by a **recessive** allele (a). Sufferers **lack** the pigment **melanin** in their skin, hair and eyes. This diagram has a separate symbol for **carriers** (Aa).

Thalassaemia

Thalassaemia is a group of inherited **blood disorders**. The blood of sufferers can't **carry oxygen** as efficiently as normal. The disorders are caused by a **recessive** allele (t).

This female must be a carrier (Tt), because she's inherited a thalassaemia allele from her mum (tt).

When two carriers have a child, there's a 25% chance that the child will have thalassaemia. You can use a genetic diagram to work it out. →

- Unaffected male
- Unaffected female
- Male with thalassaemia
- Female with thalassaemia

Tt × Tt → T t T t → TT Tt Tt tt → 1 in 4 = 25%

Cystic Fibrosis Causes the Production of Thick Sticky Mucus

1) Cystic fibrosis is caused by a **mutation** in the **gene** that codes for the **CFTR** protein (**C**ystic **F**ibrosis **T**ransmembrane Conductance **R**egulator).

2) CFTR is a **carrier protein**. It transports **chloride ions** out of cells and into mucus — this causes water to move **into** the mucus by **osmosis**, which makes mucus **watery**.

3) **Mutant** CFTR protein is much **less efficient** at transporting chloride ions **out** of the cell, so **less water moves out by osmosis**. This makes the mucus of people with CF abnormally **thick** and **sticky**.

4) This thick and sticky mucus causes **problems** in the **respiratory**, **digestive** and **reproductive systems**.

See page 34 for more on osmosis and page 36 for more on carrier proteins.

Inheritance of Genetic Disorders

Cystic Fibrosis Affects the **Respiratory System**...

Everybody has **mucus** in their respiratory system — it helps **prevent lung infections** by trapping **microorganisms**. The mucus (including the microorganisms) is transported towards the throat by **cilia** (small **hair-like** structures that beat to move mucus along). In people suffering from CF the mucus is abnormally **thick** and **sticky**, which causes some problems:

1) The cilia are **unable** to **move** the mucus towards the throat because it's so thick and sticky.
2) This means the **mucus builds up** in the **airways**.
3) Some airways can become completely **blocked** by the mucus — **gas exchange** can't take place in the area **below the blockage**.
4) This means that the **surface area** available for gas exchange is **reduced**, causing breathing difficulties.
5) Sufferers are also more prone to **lung infections** as mucus containing microorganisms can't be removed.

See page 106 for more on gas exchange in the lungs.

...the **Digestive System**...

Everyone also has mucus in their digestive system. The abnormally thick mucus produced by people suffering from CF can also cause **digestive problems** because:

1) The **tube** that connects the **pancreas** to the **small intestine** can become **blocked** with mucus — preventing **digestive enzymes** produced by the pancreas from **reaching** the small intestine. This reduces the sufferers ability to **digest food** and so **fewer nutrients** can be absorbed.
2) The mucus can cause **cysts** (**growths**) to form in the **pancreas**. These **inhibit** the **production** of **enzymes**, which also reduces the ability to digest food and absorb nutrients.
3) The mucus **lining** the **small intestine** is **abnormally thick** — this inhibits the **absorption** of nutrients.

...and the **Reproductive System**

Mucus is also secreted by the reproductive system — it helps to **prevent infections** and **transport sex cells** (sperm or eggs). The thick and sticky mucus of CF sufferers causes problems here because:

1) In men, the **tubes** connecting the **testicles** (where sperm are produced) to the **penis** are **absent** in some sufferers and can become **blocked** by the thick mucus in others. This means that any **sperm** produced **can't reach the penis**.
2) In women, thickened **cervical mucus** can **prevent** the sperm from **reaching the egg**. The sperm has to travel through this mucus to reach the egg — thick mucus reduces the **motility** of the sperm, reducing its chances of **making it** to the egg.

Jokes about genetic disorders aren't really PC — so here's a picture of a bear in a German police car and a chap sporting a silly hat.

Practice Questions

Q1 What is a genetic pedigree diagram?

Q2 Why do people suffering from cystic fibrosis have abnormally thick and sticky mucus?

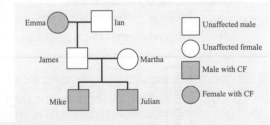

Exam Question

Q1 The genetic pedigree diagram above shows the inheritance of cystic fibrosis (CF) in one family.

a) Name one female who is homozygous for the CF allele and one individual who is a carrier. [2 marks]

b) If James and Martha have another child, what is the chance it will have CF? Show your working. [3 marks]

c) Describe and explain the effect of CF on the digestive system. [8 marks]

Pedigree Diagram — because your dog's worth it...

Pedigree diagrams aren't as scary as they look, just work through them slowly. And remember — with recessive disorders affected individuals are always homozygous, so any children they have will always have at least one recessive allele.

Genetic Screening and Gene Therapy

These pages are just for Edexcel Unit 1.

Most genetic disorders can only be treated, not cured, so it's important to be able to screen for these conditions.

There are **Three Main Uses** of **Genetic Screening**

Genetic screening involves analysing **DNA** to see if it contains **alleles** for genetic disorders. The **three** main uses are:

1 Identification of Carriers

1) **Carrier testing** is offered to individuals with a **family history** of genetic disorders.

2) It shows whether people **without** a disorder **carry an allele** that can cause a disorder (e.g. CF).

3) Couples can be tested **before having children** to determine the **chances** of any **future** children having the disorder, e.g. if both parents are **carriers** there's a **25%** chance their child will have the disorder.

4) Carrier testing allows people to make **informed decisions** about things like **whether to have children** and whether to carry out **prenatal testing** if the woman is pregnant (see below).

5) Carrier testing raises **social** and **ethical issues**:

   - Finding out you're a carrier may cause **emotional stress** or affect your ability to **find a partner**.
   - The tests **aren't** always 100% accurate — they could give a **false result**. This means decisions could be based on **incorrect information**.
   - Other genetic **abnormalities** may be found, which could cause **further stress**.
   - There are concerns that the **results** of genetic tests could be used by **employers** or **life insurance companies** — resulting in **genetic discrimination**.

2 Preimplantation Genetic Diagnosis (PGD)

1) **PGD** is carried out on **embryos** produced by *in vitro* fertilisation **(IVF)**.

2) It involves **screening** embryos for genetic disorders **before** they're implanted into the woman.

3) The **advantages** of PGD are that it **reduces** the chance of having a baby with a genetic disorder — only embryos **without** the genetic disorders tested for will be implanted. Also, because it's performed **before implantation**, it avoids the issue of **abortion** that could be raised by **prenatal testing** (see below).

4) PGD also raises **social** and **ethical issues**:

   - It can be used to find out **other characteristics** (e.g. **gender, eye colour**) — leading to concerns that **in the future**, embryos may be selected for other characteristics (**designer babies**).
   - **False results** could provide **incorrect information**.

Selecting for other characteristics is illegal in the UK.

3 Prenatal Testing

1) Prenatal tests involve screening **unborn babies** (fetuses) for genetic disorders.

2) They're offered to pregnant women with a **family history** of genetic disease.

3) There are **two** types of test —

Amniocentesis	Chorionic villus sampling (CVS)
This is carried out at **15-16 weeks** of pregnancy. A sample of **amniotic fluid** (the fluid that surrounds the fetus) is obtained using a very fine **needle**. This fluid contains fetal **cells**. The cells contain **DNA**, which can be **analysed**.	This is carried out at **8-12 weeks** of pregnancy. A sample of **cells** is taken from the **chorionic villi** (part of the fetus that connects it to its mother) using a fine **needle** or a **catheter** (a thin flexible tube). The cells contain fetal **DNA**, which can be **analysed**.

4) Prenatal testing allows parents to make **informed decisions**. If the test is positive, the parents may decide to **have the child** or to have an **abortion**. The results can also help parents to **prepare for the future care** of the child — any **medical treatment** available could be started as soon as the child is born.

5) As with the other forms of testing, prenatal testing raises **social** and **ethical issues**:

   - Prenatal tests slightly **increase** the risk of **miscarriage** (by around 1%).
   - **False results** could provide **incorrect information**.
   - Some people consider it **unethical** to **abort** a fetus because it has a genetic disorder.

Genetic Screening and Gene Therapy

Gene Therapy Could be Used to Cure Genetic Disorders

1) Gene therapy involves **altering** the **alleles** inside cells to cure **genetic disorders**.

2) How you do this depends on whether the genetic disorder is caused by a **dominant allele** or two **recessive alleles**:

Gene therapy is a new method, which isn't being used to treat people yet (some gene therapy treatments are undergoing clinical trials though).

- If it's caused by two **recessive** alleles you can **add** a working **dominant allele** to make up for them.
- If it's caused by a **dominant** allele you can 'silence' the **dominant allele** (e.g. by sticking a bit of DNA in the middle of the allele so it doesn't work any more or by stopping it being used to make the protein).

3) Alleles are inserted into cells using **vectors** (**vehicles** that **carry** the alleles).

4) Different **vectors** can be used, e.g. altered **viruses** that can carry human DNA, **plasmids** (rings of bacterial DNA that can also carry human DNA) or **liposomes** (spheres made of lipid).

5) There are **two types** of gene therapy:

- **Somatic therapy** — this involves changing the alleles in **body cells**, particularly the cells that are **most affected** by the disorder. For example, CF is very **damaging** to the **respiratory system**, so somatic therapy for CF **targets** the epithelial cells lining the lungs. Somatic therapy doesn't affect the individual's **sex cells** (sperm or eggs) though, so any **offspring** could still **inherit** the disease.
- **Germ line therapy** — this involves changing the alleles in the **sex cells**. This means that **every cell** of **any offspring** produced from these cells will be **affected** by the gene therapy and they **won't suffer from the disease**. Germ line therapy in humans is currently illegal though.

Practice Questions

Q1 What is genetic screening?

Q2 Give the two uses of genetic screening other than prenatal testing.

Q3 Describe one ethical issue raised by prenatal testing.

Q4 What does gene therapy involve?

Q5 What is somatic gene therapy?

Q6 What is germ line gene therapy?

Exam Question

Q1 Duchenne muscular dystrophy is a genetic disorder caused by a recessive allele. It's caused by a mutated gene, which normally codes for a protein needed for healthy muscle tissue.

   a) Explain why an individual with a family history of Duchenne muscular dystrophy may be offered carrier testing. [2 marks]

   b) Preimplantation genetic diagnosis is available for Duchenne muscular dystrophy.

      i)   Explain what preimplantation genetic diagnosis is. [1 mark]

      ii) Describe one benefit of preimplantation genetic diagnosis. [1 mark]

      iii) Describe two social or ethical issues raised by preimplantation genetic diagnosis. [2 marks]

   c) Explain how somatic gene therapy could be used to treat Duchenne muscular dystrophy. [2 marks]

Gene therapy — counselling for Levis...

There's lots to learn when it comes to genetic screening and gene therapy. With genetic screening, you need to understand the three main uses, the advantages of each, and all the possible ethical issues. As with any ethics question in the exam, don't forget to cover both the advantages and the issues surrounding it (whatever your personal opinion).

The Cell Cycle and DNA Replication

This page is for AQA Unit 2, Edexcel Unit 1, Edexcel Unit 2, OCR Unit 1 and OCR Unit 2.

Ever wondered how you grow from one tiny cell to a complete whole person? Or how that big cut you got in that horrific guitar strumming incident healed? No, oh... well you grow bigger and heal because your cells replicate and you need to learn the processes involved.

The **Cell Cycle** is the Process of **Cell Growth** and **Division**

AQA Unit 2, Edexcel Unit 2, OCR Unit 1.

The **cell cycle** is the process that all body cells from **multicellular organisms** use to **grow** and **divide**.

1) The cell cycle **starts** when a cell has been produced by cell division and **ends** with the cell dividing to produce two identical cells.

2) The cell cycle consists of a period of **cell growth** and **DNA replication**, called **interphase**, and a period of ⟹ **cell division**, called **mitosis**.

3) Mitosis only occupies a **small percentage** of the cell cycle.

4) Most of the cell cycle is taken up by **interphase**, during which the **genetic material** (DNA) is **copied** and **checked** for any errors that may have occurred during copying.

5) If errors in the genetic material are detected at this stage, the cell may **kill itself**. This prevents any **mutations** (errors) in the DNA from being passed on.

6) Interphase is subdivided into three separate growth stages. These are called G_1, **S** and G_2.

GAP PHASE 2
cell keeps growing and proteins needed for cell division are made

MITOSIS
(the cycle starts and ends here)

GAP PHASE 1
cell grows and new organelles and proteins are made

SYNTHESIS
cell replicates its DNA, ready to divide by mitosis

DNA is **Replicated** in **Interphase**

AQA Unit 2, Edexcel Unit 1, OCR Unit 2.

DNA copies itself before **cell division** so that each new cell has the full amount of DNA.

1) The enzyme **DNA helicase** **breaks** the **hydrogen bonds** between the two **polynucleotide** DNA strands. The helix **unzips** to form two single strands.

Helicase ↓ Breaks the hydrogen bonds

Helix

See p. 38 for more on DNA structure.

Mandy took her cells for a cycle.

2) Each **original** single strand acts as a **template** for a new strand. Free-floating DNA nucleotides join to the **exposed bases** on each original template strand by **specific base pairing** — A with T and C with G.

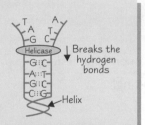

Bases match up using specific base pairing.

Specific base pairing is also called complementary base pairing.

3) The nucleotides on the new strand are joined together by the enzyme **DNA polymerase**. **Hydrogen bonds form** between the bases on the original and new strand.

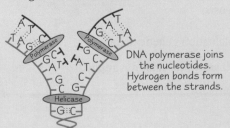

DNA polymerase joins the nucleotides. Hydrogen bonds form between the strands.

4) Each new DNA molecule contains **one strand** from the **original** DNA molecule and one **new strand**.

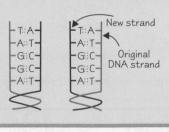

New strand

Original DNA strand

This type of copying is called **semi-conservative replication** because **half** of the new strands of DNA are from the **original** piece of DNA.

The Cell Cycle and DNA Replication

This page is for Edexcel Unit 1 only. If you're doing AQA or OCR, you can skip straight to the questions.

Meselson and Stahl Provided Evidence for Semi-conservative Replication

Before Meselson and Stahl's experiment people were unsure if DNA replication was **semi-conservative** or **conservative**. **Semi-conservative** replication would produce new DNA molecules containing **one original strand** and **one new strand**. If the method was **conservative**, the original DNA strands would **stay together** and the new DNA molecules would contain **two new strands**. Meselson and Stahl showed DNA replicated using the **semi-conservative method**. Their experiment used two **isotopes** of **nitrogen** (DNA contains nitrogen) — **heavy** nitrogen (^{15}N) and **light** nitrogen (^{14}N).

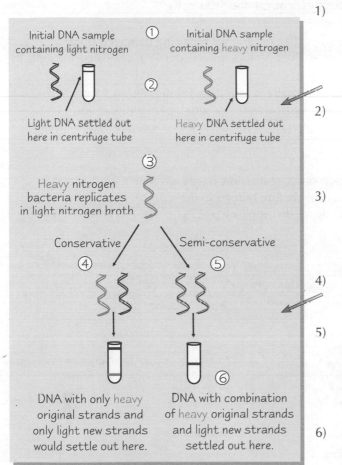

1) Two samples of bacteria were grown — one in a nutrient broth containing **light** nitrogen, and one in a broth with **heavy** nitrogen. As the **bacteria reproduced**, they **took up nitrogen** from the broth to help make nucleotides for new DNA. So the nitrogen gradually became part of the bacteria's DNA.

2) A **sample of DNA** was taken from each batch of bacteria, and spun in a **centrifuge**. The DNA from the **heavy** nitrogen bacteria settled **lower** down the **centrifuge tube** than the DNA from the **light** nitrogen bacteria — because it's **heavier**.

3) Then the bacteria grown in the **heavy** nitrogen broth were **taken out** and put in a broth containing only **light nitrogen**. The bacteria were left for **one round of DNA replication**, and then **another DNA sample** was taken out and spun in the centrifuge.

4) If replication was **conservative**, the original **heavy** DNA, which is still together, would settle at the bottom and the new **light** DNA would settle at the top.

5) If replication was **semi-conservative**, the new bacterial DNA molecules would contain **one strand** of the **old DNA** containing **heavy** nitrogen and **one strand** of **new DNA** containing **light** nitrogen. So the DNA would settle out **between** where the **light** nitrogen DNA settled out and where the **heavy** nitrogen DNA settled out.

6) The DNA settled out in the **middle**, showing that the DNA molecules contained a **mixture** of **heavy** and **light** nitrogen. The bacterial DNA had **replicated semi-conservatively** in the **light** nitrogen.

Practice Questions

Q1   Name the two main stages of the cell cycle.

Q2   Why is DNA copied before cell division?

Q3   Why is DNA replication described as semi-conservative?

Exam Question

Q1   a) Fill in the missing base pairs on the diagram opposite.   [1 mark]

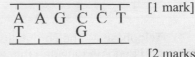

b) Draw a diagram to show the DNA molecule on the right after it has replicated. Label the original and new strands.   [2 marks]

I went through a gap phase — I just love their denim...

DNA and its self-replication is important — so make sure you understand what's going on. Diagrams are handy for learning stuff like this. I don't just put them in to keep myself amused you know — so get drawing and learning.

Cell Division — Mitosis

These pages are for AQA Unit 2, Edexcel Unit 2 and OCR Unit 1.

I don't like cell division. There, I've said it. It's unfair of me, because if it wasn't for cell division I'd still only be one cell big. It's all those diagrams that look like worms nailed to bits of string that put me off.

Mitosis is Cell Division that Produces Genetically Identical Cells

1) There are two types of cell division — **mitosis** and **meiosis** (see pages 57-59 for more on meiosis).

2) Mitosis is the form of cell division that occurs during the **cell cycle**.

3) In **mitosis** a **parent cell** divides to produce **two genetically identical daughter cells** (they contain an **exact copy** of the DNA of the parent cell).

4) Mitosis is needed for the **growth** of multicellular organisms (like us) and for **repairing damaged tissues**. How else do you think you get from being a baby to being a big, strapping teenager — it's because the cells in our bodies grow and divide.

5) Some organisms (e.g. some **plants** and **fungi**) reproduce asexually (without sex) using mitosis. This means any new organisms produced are **genetically identical** to the original, parent organism.

Mitosis has Four Division Stages

Mitosis is really one **continuous process**, but it's described as a series of **division stages** — prophase, metaphase, anaphase and telophase. **Interphase** comes **before** mitosis in the cell cycle — it's when cells grow and replicate their DNA ready for division (see p. 52).

Interphase — The cell carries out normal functions, but also prepares to divide. The cell's **DNA** is unravelled and **replicated**, to double its genetic content. The **organelles** are also **replicated** so it has spare ones, and its ATP content is increased (ATP provides the energy needed for cell division).

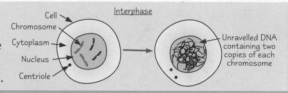

1) **Prophase** — The **chromosomes** **condense**, getting shorter and fatter. Tiny bundles of protein called **centrioles** start moving to opposite ends of the cell, forming a network of protein fibres across it called the **spindle**. The **nuclear envelope** (the membrane around the nucleus) **breaks down** and chromosomes lie free in the cytoplasm.

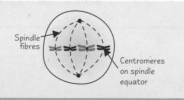

As mitosis begins, the chromosomes are made of two strands joined in the middle by a centromere. The separate strands are called chromatids.

There are two strands because each chromosome has already made an identical copy of itself during interphase. When mitosis is over, the chromatids end up as one-strand chromosomes in the new daughter cells.

2) **Metaphase** — The chromosomes (each with two chromatids) **line up** along the middle of the cell and become **attached** to the **spindle** by their **centromere**.

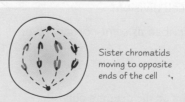

3) **Anaphase** — The centromeres divide, **separating** each pair of sister **chromatids**. The spindles contract, pulling chromatids to opposite ends of the cell, centromere first.

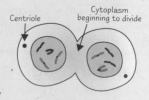

Mitosis can be a moving time.

4) **Telophase** — The chromatids reach the **opposite poles** on the spindle. They uncoil and become long and thin again. They're now called **chromosomes** again. A **nuclear envelope** forms around each group of chromosomes, so there are now **two nuclei**. The **cytoplasm divides** and there are now **two daughter cells** that are **genetically identical** to the original cell and to each other. Mitosis is finished and each daughter cell starts the **interphase** part of the cell cycle to get ready for the next round of mitosis.

Cell Division — Mitosis

You can Observe Mitosis by Staining Chromosomes

You can **stain chromosomes** so you can see them under a **microscope**. This means you can watch what happens to them **during mitosis** — and it makes high-adrenaline viewing, I can tell you. You need to be able to **recognise** each stage in mitosis from diagrams and **photographs** — lucky you. You've seen the diagrams, now enjoy the photos:

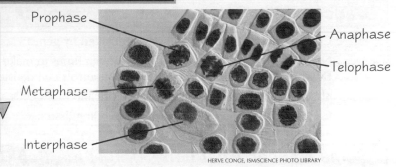

Prophase
Anaphase
Telophase
Metaphase
Interphase

HERVE CONGE, ISM/SCIENCE PHOTO LIBRARY

Staining root tips is for Edexcel only.

You need to Learn How Root Tips can be Stained to Observe Mitosis

1) **Cut** the **tip** from a **growing root** (e.g. of a broad bean). Your root tip should be about **5 mm long**.

2) Place the root tip on a **watch glass** (a small, shallow bowl) and add a few drops of **hydrochloric acid**.

3) Add a few drops of **stain** so that the **chromosomes** become **darker** and so **easier to see** under a microscope. There are loads of different stains, all with crazy names — **toluidine blue**, **acetic orcein**, **Schiff's reagent**, **Feulgen's reagent**...

4) **Warm** the watch glass (but **don't boil** the liquid) by passing it slowly through a **Bunsen burner flame**.

5) Place the root tip on a **microscope slide** and use a **mounted needle** to **break it open** and spread the cells out thinly.

6) Add a few more drops of **stain** and then place a **cover slip** over it.

7) **Squash** the cover slip down gently.

8) **Warm** the slide again for a few seconds. This will **intensify** the stain.

9) Now you can look at all the stages of mitosis under a light microscope. Lovely.

Yeast cell budding is for OCR only.

Yeast Cells Reproduce Asexually by Budding

1) Yeast are single-celled **microorganisms**. They're a type of fungi.

2) Yeast cells are **eukaryotic**, with all the usual **organelles** in the cytoplasm (see page 22) and a **nucleus** containing chromosomes (DNA).

3) Yeast can reproduce **asexually** by a process called **budding**.

4) Budding involves **mitosis** — this means the offspring produced are **genetically identical** to the parent cell.

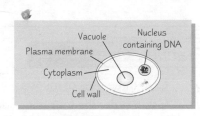

Vacuole
Nucleus containing DNA
Plasma membrane
Cytoplasm
Cell wall

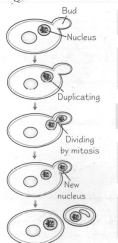

Bud
Nucleus
Duplicating
Dividing by mitosis
New nucleus

1) A **bud** forms at the surface of the cell.

2) The cell undergoes **interphase** — the **DNA** and **organelles** are **replicated** ready for the cell to divide.

3) The cell begins to undergo **mitosis**.

4) **Nuclear division** is complete — the budding cell contains a nucleus that has an **identical copy** of the parent cell's **DNA**.

5) Finally, the bud **separates** off from the parent cell, producing a new, **genetically identical** yeast cell.

Cell Division — Mitosis

This page is for AQA only. If you're doing Edexcel or OCR, you can skip straight to the questions.

Cancer is the Result of Uncontrolled Cell Division

Mutations are changes in the base sequence of an organism's DNA (see p. 42).

1) Cell growth and cell division are **controlled by genes**.

2) Normally, when cells have divided enough times to make **enough new cells**, they stop. But if there's a **mutation** in a gene that controls cell division, the cells can **grow out of control**.

3) The cells **keep on dividing** to make more and more cells, which form a **tumour**.

4) **Cancer** is a tumour that **invades** surrounding tissue.

Some Cancer Treatments Target the Cell Cycle

Some treatments for cancer are designed to **disrupt** the cell cycle.

These treatments don't **distinguish** tumour cells from normal cells though — they also **kill normal body cells** that are dividing. However, tumour cells **divide much more frequently** than normal cells, so the treatments are **more likely** to kill tumour cells. Some cell cycle **targets** of cancer treatments include:

1) <u>G1</u> **(cell growth and protein production)** — Some chemical drugs (chemotherapy) prevent the **synthesis of enzymes** needed for DNA replication. If these aren't produced, the cell is unable to enter the synthesis phase (<u>S</u>), disrupting the cell cycle and forcing the cell to **kill itself**.

2) **S phase (DNA replication)** — **Radiation** and some drugs **damage DNA**. When the cell gets to S phase it checks for **damaged DNA** and if any is detected it **kills itself**, preventing **further** tumour growth.

Because cancer treatments **kill normal cells** too certain steps are taken to **reduce the impact** on normal body cells:

1) A **chunk** of tumour is often removed first using **surgery**. This removes a lot of tumour cells and increases the access of any left to nutrients and oxygen, which triggers them to enter the **cell cycle**, making them **more susceptible** to treatment.

2) **Repeated treatments** are given with periods of **non-treatment** (breaks) in between. A **large dose** could kill **all the tumour** but also so many normal cells that the patient could **die**. Repeated treatments with **breaks** allows the body to **recover** and produce new cells. The treatment is **repeated** as any tumour cells **not killed** by the treatment will keep **dividing and growing** during the breaks too. The break period is kept short so the body can **recover** but the **cancer** can't grow back to the same size as before.

Practice Questions

These questions are for pages 54-56.

Q1 Give three uses of mitosis.

Q2 List in order the four stages of mitosis.

Q3 What process do some yeast use to reproduce?

Q4 Give one example of how a cancer treatment affects the cell cycle.

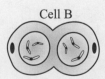

Exam Questions

Q1 The diagrams show cells at different stages of mitosis.

a) For each of the cells A, B and C state the stage of mitosis, giving a reason for your answer. [6 marks]

b) Name the structures labelled X, Y and Z in cell A. [3 marks]

Q2 Briefly describe how to prepare a root tip to observe mitosis. [8 marks]

<u>Doctor, I'm getting short and fat — don't worry, it's just a phase...</u>

Quite a lot to learn on these pages — but it's all important stuff, so no slacking. Mitosis is vital — it's how cells multiply, organisms like us grow, and some organisms (like fungi) reproduce. The best way to learn it is to get drawing those diagrams.

Cell Division — Meiosis

This page is for AQA Unit 2, Edexcel Unit 2 and OCR Unit 1.

More cell division — lovely jubbly. Meiosis is the type of cell division that produces gametes — the sex cells that come together at fertilisation to form a new organism. Meiosis results in genetic variation because the gametes produced by meiosis contain different combinations of chromosomes...

DNA from One Generation is Passed to the Next by Gametes

1) **Gametes** are the male and female **sex cells** found in all organisms that reproduce **sexually**.

2) They join together at **fertilisation** to form a **zygote**, which divides and develops into a **new organism**.

3) In animals, the male gametes are **sperm** and the females gametes are **egg cells**.

4) In plants, the male gametes are contained in **pollen grains** and the female gametes are contained in **ovules** (see p. 61).

5) Normal **body cells** of plants and animals have the **diploid number** (**2n**) of chromosomes — meaning each cell contains **two** of each chromosome (one from each parent).

6) **Gametes** have a **haploid** (**n**) number of chromosomes — there's only one copy of each chromosome.

7) At **fertilisation** (see p. 60), a **haploid male gamete** fuses with a **haploid female gamete**, making a cell with the normal diploid number of chromosomes. Half these chromosomes are from the father (e.g. sperm) and half are from the mother (e.g. egg cell).

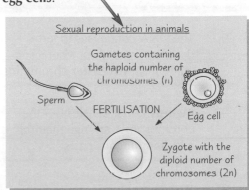

Sexual reproduction in animals

Gametes containing the haploid number of chromosomes (n)

Sperm

FERTILISATION

Egg cell

Zygote with the diploid number of chromosomes (2n)

Mammalian gamete features are for Edexcel only.

Mammalian Gametes are Specialised for Their Function

Egg cells are much larger than sperm.

Egg cell

Cell membrane

Follicle cells form protective coating

Zona pellucida — protective layer that sperm have to penetrate

Nucleus

Sperm cell

Lots of mitochondria provide energy for tail movement (swimming)

Nucleus

Flagellum (tail) allows sperm to swim towards egg cell

Acrosome contains digestive enzymes to break down the egg cell's zona pellucida and enable sperm to penetrate the egg

Gametes are Formed by Meiosis

1) **Meiosis** is a type of **cell division** that happens in the reproductive organs to **produce gametes**.

2) Cells that divide by meiosis are **diploid** to start with, but the cells that are formed from meiosis are **haploid** — the chromosome number halves.

3) Without meiosis you'd get **double** the number of chromosomes when the gametes **fused**. Not good.

4) Cells formed by meiosis are all **genetically different** because each new cell ends up with a **different combination** of chromosomes.

There was no doubt that Nelly's cells were genetically different to the rest of his herd.

Cell Division — Meiosis

These pages are for AQA Unit 2 and Edexcel Unit 2.
If you're doing OCR Unit 1 you just need to learn about homologous pairs.
You've read all about it — now see how it happens... Meiosis...

There are Two Divisions in Meiosis

As you now know, meiosis is the type of cell division that produces gametes:

1) The DNA unravels and **replicates** so there are **two** copies of **each** chromosome, called **chromatids**.

2) The DNA condenses to form double-armed chromosomes, made from **two sister chromatids**.

3) **Meiosis I** (first division) — the chromosomes arrange themselves into **homologous pairs**.

4) These homologous **pairs** are then **separated**, **halving** the chromosome number.

5) **Meiosis II** (second division) — the pairs of sister **chromatids** that make up each chromosome are **separated**.

6) **Four haploid cells** (gametes) that are **genetically different** from each other are produced.

We've only shown 4 chromosomes here for simplicity. Humans really have 46 (23 pairs).

HOMOLOGOUS PAIRS

Humans have **46 chromosomes** in total — **23 pairs**. **One chromosome** in each pair came from mum and one from dad, e.g. there are two number 1s (1 from mum and 1 from dad), two number 2s, etc. The chromosomes that make up each pair are the same size and have the **same genes**, although they could have **different versions** of those genes (called **alleles**). These pairs of chromosomes are called **homologous pairs**.

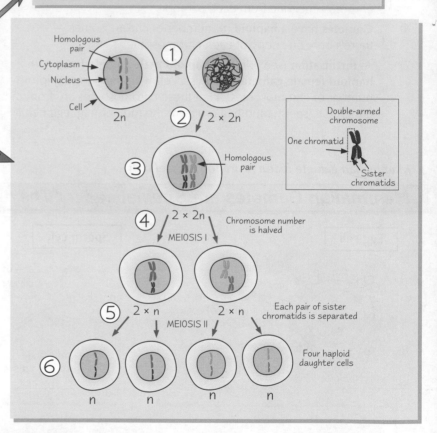

Chromatids Cross Over in Meiosis I

1) During meiosis I, **homologous pairs** of chromosomes come together and **pair up**.

2) The chromatids twist around each other and **bits of chromatids swap over** (they break off their original chromatid and rejoin onto the other chromatid).

3) The chromatids still contain the **same genes** but now have a **different combination of alleles**.

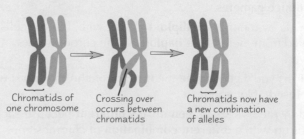

Chromatids of one chromosome → Crossing over occurs between chromatids → Chromatids now have a new combination of alleles

Luke finally gave in and crossed over to the dark side — working in a call centre...

Cell Division — Meiosis

Meiosis *Produces Cells that are* Genetically Different

Genetic variation is the **differences** that exist between **individuals' genetic material**. The reason that meiosis is so important is that it **creates** genetic variation — it makes gametes that are genetically different. It does this in two ways:

1 Crossing over of chromatids

The **crossing over** of chromatids in meiosis I means that each of the **four daughter cells** formed from meiosis contain chromatids with **different alleles**:

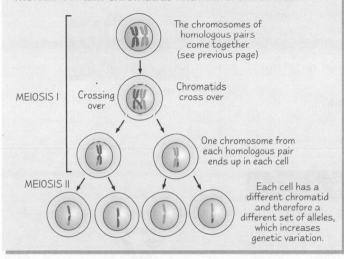

MEIOSIS I

Crossing over

Chromatids cross over

The chromosomes of homologous pairs come together (see previous page)

One chromosome from each homologous pair ends up in each cell

MEIOSIS II

Each cell has a different chromatid and therefore a different set of alleles, which increases genetic variation.

2 Independent segregation of chromosomes

1) The four daughter cells formed from meiosis have completely **different combinations** of **chromosomes**.

2) All your cells have a **combination** of chromosomes from your parents, half from your mum (**maternal**) and half from your dad (**paternal**).

3) When the gametes are produced, different **combinations** of those maternal and paternal **chromosomes** go into each cell.

4) This is called **independent segregation** (separation) of the chromosomes.

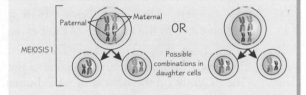

MEIOSIS I

Paternal — Maternal

OR

Possible combinations in daughter cells

Independent segregation is also called independent assortment.

Practice Questions

Q1 Explain what is meant by the terms haploid and diploid.

Q2 What happens to the chromosome number at fertilisation?

Q3 What is the zona pellucida?

Q4 How many divisions are there in meiosis?

Q5 How many cells are produced when one cell divides by meiosis?

These questions are for pages 57-59.

Exam Questions

Q1 Describe how sperm are specialised for their function. [3 marks]

Q2 Explain why it's important for gametes to have half the number of chromosomes as normal body cells. [2 marks]

Q3 Describe, using diagrams where appropriate, the process of meiosis. [6 marks]

Q4 a) Explain what crossing over is and how it leads to genetic variation. [4 marks]

b) Explain how independent segregation leads to genetic variation. [2 marks]

Reproduction isn't as exciting as some people would have you believe...

This stuff can take a while to sink in — but that's no excuse to sit there staring at the page muttering things like "I don't get it" and "guinea pigs don't have to learn this stuff — I wish I was a guinea pig". Use the diagrams to help you understand — they look evil, but they really help. And remember, meiosis produces genetically different cells.

Fertilisation

These pages are for Edexcel Unit 2 only.

Right, now that you know how gametes are formed, you can get on to some fertilisation. I won't tell you any more because it's all explained on these pages. You have to read it though — don't just giggle at the rude diagram...

Fertilisation is When Male and Female Gametes Fuse

1) **Fertilisation** is the term used to describe the **exact moment** when the **nuclei** of the male and female gametes **fuse**.

2) Since each gamete contains **half** the full number of chromosomes, fertilisation creates a cell with the **full** number of chromosomes — this cell is called the **zygote**.

3) The zygote contains **two** sets of chromosomes — one set from the **male** parent and one from the **female** parent.

4) **Combining** genetic material from **two individuals** makes offspring that are **genetically unique**.

NB: you can't fertilise farmland with sperm.

In Mammals Fertilisation Occurs in the Oviduct

1) In mammals, **sperm** are deposited high up in the female **vagina** close to the entrance of the **cervix**.

2) Once there, they have to make their way up through the **cervix** and **uterus**, and into one of the **oviducts**. The diagram on the right shows the **human** female reproductive system.

3) Once the sperm are in the oviduct **fertilisation** may occur. Here's how it works:

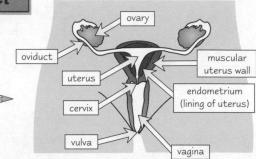

1) The sperm swim towards the **egg cell** in the oviduct.

2) Once **one** sperm makes contact with the **zona pellucida** of the egg cell (see p. 57), the **acrosome reaction** occurs — this is where **digestive enzymes** are released from the acrosome of the sperm.

3) These enzymes **digest** the zona pellucida, so that the sperm can move through it to the plasma membrane of the egg cell.

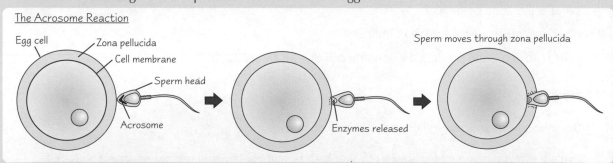

The Acrosome Reaction

Egg cell — Zona pellucida — Cell membrane — Sperm head — Acrosome

Enzymes released

Sperm moves through zona pellucida

4) The sperm head **fuses** with the **cell membrane** of the egg cell. This triggers the **cortical reaction** — the egg cell releases the contents of vesicles called **cortical granules** into the space between the cell membrane and the zona pellucida.

5) The chemicals from the cortical granules make the zona pellucida **thicken**, which makes it **impenetrable** to other sperm. This makes sure that **only one** sperm fertilises the egg cell.

6) Only the **sperm nucleus** enters the egg cell — its **tail** is **discarded.**

7) The nucleus of the sperm **fuses** with the nucleus of the egg cell — this is **fertilisation**.

A **zygote** is now formed, which has the full number of chromosomes. It immediately begins to divide by **mitosis** (see p. 54) to develop into a fully formed organism.

Fertilisation

In Flowering Plants Fertilisation Occurs in the Embryo Sac

1) A pollen grain lands on the **stigma** of a flower. The grain **absorbs water** and **splits open**.

2) A **pollen tube** grows out of the pollen grain down the **style** (the rod-like section that supports the stigma). There are **three nuclei** in the pollen tube — one **tube nucleus** at the tube's **tip** and two **male gamete nuclei** behind it. The tube nucleus makes **enzymes** that **digest** surrounding cells, making a **way through** for the pollen tube.

3) When the tube reaches the **ovary**, it grows through the **micropyle** (a tiny hole in the ovule wall) and into the **embryo sac** within the **ovule**.

4) In the embryo sac, the tube nucleus **disintegrates** and the tip of the pollen tube **bursts**, releasing the two male nuclei.

5) One male nucleus fuses with the **egg nucleus** to make a **zygote**. This divides by mitosis to become the **embryo** of the seed.

6) The second male nucleus fuses with two other nuclei (called the **polar nuclei**) at the centre of the embryo sac. This produces a cell with a **large nucleus**, which divides to become a **food store** (called the **endosperm**) for the mature seed.

7) So a **double fertilisation** has taken place (**two** male nuclei have fused with female nuclei). This only happens in flowering plants.

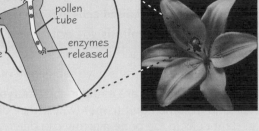

Flowering plants can only be fertilised by pollen grains from the same species (or a closely related species).

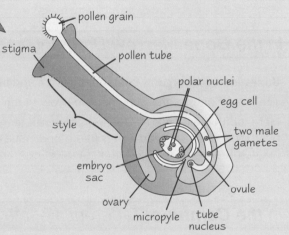

Practice Questions

Q1 What is fertilisation?

Q2 How many nuclei are found in a pollen tube?

Q3 What is the purpose of the endosperm?

Q4 What type of plants does double fertilisation occur in?

Exam Questions

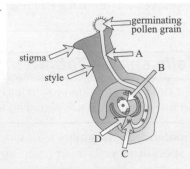

Q1 a) The diagram on the right shows the events leading to fertilisation in a flowering plant. Label parts A-D. [4 marks]

b) Explain why the pollen tube needs to secrete digestive enzymes. [2 marks]

Q2 Describe the process of fertilisation in mammals, starting with the acrosome reaction. [9 marks]

Polar nuclei — suitable for freezing...

You don't need to learn the diagram of the female reproductive system — it's just there to give words like 'oviduct' and 'uterus' some sort of meaning when you're trying to learn what goes where. See, never say that I don't try my very best to help you. Now help yourself and get this stuff learnt — then it'll be another two pages done and dusted.

Stem Cells and Differentiation

This page is for AQA Unit 2, Edexcel Unit 2 and OCR Unit 1.

After a bit of *nudge, nudge, wink, wink* you end up with a fertilised egg cell. If that single cell just divided over and over again we'd end up as a massive wobbly blob, but obviously we don't, and the reason is all down to differentiation...

Stem Cells are Able to Differentiate into Specialised Cells

1) **Multicellular organisms** are made up from many **different cell types** that are **specialised** for their function, e.g. liver cells, muscle cells, white blood cells.

2) **All** these specialised cell types originally came from **stem cells**.

3) Stem cells are **unspecialised** cells that can develop into **any** type of cell.

4) Stem cells divide (by **mitosis**) to become **new** cells, which then become **specialised**.

5) The **process** by which a cell becomes specialised is called **differentiation**.

6) All multicellular organisms have some form of stem cell.

7) In **animals**, stem cells are found in the **embryo** (where they differentiate into **all** the cells needed to form a **fetus**) and in **some adult tissues** (where they differentiate into **specialised** cells that need to be **replaced**, e.g. stem cells in the **bone marrow** can differentiate into **red blood cells**).

Joe knew his cells were specialised — specialised to look good.

Cells in the Bone Marrow Differentiate into Blood Cells

OCR only

1) **Bones** are living organs, containing nerves and **blood vessels**.

2) The main bones of the body have **marrow** in the **centres**.

3) Here, **adult stem cells** divide and **differentiate** to replace worn out blood cells — **erythrocytes** (red blood cells) and **neutrophils** (white blood cells that help to fight infection).

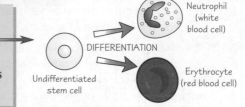

Neutrophil (white blood cell)

DIFFERENTIATION

Undifferentiated stem cell

Erythrocyte (red blood cell)

Cells in the Cambium Differentiate into Xylem and Phloem

OCR only

Plants are always growing, so stem cells are needed to make **new shoots** and **roots** throughout their lives. Stem cells in plants can **differentiate** into various plant tissues including **xylem and phloem** (the tissues that transport water and sugars around the plant).

1) In plants, **stem cells** are found in the **cambium**.

2) In the root and stem, stem cells of the **vascular cambium** divide and **differentiate** to become **xylem** and **phloem**.

3) The vascular cambium forms a **ring** inside the root and shoots.

4) The cells **divide** and grow out from the ring, **differentiating** as they **move away** from the cambium.

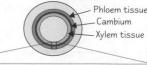

Root or shoot

Phloem tissue
Cambium
Xylem tissue

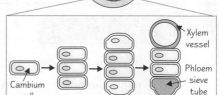

Xylem vessel

Cambium cell

Phloem sieve tube

Cambium cells divide and begin to differentiate

Xylem and phloem differentiate on either side of the cambium

Stem Cells can be Totipotent or Pluripotent

Edexcel only

The ability of stem cells to differentiate into specialised cells is called **potency** and there are **two types** you need to know about:

1) **Totipotency** — the ability to produce **all cell types**, including all the **specialised cells** in an organism and **extraembryonic cells** (cells of the placenta and umbilical cord).

2) **Pluripotency** — the ability of a stem cell to produce all the **specialised cells** in an organism (but **not** extraembryonic cells).

Totipotent stem cells in humans are only present in the **early life** of an **embryo** — they **differentiate** into **extraembryonic** cells and **pluripotent** stem cells. The pluripotent stem cells then **differentiate** into the **specialised** cells in a **fetus**.

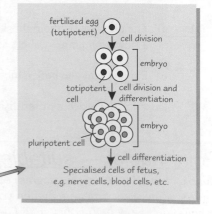

fertilised egg (totipotent)
cell division
embryo
totipotent cell
cell division and differentiation
embryo
pluripotent cell
cell differentiation
Specialised cells of fetus, e.g. nerve cells, blood cells, etc.

Stem Cells and Differentiation

This page is for Edexcel Unit 2 only. If you're doing AQA or OCR, you can skip straight to the questions.

Totipotency can be Demonstrated by Plant Tissue Culture

1) **Plants** also have **stem cells** — they're found in areas where the plant is **growing**, e.g. in roots and shoots.

2) All stem cells in plants are **totipotent** — they can produce **all cell types** and can grow into a **whole new plant**.

3) Totipotency can be shown in plants using **tissue culture**, a method used to **grow** a **plant** from a **single cell**:

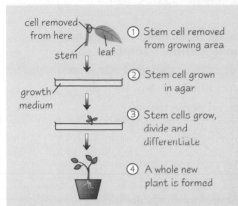

1) A **single cell** is taken from a **growing area** on a plant (e.g. a **shoot**).

2) The cell is placed in some **growth medium** (e.g. agar) that contains **nutrients** and **growth hormones**. The growth medium is **sterile**, so microorganisms can't grow and compete with the plant cells.

3) The plant cell will **grow** and **divide** into a **mass of unspecialised** cells. If the **conditions** are **suitable** (e.g. the plant cells are given the **right hormones**) the unspecialised cells will **differentiate** into **specialised** cells.

4) Eventually, the cells will grow and differentiate into an **entire plant**.

Tissue culture shows **totipotency** because a **single stem** cell can produce all the specialised cells to make a **whole plant**.

Stem Cells Become Specialised Through Differential Gene Expression

Stem cells become **specialised** because different genes in their DNA become **active** (are turned on) — in other words they **express different genes** (use different genes to make different **proteins**):

1) **Stem cells** all contain the **same genes**, but not all of them are **expressed** because not all of them are **active**.

2) Under the **right conditions**, some **genes** are **activated** and other genes are **inactivated**.

3) **mRNA** is only **transcribed** from the **active genes**.

4) The mRNA from the active genes is then **translated** into **proteins**.

5) These proteins **modify** the cell — they determine the cell **structure** and **control cell processes** (including the activation of **more** genes, which produces more proteins).

6) **Changes** to the cell produced by these proteins cause the cell to become **specialised** (**differentiate**). These changes are **difficult** to **reverse**, so once a cell has differentiated it **stays** specialised.

See pages 40-41 for more on transcription and translation.

Example — Red Blood Cells

1) **Red blood cells** are produced from a type of **stem cell** in the **bone marrow**. They contain lots of **haemoglobin** and have **no nucleus** (to make room for more haemoglobin).

2) The stem cell produces a new cell in which the genes for **haemoglobin production** are **activated**. Other genes, such as those involved in **removing the nucleus**, are **activated** too. Many other genes are activated or inactivated, resulting in a specialised red blood cell.

Practice Questions

Q1 What are stem cells?

Q2 What is the process by which a stem cell becomes specialised called?

Q3 Stem cells in bone marrow can differentiate into other cell types. Name two of these cell types.

Q4 Name the method that can be used to demonstrate totipotency in plant cells.

Exam Questions

Q1 Describe, with examples, the role of stem cells in animals. [4 marks]

Q2 Describe how differential gene expression results in the production of specialised cells. [6 marks]

And you thought differentiation was just boring maths stuff...

Stem cells are pretty amazing when you think about it — they can differentiate to become any cell in the whole body. Scientists are excited about them because they could be used to repair damaged cells, like muscle cells after a heart attack.

Stem Cells in Medicine

These pages are for Edexcel Unit 2 only.

These pages are about how stem cells can be used in medicine to replace damaged cells. It's got me thinking... perhaps I could grow another brain from some of my stem cells — then I'd be twice as clever... By jove, I think it'd work.

Stem Cells Could be Used to Treat Some Diseases

1) **Stem cells** can develop into **any** specialised cell type, so scientists think they could be used to **replace damaged tissues** in a **range** of **diseases**.

2) Some stem cell therapies **already exist**. For example, the treatment for **leukaemia** (a cancer of the bone marrow) kills all the **stem cells** in the bone marrow, so **bone marrow transplants** can be given to patients to **replace** them.

3) Scientists are **researching** the use of stem cells as a **treatment** for lots of conditions, including:

   - **Spinal cord injuries** — stem cells could be used to repair damaged **nerve tissue**.

   - **Heart disease** and **damage caused by heart attacks** — stem cells could be used to replace damaged heart tissue.

4) People who make **decisions** about the **use** of stem cells in medicine and research have to consider the **potential benefits** of stem cell therapies:

   - They could **save** many **lives** — e.g. many people waiting for organ transplants **die** before a **donor organ** becomes available. Stem cells could be used to **grow organs** for those people awaiting transplants.

   - They could **improve** the **quality of life** for many people — e.g. stem cells could be used to replace damaged cells in the eyes of people who are **blind**.

Human Stem Cells Can Come from Adult Tissue or Embryos

1) In order to **use stem cells** in medicine and research, scientists have to get them from somewhere.

2) There are **two** potential **sources** of human stem cells:

1 Adult stem cells

1) These are obtained from the **body tissues** of an **adult**. For example, adult stem cells are found in **bone marrow**.

2) They can be obtained in a relatively **simple operation** — with very **little risk** involved, but quite **a lot of discomfort**. The **donor** is anaesthetised, a **needle** is **inserted** into the centre of a **bone** (usually the hip) and a **small quantity** of bone marrow is **removed**.

3) Adult stem cells **aren't** as **flexible** as embryonic stem cells — they can only develop into a **limited** range of cells.

2 Embryonic stem cells

1) These are obtained from **early embryos**.

2) Embryos are created in a **laboratory** using *in vitro* **fertilisation** (IVF) — egg cells are **fertilised** by sperm **outside the womb**.

3) Once the embryos are approximately **4 to 5 days old, stem cells** are **removed** from them and the rest of the embryo is **destroyed**.

4) Embryonic stem cells can develop into **all types** of specialised cells.

3) Obtaining stem cells from **embryos** created by IVF raises **ethical issues** because the procedure results in the **destruction** of an embryo that's **viable** (could become a fetus if placed in a womb).

4) Many people believe that at the moment of **fertilisation** a **genetically unique individual** is formed that has the **right** to **life** — so they believe that it's **wrong** to **destroy** embryos.

5) Some people have **fewer objections** to stem cells being **obtained** from **unfertilised embryos** — embryos made from **egg cells** that **haven't** been fertilised by sperm. This is because the embryos **aren't viable** — they **can't survive** past a few days and **wouldn't** produce a fetus if placed in a womb.

6) Some people think that **scientists** should **only use** adult stem cells because their production **doesn't** destroy an embryo. But adult stem cells **can't** develop into all the specialised cell types that embryonic stem cells can.

7) The decision-makers in **society** have to take into account **everyone's views** when making decisions about **important scientific work** like stem cell research and its use in medicine.

Stem Cells in Medicine

Society Makes Decisions About the Use of Stem Cells in Medicine

1) Embryonic stem cells could be really **useful** in **medicine**, but **research** into their use raises many **ethical issues** (see previous page).

2) **Society** has to consider all the arguments **for** and **against** stem cell research before allowing it to go ahead.

3) To help society make these decisions, **regulatory authorities** have been established to consider the **benefits** and **ethical issues** surrounding embryonic stem cell research.

4) The work of regulatory authorities includes:

1) Looking at proposals of **research** to decide if they should be **allowed** — this ensures that any research involving embryos is carried out for a **good reason**. This also makes sure research isn't unnecessarily **repeated** by different groups.

Just like a regulatory authority, you'll need to consider all the benefits and issues of stem cell research when asked about it.

2) **Licensing** and **monitoring centres** involved in embryonic stem cell research — this ensures that only **fully trained staff** carry out the research. These staff will understand the **implications** of the research and **won't** waste precious resources, such as embryos. This also helps to **avoid unregulated research**.

3) Producing **guidelines** and **codes of practice** — this ensures all scientists are working in a **similar manner** (if scientists don't use similar methods their results can't be compared). It also ensures methods of **extraction** are **controlled**.

4) **Monitoring developments** in scientific research and advances — this ensures that any changes in the field are **regulated appropriately** and that all the **guidelines** are **up to date** with the latest in scientific understanding.

5) Providing **information** and **advice** to governments and professionals — this helps to **promote** the science involved in embryo research, and it helps **society** to **understand** what's involved and why it's important.

Practice Questions

Q1 Describe how stem cells could be used to treat a range of diseases.

Q2 Name two potential sources of human stem cells.

Q3 Describe the difference in flexibility between the two potential sources of human stem cells.

Exam Question

Q1 Stem cell research is permitted in the UK, but it is regulated by a number of authorities.

a) Describe one potential benefit of using stem cells in medicine. [1 mark]

b) Embryonic stem cells can be used for research.

   i) Explain how embryonic stem cells are obtained. [3 marks]

   ii) Suggest two reasons why some people are opposed to using stem cells from embryos. [2 marks]

Stem cells — I think they prove that we all evolved from plants...

Stem cells have the potential to cure or relieve the symptoms of some diseases, but as you've seen, there are some issues surrounding embryonic stem cells. Scientists are working towards producing stem cells that are as flexible as embryonic stem cells (i.e. can become any cell type) but that have come from other sources (e.g. the skin or bone marrow).

Cell Organisation

These pages are for AQA Unit 2, Edexcel Unit 2 and OCR Unit 1.

Cells are **Specialised** for their Particular Function *AQA and OCR only*

Once cells **differentiate**, they have a **specific function**. Their **structure** is **adapted** to perform that function.
Here are some examples: (If you're doing **OCR** you need to learn them all — unlucky.)

Animal cells

1) **Neutrophils** (white blood cells, e.g. phagocytes) defend the body against disease. Their **flexible shape** allows them to **engulf** foreign particles or pathogens (see p. 90). The many **lysosomes** in their cytoplasm contain **digestive enzymes** to **break down** the engulfed particles.

2) **Erythrocytes** (red blood cells) carry oxygen in the blood. The **biconcave** disc shape provides a **large surface area** for gas exchange. They have **no nucleus** so there's more room for **haemoglobin** (see p. 122), the protein that carries oxygen.

3) **Epithelial cells** cover the surfaces of organs. The cells are **joined** by **interlinking** cell membranes and a membrane at their base. Some epithelia (e.g. in the **lungs**) have **cilia** that beat to move particles away. Other epithelia (e.g. in the **small intestine**) have **microvilli** — folds in the cell membrane that increase the cell's **surface area**.

4) **Sperm cells** (male sex cells) have a **flagellum** (tail) so they can **swim** to the egg (female sex cell). They also have lots of **mitochondria** to provide the **energy** to swim. The **acrosome** contains **digestive enzymes** to enable the sperm to **penetrate** the surface of the egg.

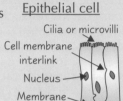

Neutrophil
- Flexible shape
- Lots of lysosomes
- Nucleus

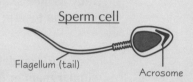

Erythrocyte
- Large surface area
- No nucleus
- Biconcave (concave on both sides)
- Cross-section

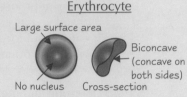

Epithelial cell
- Cilia or microvilli
- Cell membrane interlink
- Nucleus
- Membrane

Sperm cell
- Flagellum (tail)
- Acrosome

Plant cells

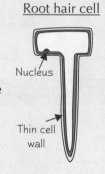

Palisade cell
- Nucleus
- Vacuole
- Cell wall
- Lots of chloroplasts
- Cytoplasm

Guard cells
- Cells turgid, stoma opens
- Cells flaccid, stoma closes

1) **Palisade mesophyll cells** in leaves do most of the **photosynthesis**. They contain **many chloroplasts**, so they can absorb a lot of sunlight. The walls are **thin**, so carbon dioxide can **easily diffuse** into the cell.

2) **Root hair cells** absorb water and mineral ions from the soil. They have a **large surface area** for absorption and a **thin**, permeable cell wall, for entry of water and ions. The cytoplasm contains **extra mitochondria** to provide the **energy** needed for **active transport** (see p. 36).

3) **Guard cells** line the **stomata** — the tiny pores in the surface of the leaf used for **gas exchange** (see p. 103). In the **light**, guard cells **take up water** and become **turgid**. Their **thin outer walls** and **thickened inner walls** force them to bend outwards, **opening** the stomata. This allows the leaf to exchange gases for photosynthesis.

Root hair cell
- Nucleus
- Thin cell wall

Similar Cells are Organised into Tissues

A **tissue** is a group of similar cells (plus any **extracellular material** secreted by them) that are specialised to **work together** to carry out a **particular function**. A tissue can contain **more than one** cell type. Learn these examples if you're doing **OCR**:

Ciliated epithelium is a layer of cells covered in **cilia**. It's found on surfaces where things need to be **moved** — in the trachea for instance, where the cilia waft mucus along.

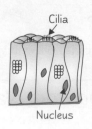

Cilia

Nucleus

Xylem tissue is a plant tissue with two jobs — it **transports water** around the plant, and it **supports** the plant. It contains **xylem vessel cells** and **parenchyma cells**.

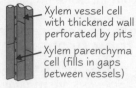

Xylem vessel cell with thickened wall perforated by pits

Xylem parenchyma cell (fills in gaps between vessels)

Squamous epithelium tissue is a **single layer** of **flat cells** lining a surface. Squamous epithelium tissue is found in many places including the alveoli in the lungs.

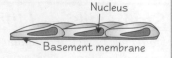

Nucleus

Basement membrane

Cell Organisation

Phloem tissue transports sugars around the plant. It's arranged in **tubes** and is made up of **sieve cells**, **companion cells**, and some **ordinary** plant cells. Each sieve cell has end walls with **holes** in them, so that sap can move easily through them. These end walls are called **sieve plates**.

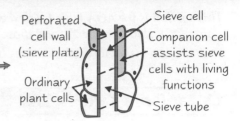

Tissues are Organised into Organs

An **organ** is a group of different tissues that **work together** to perform a particular function. Examples include:

- The **lungs** (see p. 106) — they contain **squamous epithelium** tissue (in the alveoli) and **ciliated epithelium** tissue (in the bronchi etc.). They also have **elastic connective tissue** and **vascular tissue** (in the blood vessels).
- **Leaves** — they contain **palisade tissue** for photosynthesis, as well as **epidermal** tissue, and **xylem** and **phloem** tissues in the veins.

Organs are Organised into Organ Systems

Organs work together to form **organ systems** — each system has a **particular function**. Yup, you've guessed it, another example:

The **respiratory system** is made up of all the organs, tissues and cells involved in **breathing**.

The lungs, trachea, larynx, nose, mouth and diaphragm are all part of the respiratory system.

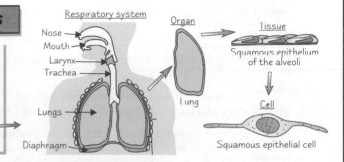

Different Tissues, Organs and Systems Cooperate Together _OCR only_

1) Multicellular organisms work **efficiently** because they have **different cells** specialised for **different functions**.
2) It's **advantageous** because **each** different cell type can carry out its specialised function **more effectively** than an **unspecialised** cell could.
3) Specialised cells can't do everything on their own though.
4) Each cell type **depends** on other cells for the functions it **can't** carry out.
5) This means the **cells**, **tissues and organs** within multicellular organisms must **cooperate** with each other to keep the organism **alive** and **running**.

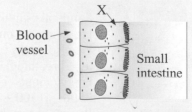

Cooperation, that's what got Hugo and Cuthbert to where they are today — National Wheel-of-Cheese-Carrying Champions.

EXAMPLES

- A **palisade cell** is good at **photosynthesising**, but it's **no good** at absorbing water and minerals from the soil. It **depends** on **root hair cells** for this.
- **Muscles cells** are great for getting you where you want to go, but to do this they need **oxygen**. They **depend** on **erythrocytes** (red blood cells) to carry oxygen to them from the **lungs**.

Practice Questions

Q1 Define what is meant by a tissue.
Q2 Name one organ found in plants and one organ found in animals.

Exam Questions

Q1 Tissue X on the right is found lining the small intestine, where nutrients are absorbed into the bloodstream. Outline how it is adapted for its function. [4 marks]

Q2 The liver is made of hepatocyte cells that form the main tissue, blood vessels to provide nutrients and oxygen, and connective tissue that holds the organ together. Discuss whether the liver is best described as a tissue or an organ. [2 marks]

Soft and quilted — the best kind of tissues...

So, similar cells group together to form tissues. Then, because they love being so helpful, tissues work together in an organ to perform a particular function. OK, well maybe you need to know a bit more detail than that, but you get the idea...

Diet and Energy

This section is for AQA Unit 1, Edexcel Unit 1 and OCR Unit 2. If you're doing AQA skip to page 76, if you're doing OCR skip to page 70, and those of you doing Edexcel just have to learn these two pages, you lucky things.

Your diet affects your weight, as does how much energy you use doing things like playing video games and stealing traffic cones. Being overweight is a risk factor for some diseases, so it's important to maintain a healthy weight.

Organisms Take In and Use Up Energy

Henri knew the cheese would push him over budget — but what harm could it do?

1) Organisms need a **supply** of **energy**, so that they can **grow**, **move**, **reproduce** etc. — in animals this energy is provided in the form of **food**.

2) **Energy budget** is a term used to describe the **amount of energy taken in** by an organism (in food) **and** the amount of energy **used up** by an organism (e.g. by moving).

Energy Imbalance Causes Changes in Weight

Ideally, a person should **take in** the **same amount** of energy as **they use up** — their energy budget should be **balanced**. If there's an **imbalance** in the energy budget, it will **affect** the **person's weight**:

WEIGHT GAIN

1) If energy **intake** is **higher** than energy **output**, the **excess energy** will be turned into **fat reserves** by the body, so the person will **gain weight**.

2) For example, if a person **consumes** food containing **4000 Calories** a day and carries out **activities** that burn **3000 Calories** a day, there'll be an **excess** of **1000 Calories** per day, so they'll put on weight.

3) If the energy difference is **a lot** and it's **sustained** over a **long period** of time, the person could become **obese**.

WEIGHT LOSS

1) If energy **intake** is **lower** than energy **output**, the body will have to **get** more energy from somewhere — it'll **turn** some of its **fat reserves** into energy, so the person will **lose weight**.

2) For example, if a person **consumes** food containing **2500 Calories** a day but carries out **activities** that burn **3000 Calories** a day, they will have an energy **deficit** of **500 Calories** per day, so they'll lose weight.

3) If this energy difference is **large** and is **sustained** over a **long period** of time, the person is likely to become **underweight**.

You May Have to Analyse Data on Energy Budgets and Diet

You may be asked to analyse data about **energy budgets** (input and output) in the exam. Here's an idea of what you might get:

1) The **recommended daily intake** of Calories is **2000** for **women** and **2500** for **men**.

2) **Different activities** use up **different amounts of Calories**, as shown in the table.

3) You can use this information to **calculate** people's **energy budgets**:

Activity	Number of Calories used per hour
Cooking	159
Dog walking	224
Gardening	328
Swimming	513

You need to multiply these figures by the number of hours the activity lasts.

- Ranjit takes in the recommended daily intake of Calories a day (**2500**). He swims for **one hour** and does **one hour** of **gardening** each day. He also **cooks** for **an hour** each day. His **bodily functions** (e.g. breathing) use up **1500** Calories per day. So his energy budget is:
  Energy input – energy output = energy budget
  2500 – (1500 + 513 + 328 + 159) = **0**
  Ranjit's energy budget is **balanced** — he takes in as much as he uses up.

- Christina takes in **2000** Calories a day. She **walks the dog** for **an hour** every **morning** and every **night**. Her **bodily functions** use up **1200** Calories per day. So her energy budget is:
  Energy input – energy output = energy budget
  2000 – (1200 + 224 + 224) = **352 Calories**
  Christina has an **excess** of **352 Calories** per day.

Diet and Energy

You Can Measure the Amount of Vitamin C in Your Food

1) You need to be able to **describe** how to carry out an **experiment** to find out **how much vitamin C** is in a **food sample**.

2) This can be done using a chemical called **DCPIP** — a **blue** dye that turns **colourless** in the presence of vitamin C.

Here's how you do it:

Melanie was the same colour as her orange juice but had less vitamin C content.

First you need to make a **calibration curve**. To do this you need to:

1) Make up several **vitamin C solutions** of **different, known concentrations**, (e.g. 10 mg/cm³, 20 mg/cm³, 30 mg/cm³). Ideally, you need about **six** different solutions.

2) Measure out a **set volume** of **DCPIP** (at a **set concentration**) into a test tube.

3) **Add** one of the **vitamin C solutions** to the DCPIP, **drop by drop**, using a pipette.

4) Gently **shake** the test tube for a **set length of time** after each drop of vitamin C solution is added.

5) When the solution turns **colourless**, **record** the **volume** (no. of drops) of vitamin C solution that has been added.

6) **Repeat** the experiment **twice more**, with the **same** solution, and take an **average** of the three readings.

7) Make sure you keep **all** the other **variables** constant during the experiment, e.g. temperature.

8) **Repeat** the above procedure with **each solution**.

9) Use the results to make a **line graph**, showing volume of vitamin C solution against its concentration — this is the **calibration curve**.

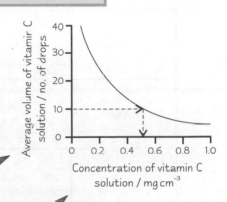

Then you can test the **unknown solution** in the same way as the known concentrations and use the calibration curve to find its concentration. E.g. 10 drops of an **unknown solution** is needed to turn DCPIP colourless. Reading **across** the calibration curve from a volume of **10 drops** shows that the concentration of vitamin C in the unknown solution is **0.5 mg/cm³**.

Practice Questions

Q1 What is an energy budget?

Q2 Explain how an energy imbalance causes weight gain.

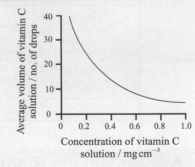

Exam Questions

Q1 The graph on the right shows a calibration curve for vitamin C concentration.

    a) 25 drops of DCPIP were needed to turn a vitamin C solution of unknown concentration colourless. Use the calibration curve to work out the concentration of the solution. Show your working on the graph. [2 marks]

    b) Suggest three variables that should be kept constant in an experiment like this. [3 marks]

Q2 A woman takes in 2000 Calories a day in food. She needs 1200 Calories each day to maintain her basic bodily functions. She also swims for two hours and does two hours of gardening.

    a) Use the table on page 68 to calculate her energy budget and explain what short-term effect this energy budget will have on her weight. [3 marks]

    b) If the woman sustained this energy budget over a long period of time, what effect would it have on her weight? [1 mark]

Eat beans to increase the amount of Calories used for bodily functions...

If you've done an hour's revision you've used up around 120 Calories (which is 90 more than you'd use just sat on your bum watching telly)... well done you — go and have a biscuit to celebrate (and even up your energy balance).

Balanced Diet

These pages are for OCR Unit 2 only.

To maintain good health you need a balanced diet containing the right amount of each essential nutrient. If you eat too much of something it can badly affect your health... and your waistline.

A **Balanced Diet** Supplies All the **Essential Nutrients**

A balanced diet gives you all the **nutrients** you need, plus **fibre** and **water**. There are **five** important nutrients — **carbohydrates**, **fats**, **proteins**, **vitamins** and **mineral salts**. Each nutrient has different functions in the body:

Nutrient	Function		Found in...
Carbohydrates	Provide energy.		Pasta is packed full of carbs.
Fats (lipids)	Act as an energy store, provide insulation, make up cell membranes, physically protect organs.		Coconut oil (the oil found in coconuts) is full of lipids.
Proteins	Needed for growth, the repair of tissues and to make enzymes.		There's more protein than you can shake a stick at in red meat.,
Vitamins	Different vitamins have different functions, e.g. vitamin D is needed for calcium absorption, vitamin K is needed for blood clotting.		Green vegetables like spinach are a good source of vitamin K.
Mineral salts	Different mineral salts have different functions, e.g. iron is needed to make haemoglobin in the blood, calcium is needed for bone formation.		There's loads of calcium in cheese.

Fibre	Aids movement of food through gut.		Eating plenty of broccoli will keep you nice and regular.
Water	It's used in chemical reactions. We need a constant supply to replace water lost through urinating, breathing and sweating.		Water is found in all sorts of places, like taps.

Not Getting the **Right Amount** of **Each Nutrient** Causes **Malnutrition**

Basically, **malnutrition** is caused by having **too little** or **too much** of some nutrients in your diet. There are three causes:

1) Not having **enough food** — you get **too little** of **every nutrient**.

2) Having an **unbalanced diet**:

   - Getting **too little** of a nutrient can lead to all kinds of **deficiency illnesses**, e.g. getting too little **iron** in your diet causes **anaemia**.
   - Getting **too many** carbohydrates or fats can lead to **obesity**.

3) Not being able to **absorb the nutrients** from digestion into your **bloodstream** properly. E.g. coeliac disease reduces absorption of nutrients from the small intestine. This also causes **deficiency illnesses**.

OK, I probably have been eating too little food.

Balanced Diet

Over-Nutrition and Lack of Exercise can Lead to Obesity

Obesity is a common **dietary condition** caused by eating **too much food**.

Hear ye, hear ye! I want more food.

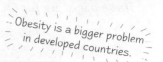
Obesity is a bigger problem in developed countries.

1) **Obesity** is defined as being **20%** (or more) **over the recommended body weight**.

2) **Too much sugary** or **fatty food** and **too little exercise** are the main causes of obesity.

3) People can also be obese due to an **underactive thyroid gland**, but this problem isn't common.

4) Obesity can increase the risk of **diabetes**, **arthritis**, **high blood pressure**, **coronary heart disease** (CHD) and even some forms of **cancer**.

An Unhealthy Diet Can Increase the Risk of Coronary Heart Disease

Coronary Heart Disease (CHD) is the result of **reduced** blood flow to the heart. It can lead to **chest pain** (angina) and **heart attacks**. It's caused by **atherosclerosis** — the narrowing and hardening of the **coronary arteries** (the blood vessels that supply the heart).

1) A diet **high** in **saturated fat** raises **blood cholesterol** level. This increases the build up of **fatty deposits** in the **arteries** (called atheromas), which **causes atherosclerosis**.

2) A diet **high in salt** can cause **high blood pressure**. This can **damage artery walls**, which **causes atherosclerosis**.

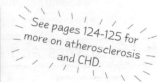
See pages 124-125 for more on atherosclerosis and CHD.

Practice Questions

Q1 Briefly describe what is meant by a balanced diet.

Q2 Give two causes of obesity.

Exam Questions

Q1 Complete the table naming all the essential nutrients and their functions. **[6 marks]**

NUTRIENTS	FUNCTIONS
Carbohydrates	Provide energy.
	Act as an energy store, provide insulation, make up cell membranes, physically protect organs.
	Needed for growth, the repair of tissues and to make enzymes.
Vitamins	
Mineral salts	

	Aids movement of food through gut.
Water	

Q2 Describe and explain three causes of malnutrition. **[5 marks]**

Healthy food tastes just as good as stuff that's bad for you — yeah right...

I hate cauliflower cheese, it looks like melted brains — but a balanced diet means eating a bit of everything and not too much of anything. So when you've finished feeding your cauliflower cheese to the dog, be sure to cover the page and write out all the essential nutrients and what they do plenty of times — your grades'll be healthier in no time.

Food Production

These pages are for OCR Unit 2 only.

The ever increasing need for food has been partly met by increasing the productivity of the plants and animals we eat. There are short-term ways to do this (like using pesticides), and long-term ways to do this (like selective breeding).

Humans *Ultimately* Depend *on* Plants *for Food*

1) Humans **rely on plants** for **food** because plants are at the **start** of **all food chains**.

2) Plants use the **energy from sunlight** to convert **carbon dioxide** and **water** into **complex organic compounds** (such as carbohydrates).

3) **Humans**, and other **animals**, eat, digest and absorb the compounds, which they use for energy and to grow.

4) We grow plants for **direct consumption** and to **feed animals**, which we then eat.

5) Many modern farming methods aim to **maximise productivity** by **increasing** plant and animal **growth**.

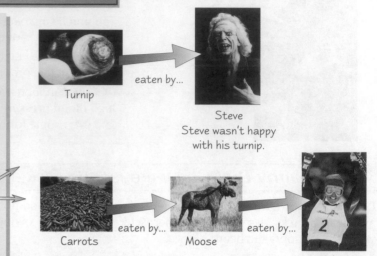

Turnip

eaten by...

Steve
Steve wasn't happy with his turnip.

Carrots

eaten by...

Moose

eaten by...

Helga
Helga's moose mousse went down a treat.

Fertilisers *and* Pesticides Increase Food Production

Fertilisers

1) Fertilisers are **chemicals** that **increase crop yields** by providing **minerals** (such as nitrate, phosphate and potassium) that plants need to grow.

2) Minerals in the soil are **used up** during crop growth. Fertilisers **replace** these minerals, so that a **lack** of minerals doesn't **limit** growth of the next crop.

3) Fertilisers can be **natural** — made by natural processes (e.g. compost and manure), or **artificial** — made by humans.

Pesticides

1) Pesticides are **chemicals** that **increase crop yields** by **killing pests** that feed on the crops. This means **fewer plants** are **damaged** or **destroyed**.

2) Pests include microorganisms, insects and mammals (e.g. rats).

3) Pesticides may be **specific** and kill only **one** pest species, or **broad**, and kill a **range** of different species — this could mean that some **non-pest species** are also harmed.

Animals *Can be Given* Antibiotics *to Increase Food Production*

1) Animals farmed for food are sometimes given **antibiotics** — chemicals that **kill** or **inhibit** the growth of **bacteria**.

2) Antibiotics help to treat or prevent **diseases** caused by bacteria.

3) Animals normally **use energy** fighting diseases, which reduces the amount of energy available for **growth**. Giving them antibiotics means animals can use **more energy** to grow, **increasing food production**.

4) Antibiotics also help to **promote** the growth of animals.

5) This is thought to be because the antibiotics **influence bacteria** in the animals' gut, allowing the animals to **digest** food **more efficiently**.

6) This can increase both the **growth rate** of the animal and its **size** when mature.

Food Production

Selective Breeding Increases Crop Yields...

1) Selective breeding involves **selecting** plants with **good characteristics** (e.g. high yield, disease resistance or pest resistance) to **reproduce** together in order to **increase productivity**.

2) Here's an example of how it's done:

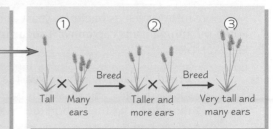

> 1) Select plants with **good characteristics** that will increase **crop yield**, e.g. a **tall** corn plant and a corn plant that produces **multiple ears**. Breed them **together**.
>
> 2) Select the **offspring** with the best characteristics, e.g. tallest with the most ears, and breed them **together**.
>
> 3) **Continue** this over **several generations** until a high-yielding plant is produced, e.g. **very tall** with **multiple ears** of corn.

③ Breed → ② Breed → ③
Tall × Many ears → Taller and more ears → Very tall and many ears

3) Selective breeding is carried out in the same way to produce plants that are **resistant to disease or pests**.

> 1) Plants showing a high level of **resistance** are **bred together**.
>
> 2) The offspring that show **most resistance** are then bred together.
>
> 3) This continues over **several generations** to produce a crop that is disease or pest resistant.

*...and the **Productivity** of **Animals***

Selective breeding can also be used to **increase** the **productivity of animals**. Useful characteristics such as **fast growth rate** and **high meat**, **milk** or **egg yields** can be developed. For example:

> 1) Select animals with **good characteristics** that will increase meat yield, e.g. the **largest** cows and bulls. Breed them **together**.
>
> 2) Select the **offspring** with the best characteristics, e.g. largest, and breed them **together**.
>
> 3) **Continue** this over **several generations** until cows with very high meat yields are produced, e.g. **very large cows**.

Daisy was a big cow, just like her mum — though she hadn't seen her around for a while...

Practice Questions

Q1 What type of organism is the basis of all food chains?

Q2 Briefly explain how fertilisers can increase crop yields.

Q3 Briefly explain how using antibiotics increases meat productivity.

Exam Question

Q1 Wheat is an important food crop that has been grown by farmers for over 5000 years.
Modern wheat plants have much larger grains than the wheat plants that were grown 5000 years ago.

a) Explain how selective breeding has led to wheat plants with larger grains than earlier wheat plants. [3 marks]

b) The Hessian fly is a pest of wheat crops. Describe how the Hessian fly infestation would affect the wheat crop yield and suggest both a short-term and a long-term solution to the infestation. [3 marks]

Better food productivity — I'm over the moooooon...

Back in the olden days the steaks weren't as fat or the potatoes so appetising... the grass was less green too. After all this talk of food you'll need a snack — go get one and have a break. I'm having one, so you'd better too. Aaah, tea...

Microorganisms and Food

These pages are for OCR Unit 2 only. When you've done these two you can move on to the next section.

The waste products of some microorganisms can be harmful and contaminate food. Other microorganisms can be useful for food production though — cheese tastes delicious until you remember it's really mouldy milk.

Microorganisms can be used to Make Food

Microorganisms such as **bacteria**, **yeast** and other **fungi** are used in the production of many foods and drinks. Some microorganisms can **convert sugar** into other substances that humans can then use for **food production**. For example:

1) **Bread** is made by mixing **yeast** (a fungus), **sugar**, **flour** and **water** into a dough. The yeast turn the sugar into **ethanol** and **carbon dioxide** — it's the carbon dioxide that makes the bread **rise**.

2) **Wine** is made by adding **yeast** to **grape juice**. The yeast turn the sugar in the grape juice into **ethanol** (alcohol) and **carbon dioxide**.

3) **Cheese** is made by adding **bacteria** to milk. The bacteria turn the sugar in the milk into **lactic acid**, which causes the milk to **curdle**. An enzyme is then used to turn the curdled milk into **curds** and **whey**. The curds are separated off and left to **ripen** into **cheese**. Nice.

4) **Yoghurt** is also made by adding bacteria to milk. The bacteria turn the sugar in the milk into **lactic acid**, causing the milk to **clot** and **thicken** into yoghurt.

Using Microorganisms to Make Food has Advantages...

1) Populations of microorganisms **grow rapidly** under the right **conditions**, so food can be produced **quickly**.
2) Microorganisms can **grow** on a **range** of **inexpensive** materials.
3) Their environment can be **artificially controlled** — so you can potentially **grow food anywhere** and at **any time of the year**.
4) Conditions for growth are **easy to create**.
5) Some of the food made using microorganisms often **lasts longer** in **storage** than the raw product they're made from, e.g. **cheese** can be stored for longer than **milk**.

...and Disadvantages

Being served microorganisms for tea pushed Geoff over the edge.

1) There's a **high risk** of **food contamination**. The conditions created to grow the **desirable** microorganisms are also favourable to **harmful** microorganisms. They could cause the foods produced to **spoil** (go off), or if eaten, cause illnesses such as **food poisoning**.
2) The conditions required to grow microorganisms can be simple to create, but **small changes** in temperature or pH can **easily kill** the microorganisms.

Microorganisms and Food

Food Spoilage by Microorganisms can be Prevented

Food spoilage can be caused by the **growth** of **unwanted microorganisms** — as the organisms grow they break down the food, **contaminating** it with **waste products**. **Preventing** food spoilage involves either **killing** the microorganisms or **depriving** the microorganisms of the conditions they need to grow — this either **slows down** or **stops** their growth.

1) Salting prevents microorganisms taking in water...

Salting is simply **adding salt** to foods. Salt **inhibits the growth** of microorganisms by interfering with their ability to **absorb water** (which they need to survive). Some **meats** are preserved by salting, and **tinned foods** are often preserved in **brine** (a mixture of salt and water).

2) ...adding sugar can have the same effect.

Adding **sugar** also **inhibits the growth** of microorganisms by interfering with their ability to **absorb water**. For example, the high sugar content of **fruit jams** reduces the growth of microorganisms, giving the jam a **long shelf life**.

3) Freezing slows the growth of microorganisms.

Freezers keep foods below −18 °C. This **slows down reactions** taking place in microorganisms and **freezes the water** in the food, so the microorganisms **can't** use it. Freezing can preserve foods for **many months**.

4) Pickling in acidic vinegar inhibits the growth of microorganisms.

Vinegar has a **low pH**, which reduces **enzyme activity** (see p. 18) in microorganisms. This means they can't function properly, **inhibiting their growth**. Vinegar is used to **pickle** foods like onions.

5) Heat treatment kills microorganisms...

Heat treatment involves heating food to a **high temperature**, which **kills** any microorganisms present. **Pasteurisation** is one form of heat treatment — it involves raising **liquids** such as **milk** to a high temperature.

6) ...and so does irradiation.

Irradiation involves exposing foods to **radiation**, e.g. **X-rays** or **gamma rays**. This treatment **kills** any microorganisms present and can **extend shelf life** considerably.

Practice Questions

Q1 Name three foods made using microorganisms.

Q2 Describe two disadvantages of using microorganisms in food production.

Q3 Describe how pickling preserves food.

Exam Question

Q1 Mycoprotein is a protein-rich food produced from an edible fungus. The fungus is grown in an environment where conditions are carefully controlled. It's then heat-treated before being processed into the final product.

a) Explain why the mycoprotein is heat-treated. [2 marks]

b) Suggest three advantages of producing protein-rich foods from fungi compared to producing protein-rich foods from cows. [3 marks]

Hmm — I believe I'll have the irradiated beef with the pickled sprouts...

Ye scurvy dogs! You see, pirates didn't just eat salted pork because they liked the taste — they knew a thing or two about food spoilage. Pity they couldn't say the same about the whole fresh fruit/scurvy/nice teeth thing. Learn the six ways of preventing food spoilage and you'll find your way to a great chest of treasure. Well, quite a few marks anyway...

The Digestive System

These pages are for AQA Unit 1 only.

The digestive system is a long tube that goes from your mouth to your bum (which is a bit weird really if you think about it — you've got a hole right through your body). What's even weirder is all the different things that go on in between...

Digestion Breaks Down Large Molecules into Smaller Molecules

1) Many of the molecules in our **food** are **polymers**.

2) These are **large**, complex molecules composed of long chains of **monomers** — small **basic molecular units**.

3) **Proteins** and some **carbohydrates** are **polymers**. In carbohydrates, the monomers are called **monosaccharides**. They contain the elements **carbon**, **hydrogen** and **oxygen**. In proteins the monomers are called **amino acids**. They contain **carbon**, **hydrogen**, **oxygen**, **nitrogen**.

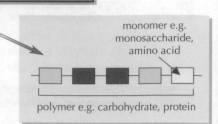

monomer e.g. monosaccharide, amino acid

polymer e.g. carbohydrate, protein

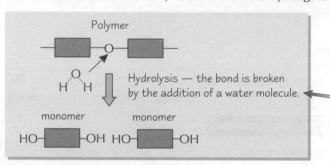

Polymer

Hydrolysis — the bond is broken by the addition of a water molecule.

monomer   monomer

4) The polymers in our food are **insoluble** — they can't be directly **absorbed** into our bloodstream and **assimilated** (made) into new products.

5) The polymers have to be **hydrolysed** (broken down) into **smaller**, more **soluble** molecules by **adding water**.

6) This process happens during **digestion**.

7) **Hydrolysis** is catalysed by **digestive enzymes**.

Each Part of the Digestive System Has a Specific Function

All the organs in the **digestive system** have a **role** in **breaking down** food and **absorbing nutrients**:

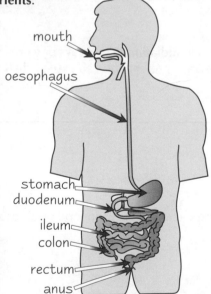

mouth
oesophagus
stomach
duodenum
ileum
colon
rectum
anus

1 Oesophagus

The **tube** that takes **food** from the **mouth** to the **stomach** using waves of **muscle contractions** called **peristalsis**. **Mucus** is secreted from tissues in the walls, to **lubricate** the food's passage downwards.

2 The Stomach

The stomach is a **small sac**. It has lots of **folds**, allowing the stomach to **expand** — it can hold up to 4 litres of food and liquid. The entrance and exit of the stomach are controlled by **sphincter muscles**. The stomach walls produce **gastric juice**, which helps break down food. Gastric juice consists of **hydrochloric acid** (HCl), **pepsin** (an enzyme) and **mucus**. Pepsin hydrolyses **proteins**, into smaller polypeptide chains. It only works in **acidic conditions** (provided by the HCl). **Peristalsis** of the stomach turns food into an acidic fluid called **chyme**.

3 The Small Intestine

The small intestine has two main parts — the **duodenum** and the **ileum**. **Chyme** is moved along the small intestine by **peristalsis**. In the duodenum, **bile** (which is alkaline) and **pancreatic juice neutralise** the **acidity** of the chyme and break it down into **smaller molecules**. In the ileum, the small, soluble molecules (e.g. glucose and amino acids) are **absorbed** through structures called **villi** that line the gut wall. Molecules are absorbed by **diffusion**, **facilitated diffusion** and **active transport** (see pages 34-36 for more).

4 Large intestine

The large intestine (colon) absorbs **water**, **salts** and **minerals**. Like other parts of the digestive system, it has a **folded wall** — this provides a **large surface area** for absorption. **Bacteria** that **decompose** some of the undigested nutrients are found in the large intestine.

5 Rectum

Faeces are stored in the rectum and then pass through **sphincter** muscles at the **anus** during **defecation**. Nice.

The Digestive System

The **Pancreas** and **Salivary Glands** Play Important Roles in **Digestion**

Glands along the **digestive system** release **enzymes** to help **break down** food.
You need to know about two of these glands — the **salivary glands** and the **pancreas**.

The Salivary Glands

There are three main pairs of salivary glands in the mouth.
They secrete **saliva** that consists of **mucus**, **mineral salts** and
salivary amylase (an enzyme). Salivary amylase breaks
down **starch** into **maltose**, a disaccharide. Saliva has other
roles in digestion — e.g. it helps to **lubricate** food, making
it easier to **swallow**.

Dudley quite fancied swopping mucus, mineral
salts and salivary amylase with Mildred.

The Pancreas

The pancreas releases **pancreatic juice** into the **duodenum** (see previous page) through
the **pancreatic duct**. Pancreatic juice contains **amylase**, **trypsin**, **chymotrypsin** and
lipase (the functions of these enzymes are on the next page). It also contains **sodium
hydrogencarbonate**, which **neutralises** the acidity of **hydrochloric acid** from the **stomach**.

Practice Questions

Q1　What chemical elements do proteins contain?

Q2　What is hydrolysis?

Q3　Describe the structure and function of the stomach.

Q4　Describe the structure and function of the small intestine.

Q5　Describe the structure and function of the large intestine.

Exam Questions

Q1　There are several glands associated with the digestive system.

　　a) Describe how the pancreas aids digestion.　　　　　　　　　　　　　　　　[6 marks]

　　b) Name one other gland associated with the digestive system.　　　　　　　[1 mark]

Q2　Name the parts of the digestive system labelled in the diagram.　　　　　　[4 marks]

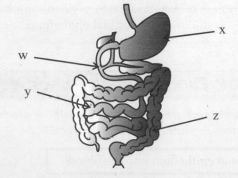

Gastric juice — not for me thanks, think I'll stick to orange...

_So when I eat a biscuit, first it gets chomped up by my teeth. Then it gets churned up, acidified and neutralised before all
those smaller, more soluble molecules are absorbed and, most likely, deposited on my hips. Then there's the messy
business of defecation. Learn all this stuff on the digestive system inside out — it might just save your life._

Enzymes and Carbohydrate Digestion

These pages are for AQA Unit 1 only.

Enzymes are needed to speed up digestion — without them it wouldn't happen fast enough and you'd be full of week-old mouldy pizza and chips... Nice.

Enzymes Help us to Digest Food Molecules

Digestive enzymes can be divided into three classes.

1) **Carbohydrases** catalyse the hydrolysis of **carbohydrates**.

2) **Proteases** catalyse the hydrolysis of **proteins**.

3) **Lipases** catalyse the hydrolysis of **lipids**.

You need to learn what amylase, maltase, sucrase and lactase break down.

The table shows some more specific enzyme reactions.

LOCATION	ENZYME	CLASS	HYDROLYSES	INTO
salivary glands	**amylase**	carbohydrase	starch	maltose
stomach	**pepsin**	protease	protein	peptides
pancreas	**amylase**	carbohydrase	starch	maltose
	trypsin	protease	protein	peptides
	chymotrypsin	protease	protein	peptides
	carboxypeptidase	protease	peptides	amino acids
	lipase	lipase	lipids	fatty acids + glycerol
ileum	**maltase**	carbohydrase	maltose	glucose
	sucrase	carbohydrase	sucrose	glucose + fructose
	lactase	carbohydrase	lactose	glucose + galactose
	peptidase	protease	peptides	amino acids

Two Enzymes are Needed to Break Down Starch into Glucose

1) Starch is made up of a mixture of two polysaccharides — **amylose** and **amylopectin** (see p. 10).

2) Both are composed of **long chains** of α-**glucose** linked together by glycosidic bonds, formed in condensation reactions.

3) When starch is digested, it's first broken down into **maltose** by **amylase** — an enzyme released by the **salivary glands** and the **pancreas** (see p. 77).

4) Maltose is then broken down into α-**glucose molecules** by **maltase**, which is released by the **intestinal epithelium**.

The Products of Carbohydrate Digestion are Absorbed in Different Ways

Diffusion, **facilitated diffusion** and **active transport** are essential to **absorb** the **products** of **carbohydrate digestion** (e.g. glucose) across the **intestinal epithelium cells**:

See pages 34-36 for a recap of diffusion, facilitated diffusion and active transport.

> Some **glucose diffuses** across the **intestinal epithelium** into the **blood**

When carbohydrates are first broken down, there's a **higher concentration** of **glucose** in the **small intestine** than in the **blood** — there's a **concentration gradient**. Glucose moves across the **epithelial cells** of the small intestine into the blood by **diffusion**. When the concentration in the lumen becomes **lower** than in the blood diffusion **stops**.

Enzymes and Carbohydrate Digestion

Some glucose enters the intestinal epithelium by active transport with sodium ions

The remaining glucose is absorbed by **active transport**. Here's how it all works:

1) **Sodium ions** are **actively transported out** of the small intestine epithelial **cells**, into the **blood**, by the **sodium-potassium pump**. This creates a **concentration gradient** — there's now a higher concentration of sodium ions in the small intestine lumen than inside the cell.

2) This causes sodium ions to diffuse from the small intestine lumen into the cell, down their concentration gradient. They do this via the **sodium-glucose co-transporter proteins**.

3) The co-transporter carries **glucose** into the cell with the sodium. As a result the concentration of **glucose** inside the cell **increases**.

4) Glucose diffuses out of the cell, into the blood, down its concentration gradient through a protein channel, by **facilitated diffusion**.

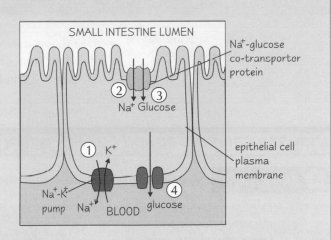

---

*Lactose-Intolerance is Caused by a **Lack** of the Digestive Enzyme **Lactase***

If you haven't got the **right enzyme** to break down a carbohydrate, you won't be able to **properly digest** foods with it in.

1) **Lactose** is a **sugar** found in milk.

2) It's digested by an **enzyme** called **lactase**, found in the intestines.

3) If you **don't** have enough of the enzyme lactase, you won't be able to break down the lactose in milk properly — a condition called **lactose-intolerance**.

4) Undigested lactose is fermented by bacteria and can cause a whole host of **intestinal complaints** such as **stomach cramps**, excessive **flatulence** (wind) and **diarrhoea**.

5) Milk can be artificially treated with purified lactase to make it suitable for lactose-intolerant people.

6) It's fairly **uncommon** to be lactose **tolerant** though — around 15% of Northern Europeans, 50% of Mediterraneans, 95% of Asians and 90% of people of African descent are lactose intolerant.

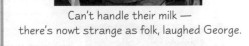

Can't handle their milk — there's nowt strange as folk, laughed George.

Practice Questions

Q1 Name the enzymes that break down: i) sucrose, ii) maltose, iii) lactose.

Q2 Name the two polysaccharides present in starch.

Exam Questions

Q1 Describe and explain how the glucose produced from starch digestion is absorbed into the blood by diffusion and active transport. [10 marks]

Q2 Describe the cause and symptoms of lactose intolerance. [4 marks]

Milk — you can't touch this — break it down...

If you don't have an enzyme for a particular substance you won't be able to break it down, simple as that. Most of the time it's not a problem — the substance just goes straight through you. The problem with lactose is that it's a feast for gut bacteria, and those bacteria produce gas (which results in a smelly social faux pas more often than you'd like).

Health and Disease

These pages are for AQA Unit 1 and OCR Unit 2. If you're doing Edexcel you can skip to Section 9.
Health can be affected by loads of things, especially infection with microorganisms...

Health isn't just Absence of Disease   *OCR only*

In the exam you could be asked to **discuss** what **health** and **disease** mean. So here goes...

- **Health** is a **state** of **physical**, **mental** and **social well-being**, which includes the **absence** of **disease** and **infirmity** (weakness of body or mind).
- **Disease** is a **condition** that **impairs** the **normal functioning** of an **organism**.

Disease can be Caused by Different Things

1 PATHOGENS   A **pathogen** is an organism that can cause **damage** to the organism it **infects** (the host).

1) Pathogens include **microorganisms** and some larger organisms, such as **tapeworms**.
2) Pathogenic microorganisms include some **bacteria**, some **fungi** and all **viruses**.

If you're doing **OCR** you also need to be able to discuss what the term parasite means, which is a little trickier:

> A **parasite** is an organism that **lives on** or **in** another organism (the host) and causes **damage** to that organism.

A pathogen and a parasite are actually the **same** thing, but traditionally people tend to call **bacteria**, **fungi** and **viruses** pathogens, and things like **tapeworms**, **roundworms** and **fleas** parasites.

2 LIFESTYLE

Certain **lifestyles** can affect your **risk** of developing some diseases. Here are two examples:

Coronary heart disease (CHD) is a disease that affects your **heart**. A **diet high** in **saturated fat** or **salt**, **smoking**, a **lack of exercise**, **excessive alcohol intake** and being **obese** can all lead to an **increased risk** of CHD (see p. 126 for more).

Cancer is the result of **uncontrolled cell division** (see p. 56). Factors that **increase the risk** of developing cancer include **smoking** (mouth, throat and lung cancer), **excessive exposure to sunlight** (skin cancer) and **excessive alcohol intake** (liver cancer).

3 OTHER FACTORS   Diseases can also be caused by **genetic defects**, **nutritional deficiencies** and other **environmental factors** (e.g. toxic chemicals).

It's never Too Late to Change Your Lifestyle   *AQA only*

Changing your **lifestyle** for the **better** (e.g. reducing your alcohol intake, doing more exercise, eating healthily etc.) doesn't mean you'll **never** develop these diseases, but it can **reduce the risk**. So it's never too late to change. For example, studies have shown that the risk to a **smoker** of developing **lung cancer** is reduced if they stop smoking. ⟹

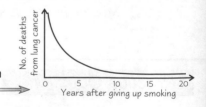

AIDS is Caused by the HIV Virus   *OCR only*

1) The **human immunodeficiency virus** (**HIV**) infects human white blood cells.
2) HIV (and all other viruses) can only **reproduce inside** the **cells** of the organism it has infected because it doesn't have the equipment (such as enzymes and ribosomes) to replicate on its own.
3) After the virus has reproduced, it **kills** the **white blood cells** as it **leaves**.
4) HIV infection leads to **acquired immune deficiency syndrome** (**AIDS**).
5) AIDS is a condition where the **immune system deteriorates** and eventually **fails** due to the loss of white blood cells. It makes the sufferer more **vulnerable** to **other infections**, like pneumonia.
6) HIV is **transmitted** in **three** main ways: ⟹   ⟹

- Via unprotected **sexual intercourse**.
- Through **infected bodily fluids** (like blood), e.g. **sharing needles**, **blood transfusions**.
- From **mother** to **fetus** (through the placenta, breast milk or during childbirth).

Health and Disease

This page is for OCR only, so if you're doing AQA you can go straight to the questions now.

Malaria is Caused by the Parasite Plasmodium

1) *Plasmodium* is a **eukaryotic, single-celled parasite**.
2) It's **transmitted** by **mosquitoes** — insects that **feed** on the **blood of animals**, including **humans**.
3) The mosquitoes are **vectors** — they **don't** cause the disease themselves, but they **spread** the infection by **transferring** the parasite from one host to another.
4) Mosquitoes **transfer** the *Plasmodium* parasite into an animal's blood when they **feed** on them.
5) *Plasmodium* infects the **liver** and **red blood cells**, and **disrupts** the **blood supply** to vital organs.

AIDS/HIV, Malaria and Tuberculosis Have a Global Impact

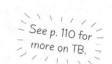
See p. 110 for more on TB.

1) **HIV**, **malaria** and **tuberculosis** (TB — a bacterial lung disease) are most **common** in **sub-Saharan Africa** and other **developing countries**. This is because:

- There's **limited access** to good **healthcare** — **drugs** are **not** always **available**, people are **less likely** to be **diagnosed** and **treated**, **blood donations** aren't always **screened** for infectious diseases and **surgical equipment** isn't always **sterile**.
- There's **limited health education** to inform people how to **avoid infectious diseases** — e.g. fewer people know about the **transmission** of **HIV** and that it can be **prevented** by **safe-sex** practices, e.g. using condoms.
- There's **limited equipment** to **reduce** the **spread** of infections — e.g. fewer people have **mosquito nets** to reduce the chance of infection with **malaria**.
- There are **overcrowded** conditions — this **increases** the **risk of TB infection** by **droplet transmission** (see previous page).

2) The **prevalence** of HIV, malaria and TB in developing countries, like sub-Saharan Africa, **slows** down **social** and **economic development** because these diseases **increase death rates**, **reduce productivity** (fewer people are able to work) and result in **high healthcare costs**.

3) **Studying** the **global distribution** of these diseases is **important** for many reasons:

- The information can be used to find out **where** people are most **at risk**.
- Any data collected can be used to **predict** where **epidemics** are most likely to occur.
- It's important for **research** (e.g. into how it's spread).
- It allows organisations to provide **aid** where it's **needed most**.

Practice Questions

Q1 Explain what is meant by the term disease.
Q2 List three lifestyle factors that affect the risk of developing CHD.

Exam Question

Q1 TB is an infectious lung disease caused by a bacterial pathogen.

a) Describe what a pathogen is. [1 mark]

b) Other than bacteria, list two types of pathogen. [2 marks]

My computer has a virus — I knew I shouldn't have sneezed on it...

Phew, they were a tough two pages — lots of definitions to get your head around. All infectious diseases (those that can be passed between individuals) are caused by pathogens, but there are other things to watch out for (like a bad lifestyle).

Cholera

These pages are for AQA Unit 1 only. If you're doing OCR you can go on to the next section.

There's a specific infectious disease that you need to learn all about — cholera. It's a pretty nasty disease caused by a bacterial pathogen.

Pathogens Cause Disease by Producing Toxins and Damaging Cells

If pathogens **successfully enter** an organism's body they can **cause disease** in **two** ways:

The cell the pathogen has invaded and is reproducing inside is called the host cell.

Production of toxins

Many bacteria **release toxins** (harmful molecules) into the body. For example, the bacterium that causes **tetanus** produces a toxin that **blocks** the function of certain **nerve cells**, causing **muscle spasms**. The bacterium that causes **cholera** produces a toxin that upsets the exchange of substances in and out of cells (see below).

Cell damage

Pathogens can physically damage host cells by:

- **Rupturing** them to **release nutrients** (proteins etc.) inside them.

- **Breaking down** nutrients inside the cell for their own use. This starves and eventually **kills** the **cell**.

- **Replicating** inside the cells and **bursting** them when they're released, e.g. some **viruses** do this.

Cholera Bacteria Produce a Toxin That Affects Chloride Ion Exchange

Cholera bacteria produce a **toxin** when they infect the body. This toxin causes a fair old bit of havoc...

The bacterium that causes cholera is a prokaryotic organism (see p. 22).

1) The toxin causes **chloride ion protein channels** in the plasma membranes of the small intestine epithelial cells to **open**.

2) Chloride ions move **into** the **small intestine lumen**. The build up of chloride ions **lowers** the **water potential** of the lumen.

3) **Water** moves **out** of the **blood**, across the epithelial cells, and **into** the **small intestine lumen** by **osmosis** (to even up the water concentration).

4) The massive increase in water secretion into the intestine lumen leads to **really, really, really bad diarrhoea** — causing the body to become extremely **dehydrated**.

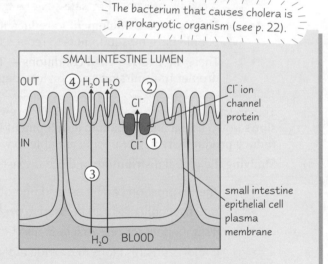

Oral Rehydration Solutions are used to Treat Diarrhoeal Diseases

People suffering from **diarrhoeal diseases** like cholera need to **replace** all the **fluid** that they've **lost** in the diarrhoea. The quickest way to do this is by inserting a **drip** into a person's **vein**. However, not everywhere in the world has access to drips, so **oral rehydration solutions** are used instead.

Oral Rehydration Solutions (ORSs)

1) An oral rehydration solution is a **drink** that contains large amounts of **salts** (such as sodium ions and chloride ions) and **sugars** (such as glucose and sucrose) dissolved in water.

2) **Sodium** ions are included to increase **glucose** absorption (sodium and glucose are **co-transported** into the epithelium cells in the intestine — see p. 79).

3) Getting the **concentration** of the ORS right is essential for effective treatment.

4) An ORS is a very **cheap** treatment and the people administering it **don't** require much **training**. This makes it great for treating diarrhoeal diseases in **developing countries** (where they're a huge problem).

Cholera

New **Oral Rehydration Solutions** can be **Tested on Humans**

ORS are so important in treating diarrhoeal disease that research into the development of **new**, **improved** ORS is always being carried out. But before a new ORS can be put into use, scientists have to show that it's **more effective** than the old ORS and that it's **safe**. This is done by **clinical testing** on humans.

> There are some **ethical issues** associated with **trialling ORSs**
>
> 1) **Diarrhoeal diseases** mostly affect **children**, so many **trials** involve **children**. **Parents** decide whether the child will **participate** in the trial. The child doesn't make their **own decision** — some people think this is unethical.
>
> 2) But scientists believe the treatment must be trialled on children if it's to be shown to be **effective** against a **disease** that mainly affects children.
>
> 3) Clinical trials usually involve a **blind trial**. This is where some patients who are admitted into hospital with diarrhoeal diseases are given the **standard ORS** and others are given the **new ORS**. This means that the two can be **compared**. It's called a blind trial because the patients **don't know** which treatment they've been given. Some people don't agree with this — they think that people have the **right** to **know** and **decide** on the **treatment** that they're going to have.
>
> 4) Scientists argue that a blind trial is important to eliminate any **bias** that may **skew** the **data** as a result of **patients knowing** which treatment they've received.
>
> 5) When a new ORS is first trialled, there's no way of knowing whether it'll be **better** than the current ORS — there is a **risk** of the patient **dying** when the original, better treatment was available.

Geysers — plenty of water but oddly not that rehydrating.

Practice Questions

Q1 Give two ways in which a pathogen can cause disease.

Q2 What type of pathogen causes cholera?

Q3 Suggest a reason why oral rehydration solutions contain sodium ions.

Q4 Suggest two reasons why oral rehydration solutions are useful for treating diarrhoeal diseases in developing countries.

Exam Questions

Q1 Describe three ways in which a pathogen may damage host cells. [3 marks]

Q2 Explain how infection with the cholera bacterium leads to diarrhoea. [5 marks]

Q3 Give one argument for and one argument against trialling new oral rehydration solutions on children. [2 marks]

<u>Diarrhoea is hereditary — it runs in your jeans...</u>

Well, I don't know about you but all I can think about now is poo. With cholera, it's actually the poo that can kill you, so to speak, because you lose so much water with it. Antibiotics can help to clear the cholera bacterium, but if you aren't rehydrated straightaway you could die because your cells need plenty of water to carry out all their chemical reactions.

Antibiotic Action and Resistance

The rest of this section is for AQA Unit 2 only.

These pages are all about antibiotics and how they kill (or inhibit) bacteria. But don't feel sorry for the bacteria — they're getting their own back by evolving antibiotic resistance. Sneaky...

Antibiotics Are Used to Treat Bacterial Diseases

1) Antibiotics are **chemicals** that either **kill** or **inhibit** the **growth** of bacteria.

2) **Different types** of antibiotics kill or inhibit the growth of bacteria in **different ways**.

3) Some **prevent growing** bacterial cells from **forming** the bacterial **cell wall**, which usually gives the cell structure and support (see p. 22).

4) This can lead to **osmotic lysis**:

> 1) The antibiotics **inhibit enzymes** that are needed to make the **chemical bonds** in the cell wall.
>
> 2) This **prevents** the cell from growing properly and **weakens** the cell wall.
>
> 3) **Water** moves **into the cell** by **osmosis**.
>
> 4) The **weakened cell wall** can't withstand the increase in **pressure** and bursts (**lyses**).

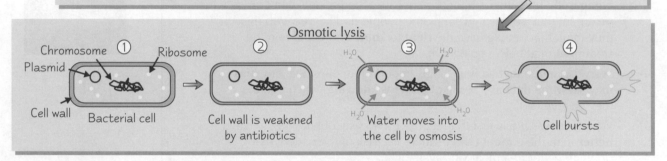

Osmotic lysis

① Bacterial cell — Plasmid, Chromosome, Ribosome, Cell wall ② Cell wall is weakened by antibiotics ③ Water moves into the cell by osmosis ④ Cell bursts

Mutations in Bacterial DNA can Cause Antibiotic Resistance

1) The **genetic material** in bacteria is the same as in most other organisms — **DNA**.

2) The DNA of an organism contains **genes** that carry the instructions for different **proteins**. These proteins determine the organism's **characteristics**.

3) **Mutations** are **changes** in the **base sequence** of an organism's DNA.

4) If a mutation occurs in the DNA of a gene it could change the protein and cause a **different characteristic**.

5) Some mutations in bacterial DNA mean that the bacteria are **not affected** by a particular antibiotic any more — they've developed **antibiotic resistance**.

See p. 38 for more on DNA and p. 42 for more on mutations.

Example

> **Methicillin** is an antibiotic that inhibits an enzyme involved in **cell wall formation** (see above).
> Some bacteria have developed resistance to methicillin, e.g. methicillin-resistant *Staphylococcus aureus* (**MRSA**).
> Usually, **resistance** to methicillin occurs because the **gene** for the **target enzyme** of methicillin has **mutated**.
> The mutated gene produces an **altered enzyme** that methicillin no longer **recognises**, and so **can't inhibit**.

Carol wished she had resistance to catalogue poses.

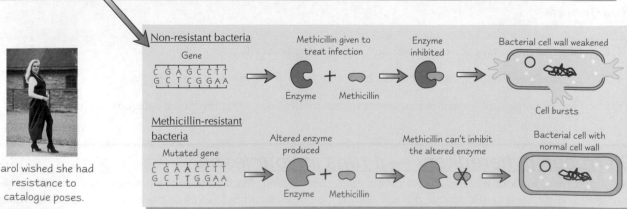

Non-resistant bacteria — Gene C G A G C C T T / G C T C G G A A → Methicillin given to treat infection (Enzyme + Methicillin) → Enzyme inhibited → Bacterial cell wall weakened, Cell bursts

Methicillin-resistant bacteria — Mutated gene C G A A C C T T / G C T T G G A A → Altered enzyme produced (Enzyme + Methicillin) → Methicillin can't inhibit the altered enzyme → Bacterial cell with normal cell wall

Antibiotic Action and Resistance

Antibiotic Resistance can be Passed On Vertically...

Vertical gene transmission is where genes are passed on during **reproduction**.

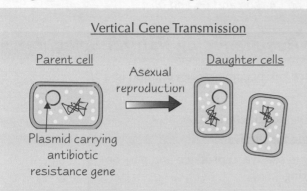

Vertical Gene Transmission

Parent cell → Asexual reproduction → Daughter cells

Plasmid carrying antibiotic resistance gene

1) Bacteria reproduce **asexually**, so each daughter cell is an **exact copy** of the parent.

2) This means that **each** daughter cell has an exact copy of the parent cell's **genes**, including any that give it **antibiotic resistance**.

3) Genes for antibiotic resistance can be found in the bacterial **chromosome** or in **plasmids** (small **rings of DNA** found in bacterial cells, see p. 22).

4) The chromosome and any plasmids are passed on to the daughter cells during reproduction.

...or Horizontally

1) Genes for resistance can also be passed on **horizontally**.

2) Two bacteria **join together** in a process called **conjugation** and a **copy of a plasmid** is passed from one cell to the other.

3) Plasmids can be passed on to a member of the **same species** or a totally **different species**.

Horizontal Gene Transmission

Bacterial cell with <u>antibiotic resistance gene</u> in plasmid + Bacteria <u>without</u> plasmid

<u>Bacterial conjugation</u> — copy of plasmid transferred through stalk called a pilus

Both bacterial cells have a copy of the plasmid containing the antibiotic resistance gene

Practice Questions

Q1 What is osmotic lysis?

Q2 What is the genetic material in bacteria?

Q3 What is the difference between vertical and horizontal gene transmission?

Exam Question

Q1 More and more bacteria are becoming resistant to antibiotics such as penicillin.

a) Describe how resistance to an antibiotic arises in bacteria. [3 marks]

b) Describe how resistance to antibiotics is spread between two bacteria. [3 marks]

c) Penicillin is a cell wall inhibitor antibiotic. Explain how penicillin kills bacteria. [4 marks]

Horizontal gene transmission — that's not what it was called in my day...

There are lots of nice, colourful pictures on this page, but they're not just here to make the place look pretty you know. They're here to help you learn the different processes you need to understand for your exam — osmotic lysis, vertical transmission and horizontal transmission — so get scribblin' and learnin'. Go on, go on, go on...

Antibiotic Resistance

These pages are for AQA Unit 2 only.

Mutations arise by accident but if they're useful, e.g. give antibiotic resistance, then natural selection will make sure they're passed on and on and on and on and on and on and on (and on and on and on)...

Bacterial Populations Evolve Antibiotic Resistance by Natural Selection

An **adaptation** (a useful characteristic) like antibiotic resistance can become **more common** in a **population** because of **natural selection**:

1) Individuals within a population **show variation** in their **characteristics**.

2) **Predation**, **disease** and **competition** create a **struggle for survival**.

3) Individuals with **better adaptations** are **more likely** to **survive**, **reproduce** and **pass on** the **alleles** that cause the adaptations to their **offspring**.

4) Over time, the **number** of individuals with the advantageous adaptations **increases**.

5) Over generations this leads to **evolution** as the favourable adaptations become **more common** in the population.

Adaptations are caused by gene mutations.

Here's how populations of antibiotic-resistant bacteria evolve by natural selection:

1) Some individuals in a population have alleles that give them **resistance** to an **antibiotic**.

2) The population is **exposed** to that antibiotic, **killing** bacteria **without** the antibiotic resistance allele.

3) The **resistant bacteria survive** and **reproduce** without competition, passing on the allele that gives antibiotic resistance to their offspring.

4) After some time **most** organisms in the population will carry the antibiotic resistance allele.

Natural Selection also Occurs in Other Organisms

1) Natural selection happens in **all populations** — not just in bacterial populations.

2) There are loads of examples, but they all follow the same basic principle — the organism has a **characteristic** that makes it more likely to **survive**, **reproduce** and pass on the **alleles** for the better characteristic.

3) In your **exam** you might be asked to explain why certain characteristics are common (or have increased).

4) To do this you should **identify** why the **adaptations** (**characteristics**) are useful and **explain** how they've become more common due to **natural selection**.

5) Here are some examples of the kinds of characteristics that can help organisms to survive:

Adaptations that could increase chance of survival	How the adaptations could increase survival
Streamlined body, camouflage, larger paws for running quicker etc.	They help to escape from predators.
Streamlined body, camouflage, larger paws for running quicker, larger claws, longer neck etc.	They help to catch prey/get food.
Shorter/longer hairs, large ears, increased water storage capacity etc.	They make the animal more suited to the climate.

Dave wasn't convinced his camouflage was working.

Antibiotic Resistance

Antibiotic Resistance Makes it Difficult to Treat Some Diseases

Diseases caused by bacteria are treated using **antibiotics**. Because bacteria are becoming resistant to different antibiotics through **natural selection** it's becoming more and more **difficult** to treat some bacterial infections, such as tuberculosis (**TB**) and methicillin-resistant *Staphylococcus aureus* (**MRSA**).

Tuberculosis

1) **TB** is a **lung disease** caused by bacteria.

2) TB was once a **major killer** in the UK, but the number of people dying from TB **decreased** with the development of **specific antibiotics** that killed the bacterium. Also the number of people catching TB **dropped** due to a vaccine (see p. 94).

3) More recently, some populations of TB bacteria have **evolved** resistance to the **most effective** antibiotics. **Natural selection** has led to populations that are resistant to a **range** of different antibiotics — the populations (strains) are **multidrug-resistant**.

4) To try to combat the **emergence** of resistance, TB treatment now involves taking a **combination** of different antibiotics for about **6 months**.

5) TB is becoming harder to treat as multidrug-resistant strains are **evolving quicker** than **drug companies** can develop new antibiotics.

There's more about TB on page 110.

MRSA

1) **Methicillin-resistant *Staphylococcus aureus*** (MRSA) is a strain of the *Staphylococcus aureus* bacterium that has evolved to be resistant to a number of commonly used antibiotics, including **methicillin**.

2) *Staphylococcus aureus* causes a **range** of illnesses from **minor skin infections** to **life-threatening diseases** such as **meningitis** and **septicaemia**.

3) The major problem with MRSA is that some strains are resistant to **nearly all** the antibiotics that are available.

4) Also, it can take a long time for **clinicians** to determine which antibiotics, if any, will **kill** the strain each individual is infected with. During this time the **patient** may become **very ill** and even **die**.

5) **Drug companies** are trying to **develop alternative ways** of treating MRSA to try to combat the emergence of resistance.

Lab tests are carried out to see if any antibiotics can kill a strain of MRSA.

Practice Questions

Q1 Briefly describe the process of natural selection.

Q2 Why is it becoming more difficult to treat TB infections?

Exam Questions

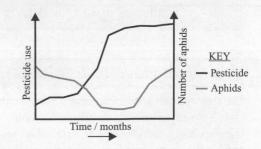

Q1 The graph shows the use of an anti-aphid pesticide on a farm and the number of aphids found on the farm over a period of time.

Describe and explain the change in aphid numbers shown in the graph. [6 marks]

Q2 The bat *Anoura fistulata* has a very long tongue (up to one and a half times the length of its body). The tongue enables the bat to feed on the nectar inside a deep tubular flower found in the forests of Ecuador.

Describe how natural selection can explain the evolution of such a long tongue. [3 marks]

Why do giraffes have long necks?...*

Adaptation and selection aren't that bad really... just remember that any characteristic that increases the chances of an organism getting more dinner, getting laid or avoiding being gobbled up by another creature will increase in the population (due to the process of natural selection). Now I know why mullets have disappeared... so unattractive...

*So they can reach food found high up. This means they're more likely to survive, reproduce and pass on their alleles (genes). So no, it's not because they've got smelly feet.

Evaluating Resistance Data

These pages are for AQA Unit 2 only.

The number of infections caused by resistant bacteria is rising, so it's important to keep an eye on them and any new ones that pop up. Like they say, you need to know your enemies if you want to beat them (OK, so I don't know who says it, but someone does. I think I heard it on Catchphrase once...).

You Need to be Able to **Evaluate Data** About **Antibiotic Resistance**

It's very possible that you could get some data from a **study** into antibiotic resistance in the exam.
You need to be able to **evaluate** the **methodology**, **data** and any **conclusions** drawn.
Here's an example:

This study investigated the **number** of **death certificates mentioning** *Staphylococcus aureus* (**S. aureus**) and methicillin-resistant *S. aureus* (**MRSA**) in the UK between 1993 and 2002. The data was collected from **UK death certificates** issued between 1993 and 2002. The **results** are shown in the graph opposite.

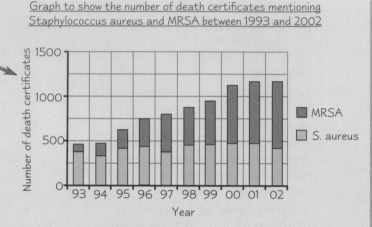

Graph to show the number of death certificates mentioning *Staphylococcus aureus* and MRSA between 1993 and 2002

Here are a couple of things you might be asked to do:

1) <u>Describe the data</u> — This study shows that the number of death certificates mentioning **all forms** of *S. aureus* **increased** between 1993 and 2002. The number mentioning **MRSA increased** while the number mentioning *S. aureus* stayed relatively level.

2) <u>Check the evidence backs up any conclusions</u> — Dr Bottril said, 'This data shows that the number of deaths **caused** by MRSA is rising'. Does the data support this conclusion? No. The study only looked at death certificates **mentioning** MRSA, not deaths **caused** by MRSA.

3) <u>Other points to consider</u>
   - This study looked at the number of **death certificates** mentioning MRSA. Studying the number of **reported** MRSA **infections** each year may have been a **better way** of investigating the occurrence of bacterial resistance.
   - Some death certificates may not have mentioned MRSA because it wasn't the **cause of death**, but the people may have been **infected** at the time. This means the data **doesn't** reflect the number of infections.
   - Increased **awareness** of MRSA may have influenced the decision to include MRSA on the death certificate, **biasing** the data.

You Might Have to **Evaluate Experimental Data**

The theory's the same for experimental data — **evaluate** the **methodology**, **data** and **conclusions**.
Here's an experimental example for you — A clinician needs to find out which antibiotics will treat a **patient's infection**. They spread a sample of bacteria taken **from the patient** onto an agar plate. Then they place paper discs **soaked** with **antibiotics** onto the plate, grow the bacteria and **measure the areas of growth inhibition** after a set period of time:

1) <u>Draw conclusions</u> — Be **precise** about what the data shows. A 250 mg dose of **streptomycin inhibited** growth the most. A 250 mg dose of **tetracycline inhibited** growth a small amount. The bacteria appear to be **resistant** to **methicillin** up to **250 mg**.

2) <u>Evaluate the methodology</u> — the experiment included a **negative control**, which is good. The negative control is a paper disc soaked in sterile water. The bacteria grew around this disc, which shows the paper disc **alone** doesn't kill the bacteria.

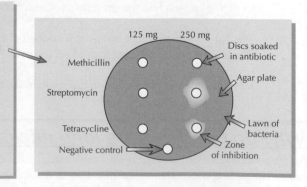

Evaluating Resistance Data

Decisions are Made Using Scientific Knowledge

Bacteria **will develop** antibiotic resistance by natural selection — it's nature. But scientific research has shown that certain things can be done to **slow down** the natural process. People working in the **public health sector**, together with patients, have to be made aware of recent **scientific findings** so that they can **act** upon them. Here are two examples:

Scientific Knowledge: Using an **antiseptic gel** to wash hands can help to **reduce the spread** of infectious diseases by **person-to-person contact**.

Decision: Health workers should **reduce spread** by washing their hands with **antiseptic gel** (placed at all hand basins) before and after **visiting each patient** on a ward.

Scientific knowledge: Bacteria become resistant to antibiotics **more quickly** when antibiotics are **misused** and patients **don't finish the course**.

Decision: Doctors should only prescribe antibiotics when **absolutely necessary**. Patients have to be told the **importance** of finishing **all the antibiotics** even if they start to feel better.

There are Ethical Issues Surrounding the Use of Antibiotics

People are very concerned about the spread of antibiotic-resistant bacteria. **Limiting the use** of antibiotics is one way of helping to slow down the emergence of resistance, but this raises some **ethical issues**.

1) Some people believe that antibiotics should only be used in **life-threatening situations** to reduce the increase of resistance. Others argue against this because people would take **more time off work** for illness, it could **reduce** people's **standard of living**, it could increase the **incidence of disease** and it could cause **unnecessary suffering**.

2) A few people believe doctors shouldn't prescribe antibiotics to those suffering **dementia**. They argue that they may forget to take them, increasing the chance of **resistance** developing. However, some people argue that **all patients** have the **right to medication**.

3) Some also argue that **terminally ill** patients shouldn't receive antibiotics because they're going to die. But **withholding** antibiotics from these patients could reduce their **length of survival** and **quality of life**.

4) Some people believe **animals shouldn't** be given antibiotics (as this may increase antibiotic resistance). Other people argue that this could cause **unnecessary suffering** to the animals.

Practice Questions

Q1 Briefly describe a method for testing the antibiotic resistance of bacteria.

Q2 Briefly describe one situation where scientific knowledge has affected the decision-making surrounding antibiotic resistance.

Exam Questions

Q1 Put forward arguments for and against giving antibiotics to someone suffering from dementia. [2 marks]

Q2 A mother takes her son, who is suffering from a mild chest infection, to the doctor to get some antibiotics.

a) Why might the doctor be reluctant to prescribe the child antibiotics? [2 marks]
b) Why might the mother disagree if the doctor refuses to prescribe antibiotics? [2 marks]

Q3 A study was carried out to determine if the increase in the national rate of bacterial resistance to antibiotic X is linked to people not finishing their course of the antibiotic. Part of the study involved sending out questionnaires to 300 patients from one GP surgery in East Anglia.

Evaluate the methodology of this study. [3 marks]

R-E-S-I-S-T-A-N-T — find out what it means to me...

You're probably a bit bored of me ramming it down your throat now but you need to be able to evaluate any data or study you're presented with. Remember to look at the methodology, evidence and conclusions, and look out for anywhere there may be problems. And if you're ever asked to consider any ethical issues, think of the arguments for and against.

The Immune Response

These pages are for AQA Unit 1 and OCR Unit 2 only. If you're doing Edexcel you can skip to the next section.

Well, all that stuff about disease is making me feel a bit on edge. Fortunately, your body has some state-of-the-art defences to protect you against pathogens...

Pathogens can Penetrate an Organism's Interface with the Environment
AQA only

Pathogens need to **enter** the body to cause disease — they **get in** through an organism's **surface of contact** (**interface**) with the **environment**, e.g. nose, eyes, a cut. An organism has **three** main interfaces with the environment:

1) **Skin** — If you **damage** your skin, **pathogens** on the surface can enter your **bloodstream**.

2) **Digestive System** — If you **eat** or **drink food** that contains **pathogens**, most of them will be **killed** by the **acidic** conditions of the **stomach**. However, some may **survive** and pass into the intestines where they can invade **cells** of the **gut wall** and cause disease.

3) **Gas-Exchange System** — If you breathe in **air** that contains **pathogens**, most of them will be trapped in **mucus** lining the lung epithelium (the outer layer of cells in the passages to the lungs). These cells also have **cilia** (hair-like structures) that **beat** and **move** the mucus up the trachea to the mouth, where it's removed. Unfortunately, some pathogens are still able to reach the **alveoli** where they can **invade** cells and cause **damage**.

The Skin and Mucous Membranes are Primary Defences
OCR only

Your body has a number of **primary defences** that help **prevent pathogens** from **entering** it. These include the **skin** and **mucous membranes**:

SKIN

This acts as a **physical barrier**, **blocking pathogens** from **entering** the body. It also acts as a **chemical barrier** by producing **chemicals** that **inhibit** the **growth** of pathogens.

MUCOUS MEMBRANES

They **protect body openings** that are **exposed** to the **environment** (such as the mouth, nostrils, ears, genitals and anus). Some membranes **secrete mucus** — a sticky substance that **traps pathogens** and contains **antimicrobial enzymes**.

If a Pathogen Enters the Body, the Immune System Responds

1) An **immune response** is the body's **reaction** to a **foreign antigen**.

2) **Antigens** are **molecules** (usually proteins or polysaccharides) found on the **surface** of **cells**.

3) When a pathogen (like a bacterium) **invades** the body, the antigens on its cell surface are **identified as foreign**, which **activates** cells in the immune system.

There are Four Main Stages Involved in the Immune Response

① Phagocytes Engulf Pathogens

A **phagocyte** (e.g. a macrophage) is a type of **white blood cell** that carries out **phagocytosis** (engulfment of pathogens). They're found in the **blood** and in **tissues** and are the **first** cells to **respond** to a pathogen inside the body. Here's how they work:

1) A phagocyte **recognises** the **antigens** on a pathogen.

2) The cytoplasm of the phagocyte moves round the pathogen, **engulfing** it.

3) The pathogen is now contained in a **phagocytic vacuole** (a bubble) in the cytoplasm of the phagocyte.

4) A **lysosome** (an organelle that contains **lysosomal enzymes**) **fuses** with the phagocytic vacuole. The lysosomal enzymes **break down** the pathogen.

5) The phagocyte then **presents** the pathogen's antigens. It sticks the antigens on its **surface** to **activate** other immune system cells.

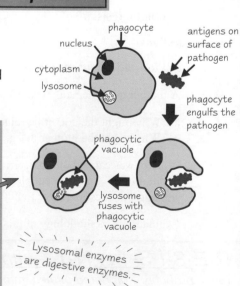

phagocyte
nucleus
antigens on surface of pathogen
cytoplasm
lysosome
phagocyte engulfs the pathogen
phagocytic vacuole
lysosome fuses with phagocytic vacuole

Lysosomal enzymes are digestive enzymes.

The Immune Response

2) Phagocytes **Activate T-cells**

T-cells are also called T lymphocytes.

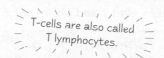

1) A **T-cell** is another type of **white blood cell**.
2) Their surface is covered with **receptors**.
3) The receptors **bind to antigens** presented by the phagocytes.
4) Each T-cell has a **different receptor** on its surface.
5) When the receptor on the surface of a T-cell meets a **complementary antigen**, it binds to it — so each T-cell will bind to a **different antigen**.
6) This **activates** the T-cell — it **divides** and **differentiates** into **different types** of T-cells that carry out **different functions**:

> 1) Some activated T-cells **release substances** to **activate B-cells** (see below).
> 2) Some **attach** to antigens on a pathogen and **kill** the cell.
> 3) Some become **memory cells** (see next page).

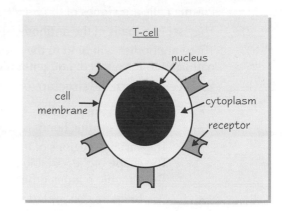

T-cell

cell membrane — nucleus — cytoplasm — receptor

A complementary antigen means its shape fits into the shape of the receptor.

3) T-cells **Activate B-cells**, which Divide into **Plasma Cells**

B-cells are also called B lymphocytes.

1) **B-cells** are another type of **white blood cell**.
2) They're covered with **antibodies**.
3) Antibodies are **proteins** that **bind to antigens** to form an **antigen-antibody complex**.
4) Each B-cell has a **different shaped antibody** on its surface.
5) When the antibody on the surface of a B-cell meets a **complementary shaped antigen**, it binds to it — so each B-cell will bind to a **different antigen**.
6) This, together with substances **released** from the T-cell, **activates** the B-cell.
7) The activated B-cell **divides**, by mitosis, into **plasma cells** and **memory cells** (see next page).

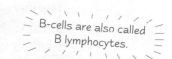

B-cell

cell membrane — nucleus — cytoplasm — antibody

Cell signalling is just for OCR.

> **Cell Signalling**
>
> 1) Cell signalling is basically how **cells communicate**.
> 2) A cell may **release** (or present) a **substance** that **binds to** the **receptors** on **another cell** — this causes a **response** of some kind in the other cell.
> 3) Cell signalling is really important in the **immune response** because it helps to **activate** all the **different types** of **white blood cells** that are needed.
> 4) For example, **T-cells** release substances that bind to receptors on **B-cells**. This **activates** the B-cells — the T-cells aresignalling to the B-cells that there's a pathogen in the body.

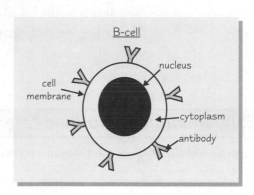

Deidre was getting quite fed up with the way Harold signalled he wanted a cup of tea.

See p. 33 for more on cell signalling.

The Immune Response

These pages are for AQA Unit 1 and OCR Unit 2.

4 Plasma Cells Make More Antibodies to a Specific Antigen

1) Plasma cells are **clones** of the B-cell (they're **identical** to the B-cell).

2) They secrete **loads** of the **antibody**, **specific** to the antigen, into the blood.

3) These antibodies will bind to the antigens on the surface of the pathogen to form **lots** of **antigen-antibody complexes**.

4) You need to **learn** the **structure** of antibodies:

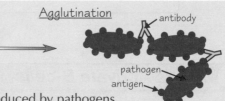

An Antigen-Antibody Complex

- Antibodies are **proteins** — they're made up of chains of **amino acids** linked by **peptide bonds** (see p. 6 for more on proteins).
- The **variable regions** of the antibody form the **antigen binding sites**. The **shape** of the variable region is **complementary** to a particular antigen. The variable regions **differ** between antibodies (due to different **amino acid sequences**).
- The **hinge region** allows **flexibility** when the antibody binds to the antigen.
- The **constant regions** allow binding to **receptors** on **immune system cells**, e.g. phagocytes. The constant region is the **same in all** antibodies.
- **Disulfide bridges** (a type of bond) hold the polypeptide chains together.

5) Antibodies **help** to **clear** an **infection** by:

1) **Agglutinating pathogens** — each antibody has **two binding sites**, so an antibody can **bind** to **two pathogens** at the **same time** — the pathogens become **clumped together**. Phagocytes then bind to the antibodies and phagocytose a lot of pathogens **all at once**.

Agglutination

2) **Neutralising toxins** — antibodies can **bind** to the **toxins** produced by pathogens. This **prevents** the toxins from **affecting human cells**, so the toxins are **neutralised** (inactivated). The toxin-antibody complexes are also phagocytosed.

3) **Preventing the pathogen binding to human cells** — when antibodies bind to the antigens on pathogens, they may **block** the cell surface receptors that the pathogens need to **bind to the host cells**. This means the pathogen **can't attach to** or **infect** the host cells.

The Immune Response Can be Split into Cellular and Humoral   *AQA only*

Just to add to your fun, the **immune response** is often split into **two** — the **cellular response** and the **humoral response**.

> Both types of response are needed to remove a pathogen from the body.

1) **Cellular** — The **T-cells** and **other** immune system **cells** that they **interact** with, e.g. phagocytes, form the cellular response.

2) **Humoral** — **B-cells** and the production of **antibodies** form the **humoral response**.

The Primary Response is Slow...

1) When an antigen enters the body for the **first time** it activates the immune system. This is called the **primary response**.

2) The primary response is **slow** because there **aren't many B-cells** that can make the antibody needed to bind to it.

3) Eventually the body will produce **enough** of the right antibody to overcome the infection. Meanwhile the infected person will show **symptoms** of the disease.

4) After being exposed to an antigen, both T- and B-cells produce **memory cells**. These memory cells **remain in the body** for a **long** time. Memory T-cells remember the **specific antigen** and will recognise it a second time round. Memory B-cells record the specific **antibodies** needed to bind to the antigen.

5) The person is now **immune** — their immune system has the **ability** to respond **quickly** to a second infection.

The Immune Response

...the Secondary Response is Faster

1) If the **same pathogen** enters the body again, the immune system will produce a **quicker**, **stronger** immune response — the **secondary response**.

2) **Memory B-cells** divide into **plasma cells** that produce the right antibody to the antigen. **Memory T-cells** divide into the **correct type** of **T-cells** to kill the cell carrying the antigen.

3) The secondary response often gets rid of the pathogen **before** you begin to show any **symptoms**.

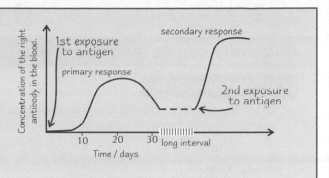

You May Be asked to Compare the Primary and Secondary Responses

OCR only

If you're asked to **compare** and **contrast** two things, like the primary and secondary responses, you need to say how they're **similar** and how they're **different**. These are summarised in this table:

	Primary response	Secondary response
Pathogen	Enters for 1st time	Enters for 2nd time
Speed of response	Slow	Fast
Cells activated	B- and T-cells	Memory cells
Symptoms	Yes	No

Practice Questions

Q1 What are the three main interfaces that pathogens can penetrate?

Q2 How does the skin prevent pathogens from entering the body?

Q3 Define the term immune response.

Q4 What are antigens?

Q5 What are the functions of T-cells?

Q6 What is the function of B-cells?

Q7 Draw and label the structure of an antibody.

Q8 Briefly describe the primary and secondary response.

These questions cover pages 90-93.

Exam Questions

Q1 Describe how a phagocyte responds to an invading pathogen. [6 marks]

Q2 Describe the function of antibodies. [3 marks]

Q3 Emily had chickenpox as a child. She was exposed to the virus that causes it as a teenager but did not experience any symptoms. Explain why. [10 marks]

The student-revision complex — only present the night before an exam...

Memory cells are still B- and T-cells, but they're the ones that stick around for a long time. So if a pathogen is stupid enough to invade the body again, these cells can immediately divide into more of themselves, and release antibodies specifically against the pathogen or bind to the pathogen and destroy it. Ha ha (evil laugh).

Immunity and Vaccinations

These pages are for AQA Unit 1 and OCR Unit 2.

The primary response gives you immunity against a disease, but only after you've gotten ill. If only there was a way to stimulate memory cell production without getting the disease... Well, there is — vaccination.

Immunity can be Active or Passive   *OCR only*

ACTIVE IMMUNITY

This is the type of immunity you get when **your immune system makes its own antibodies** after being **stimulated** by an **antigen**. There are **two** different types of active immunity:

1) **Natural** — this is when you become immune after **catching a disease**.

2) **Artificial** — this is when you become immune after you've been given a **vaccination** containing a harmless dose of antigen (see below).

PASSIVE IMMUNITY

This is the type of immunity you get from being **given antibodies made by a different organism** — your immune system **doesn't** produce any antibodies of its own. Again, there are **two** types:

1) **Natural** — this is when a **baby** becomes immune due to the antibodies it receives from its **mother**, through the **placenta** and in **breast milk**.

2) **Artificial** — this is when you become immune after being **injected** with **antibodies** from **someone else**. E.g. If you contract tetanus you can be injected with antibodies against the tetanus toxin, collected from blood donations.

In the exam you might be asked to **compare** and **contrast** these types of immunity:

Active immunity	Passive immunity
Exposure to antigen	No exposure to antigen
It takes a while for protection to develop	Protection is immediate
Protection is long-term	Protection is short-term
Memory cells are produced	Memory cells aren't produced

Vaccines can Protect Individuals and Populations Against Disease

1) While your B-cells are busy **dividing** to build up their numbers to deal with a pathogen (i.e. the **primary response** — see p. 92), you **suffer** from the disease. **Vaccination** can help avoid this.

2) Vaccines **contain antigens** that cause your body to **produce memory cells** against a particular pathogen, **without** the pathogen **causing disease**. This means you become **immune** without getting any **symptoms**... genius.

3) Vaccines **protect individuals** that have them and, because they reduce the **occurrence** of the disease, those **not** vaccinated are also less likely to catch the disease (because there are fewer people to catch it from). This is called **herd immunity**.

4) Vaccines always contain antigens — these may be **free** or **attached** to a **dead** or **attenuated** (weakened) **pathogen**.

5) Vaccines may be **injected** or taken **orally**. The **disadvantages** of taking a vaccine orally are that it could be **broken down** by **enzymes** in the gut or the **molecules** of the vaccine may be **too large** to be **absorbed** into the blood.

6) Sometimes **booster** vaccines are given later on (e.g. after several years) to **make sure** that memory cells are produced.

Paul couldn't understand why his herd immunity wasn't working...

Immunity and Vaccinations

Antigenic Variation Helps Some Pathogens Evade the Immune System

1) **Antigens** on the surface of pathogens **activate** the **primary response**.

2) When you're **infected** a **second time** with the **same pathogen** (which has the **same antigens** on its surface) they **activate** the **secondary response** and you don't get ill.

3) However, some sneaky pathogens can **change** their surface antigens. This is called **antigenic variation**. (Different antigens are formed due to changes in the **genes** of a pathogen.)

4) This means that when you're infected for a **second time**, the **memory cells** produced from the **first infection** will **not recognise** the **different antigens**. So the immune system has to start from scratch and carry out a **primary response** against these new antigens.

5) This **primary response** takes **time** to get rid of the infection, which is why you get **ill again**.

6) **Examples** of pathogens that show antigenic variation include **HIV**, *S. pneumoniae* bacteria and the **influenza virus**.

You need to **learn** how it works in influenza:

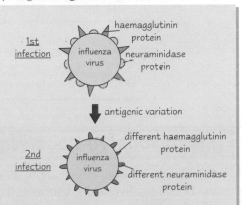

Antigenic variation in the influenza virus

1) The **influenza virus** causes **influenza** (flu).

2) **Proteins** (**neuraminidase** and **haemagglutinin**) on the **surface** of the influenza virus act as **antigens**, **triggering** the immune system.

3) These antigens can **change regularly**, forming **new strains** of the virus.

4) **Memory cells** produced from **infection** with **one strain** of flu will **not recognise** other strains with **different antigens**.

5) So this means you can **suffer from flu** more than once — each time you're infected with a **new strain**.

New Influenza Vaccines Have to be Developed Every Year   *OCR only*

1) **Memory cells** produced from **vaccination** with **one strain** of flu will **not recognise** other strains with **different antigens** — so a flu vaccination will only protect you against a **specific strain** of flu.

2) Every year there are **different strains** of the influenza virus **circulating** in the **population**, so a **different vaccine** has to be made.

3) **Laboratories** collect **samples** of these different strains, and organisations, such as the **WHO** (World Health Organisation) and **CDC** (Centre for Disease Control), **test** the **effectiveness** of different influenza **vaccines** against them.

4) **New vaccines** are **developed** and one is chosen **every year** that is the **most effective** against the **recently** circulating influenza viruses.

5) Governments and health authorities then implement a **programme** of **vaccination** using this most **suitable** vaccine. This is a good example of how society uses science to inform **decision making**.

Practice Questions

Q1   Give three differences between active and passive immunity.

Q2   How do vaccines cause immunity?

Q3   Give two advantages of vaccination.

Exam Question

Q1   Explain why it is possible to suffer from the flu more than once.   [4 marks]

An injection of dead bugs — roll on my next vaccine...

The influenza virus is so clever that it would almost make you think it had a mind of its own. I mean, as soon as your immune system has caught up with it, off it goes and changes its surface antigens again. Influenza virus: one, humans: nil. This is one of the ways viruses have evolved to avoid your immune system. Well, clever them.

Antibodies in Medicine

These pages are for AQA Unit 1 only.

Antibodies aren't only used by the immune system — they're also used by doctors as delivery boys (for drugs) and medical detectives (to diagnose conditions). Poirot eat your heart out.

Monoclonal Antibodies can be used to Target Specific Substances or Cells

1) **Monoclonal antibodies** are antibodies **produced** from a **single group of genetically identical B-cells** (plasma cells). This means that they're all **identical** in **structure**.

2) As you know, antibodies are **very specific** because their binding sites have a **unique structure** that only one particular antigen will fit into (one with a **complementary shape**).

3) You can make monoclonal antibodies **that bind to anything** you want, e.g. a cell antigen or other substance, and they will only bind to (target) this molecule.

Monoclonal Antibodies can be used to Target Cells

You can make monoclonal antibodies that bind to **specific cells** in the body (e.g. liver cells, cancer cells) because **different cells** have **different** cell-surface **antigens**.

Peggy Sue was determined to prove that she could be just as accurate as an antibody...

EXAMPLE

Monoclonal antibodies can be used to target **anti-cancer drugs** to **cancer cells**:

1) Cancer cells have **antigens** on their **cell membranes** that **aren't** found on normal body cells. They're called **tumour markers**.

2) In the lab, **monoclonal antibodies** are made that will bind to the tumour markers.

3) An **anti-cancer drug** is attached to the antibodies.

4) The antibodies are **administered** to a cancer patient.

5) When the antibodies come into **contact** with the cancer cells they will **bind** to the tumour markers, via their **antigen binding sites** (see p. 92).

6) This means the drug will **only accumulate** in the body where there are **cancer cells**.

7) So, the **side effects** of an antibody-based drug are lower than for other drugs because they accumulate near **specific cells**.

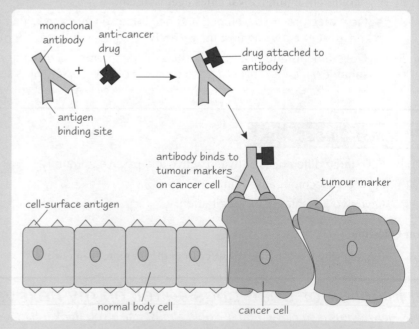

Antibodies in Medicine

Monoclonal Antibodies can Also be used to Detect Specific Substances

You can make antibodies that bind to **specific substances** because **different substances** have **different shapes**.

EXAMPLE

Pregnancy tests are a good example of how monoclonal antibodies can be used to detect specific substances. The substance being detected in pregnancy tests is a hormone called **human chorionic gonadotropin (hCG)**. It's produced by cells of the placenta and embryo, and ends up in the mother's urine, so it's a good indication of a pregnancy. Here's how it works:

1. The application area (the bit of the stick you wee on) contains **antibodies for hCG** that are attached to a **coloured bead** (**blue**). The test strip contains more **antibodies for hCG** that are stuck in place (**immobilised**) — but these ones don't have beads attached.

2. When urine is applied to the application area any hCG will **bind** to the antibody on the beads, forming an **antibody-antigen complex**.

3. The urine **moves** up the stick to the **test strip**, **carrying** any **beads** with it.

   If there <u>is</u> hCG present the **test strip turns blue** because the **immobilised** antibody binds to any **hCG** — concentrating the hCG-antibody complex with the **blue beads** attached.

   If <u>no</u> **hCG** is present, the beads will **pass through** the test area **without** binding to anything, and so it **won't** go blue.

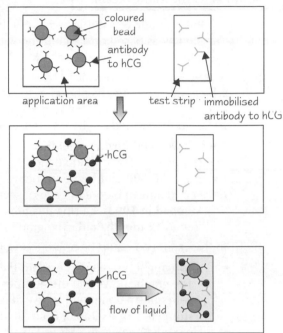

coloured bead
antibody to hCG
application area · test strip · immobilised antibody to hCG
hCG
hCG · flow of liquid

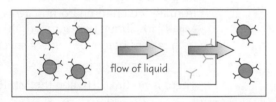

flow of liquid

Practice Questions

Q1   What are monoclonal antibodies?

Q2   What do monoclonal antibodies recognise on the surface of cells?

Q3   Give one advantage of using monoclonal antibodies to target cells.

Exam Questions

Q1   A pregnancy test contains antibodies that bind to the hormone human chorionic gonadotropin (hCG). Explain how this makes the pregnancy test specific to the hormone hCG.   [3 marks]

Q2   Describe how monoclonal antibodies can be used to target a drug to cancer cells.   [4 marks]

Monoclonal antibodies — sound like monsters out of Dr. Who to me...

Using antibodies to target drugs is at the forefront of science. As scientists find more cancer-specific antigens, more monoclonal antibodies can be developed, to target drugs to more types of cancer. So antibodies are pretty useful really. I wonder if they've made antibodies to target fat cells... that'd clear up my cellulite a treat...

Interpreting Vaccine and Antibody Data

These pages are for AQA Unit 1 only.

If someone claims anything about a vaccine or an antibody the claim has to be validated (confirmed) before it's accepted.

New Knowledge *About* Vaccines *and* Antibodies *is* Validated *by* Scientists

When a **study** presents evidence for a **new theory** (e.g. that a vaccine has a dangerous side effect) it's important that other scientists come up with **more evidence** in order to **validate** (confirm) the theory. To validate the theory other scientists may **repeat** the study and try to **reproduce** the results, or **conduct other studies** to try to prove the same theory (see p. 2).

EXAMPLE 1: The MMR Vaccine

1) In 1998, a study was published about the **safety of the measles, mumps and rubella (MMR) vaccine**. The study was based on **12 children** with **autism** (a life-long developmental disability) and concluded that there may be a **link** between the MMR vaccine and autism.

2) Not everyone was convinced by this study because it had a **very small sample size** of 12 children, which increased the likelihood of the results being due to **chance**. The study may have been **biased** because one of the scientists was helping to gain evidence for a **lawsuit** against the MMR vaccine manufacturer. Also, studies carried out by different scientists found no link between autism and the MMR vaccine.

3) There have been **further scientific studies** to sort out the **conflicting** evidence. In **2005**, a **Japanese** study was published about the incidence of autism in Yokohama (an area of Japan). They looked at the medical records of **30 000 children** born between **1988 and 1996** and counted the number of children that developed **autism** before the age of seven. The **MMR jab** was first **introduced in Japan in 1989** and was **stopped in 1993**. During this time the MMR vaccine was administered to children at **12 months old**. The graph shows the results of the study.

4) In the exam you could be asked to **evaluate evidence** like this.

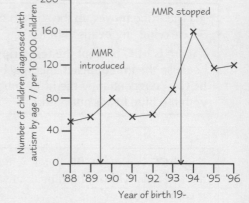

- You might be asked to **explain the data...**
  The graph shows that the number of children diagnosed with autism continued to **rise** after the MMR vaccine was **stopped**. For example, from all the children born in 1992, who did receive the MMR jab, about 60 out of 10 000 were diagnosed with autism before the age of seven. However, from all the children born in 1994, who did not receive the MMR jab, about 160 out of 10 000 of them were diagnosed with autism before the age of seven.

- **...or draw conclusions**
  There is **no link** between the MMR vaccine and autism.

- **... or evaluate the methodology**
  You can be much more confident in this study, compared to the 1998 study, because the **sample size** was so **large** — 30 000 children were studied. A larger sample size means that the results are less likely to be due to **chance**.

See pages 174-176 for more about evaluating data.

EXAMPLE 2: Herceptin — Monoclonal Antibodies

About **20%** of **women with breast cancer** have tumours that produce more than the usual amount of a **receptor** called **HER2**. **Herceptin** is a **drug** used to treat this type of breast cancer — it contains **monoclonal antibodies** that **bind the HER2 receptor** on a **tumour cell** and **prevent** the cells from growing and dividing.

In **2005**, a study **tested** Herceptin on women who had already undergone **chemotherapy** for HER2-type **breast cancer**. **1694** women took the **drug** for a **year** after chemotherapy and another **1694** women were **observed** for the **same time** (the control group). The results are shown in the graph on the right.

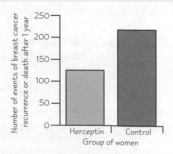

Describe the data: Almost **twice as many** women in the **control group** developed breast cancer again or died **compared** to the group taking Herceptin.

Draw conclusions: A **one-year treatment** with Herceptin, after chemotherapy, **increases** the disease-free survival rate for women with HER2-type breast cancer.

Interpreting Vaccine and Antibody Data

We use *Scientific Knowledge* to Make *Decisions*

When **new scientific information** about **vaccines** and **monoclonal antibodies** has been **validated** by scientists, **society** (organisations and the public) can **use** this information to make **informed decisions**. **Two examples** are given below:

EXAMPLE 1: The MMR Vaccine

Scientific knowledge:

The **validity** of the 1998 study that linked MMR and autism is in doubt. **New studies** have shown **no link** between the vaccine and autism.
Decision:

Scientists and doctors still recommended that parents **immunise** their **children** with the **MMR vaccine**.

EXAMPLE 2: Herceptin — Monoclonal Antibodies

Scientific knowledge:

Early studies about Herceptin showed **severe heart problems** could be a **side effect** of the drug.
Decision:

All patients receiving Herceptin must be **monitored** for heart problems, e.g. by having **heart tests** done.

Use of *Vaccines* and *Antibodies* Raises *Ethical Issues*

Ethical issues surrounding vaccines include:

1) All vaccines are **tested on animals** before being tested on humans — some people **disagree** with animal testing. Also, **animal based substances** may be used to **produce** a vaccine, which some people disagree with.

2) **Testing** vaccines on **humans** can be **tricky**, e.g. volunteers may put themselves at **unnecessary risk** of contracting the disease because they think they're fully protected (e.g. they might have unprotected sex because they have had a new HIV vaccine and think they're protected — and the vaccine might not work).

3) Some people **don't** want to take the vaccine due to the **risk** of **side effects**, but they are **still protected** because of **herd immunity** (see p. 94) — other people think this is **unfair**.

4) If there was an **epidemic** of a **new disease** (e.g. a new influenza virus) there would be a rush to **receive** a vaccine and **difficult decisions** would have to be made about **who** would be the **first** to receive it.

Ethical issues surrounding monoclonal antibody therapy often involve animal rights issues. **Animals** are used to **produce the cells** from which the monoclonal antibodies are produced. Some people **disagree** with the use of animals in this way.

Practice Questions

Q1 Suggest one ethical issue surrounding vaccines.

Q2 Suggest one ethical issue surrounding monoclonal antibodies.

Exam Question

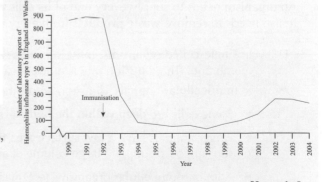

Q1 The graph on the right shows the number of laboratory reports of *Haemophilus influenzae* type b (Hib), in England and Wales, from 1990 to 2004. Hib affects children and can lead to meningitis and pneumonia.

a) Why did the number of cases of Hib decrease after 1992? [2 marks]

b) Due to a shortage of the normal vaccine in 2000-2001, a different type of Hib vaccine was used. What effect did this have on the number of cases of Hib? [1 mark]

Some scientists must have to validate the taste of chocolate — nice job...

After the 1998 study, some parents were worried about giving their kids the MMR vaccine, so the number of children given the vaccine fell. With fewer children in each community protected by the vaccine, herd immunity decreased. This meant that more people were vulnerable to the diseases, so the number of cases of measles, mumps and rubella went up.

Size and Surface Area

This page is for AQA Unit 2, OCR Unit 1 and Edexcel Unit 1.

Exchanging things with the environment is pretty easy if you're a single-celled organism, but if you're multicellular it all gets a bit more complicated... and it's all down to this 'surface area to volume ratio' malarkey.

Organisms Need to **Exchange Substances** with their **Environment**

Every organism, whatever its size, needs to exchange things with its environment.

1) Cells need to take in **oxygen** (for aerobic respiration) and **nutrients**.

2) They also need to excrete **waste products** like **carbon dioxide** and **urea**.

3) Most organisms need to stay at roughly the **same temperature**, so **heat** needs to be exchanged too.

Raj was glad he'd exchanged his canoe for a bigger boat.

How easy the exchange of substances is depends on the organism's **surface area to volume ratio**.

Smaller Animals have *Higher Surface Area : Volume Ratios*

A mouse has a bigger surface area **relative to its volume** than a hippo. This can be hard to imagine, but you can prove it mathematically. Imagine these animals as cubes:

The hippo could be represented by a block measuring
2 cm × 4 cm × 4 cm.

Its **volume** is 2 × 4 × 4 = **32 cm³**

Its **surface area** is 2 × 4 × 4 = 32 cm² (top and bottom surfaces of cube)
+ 4 × 2 × 4 = 32 cm² (four sides of the cube)

Total surface area = **64 cm²**

So the hippo has a **surface area : volume ratio** of 64 : 32 or **2 : 1**.

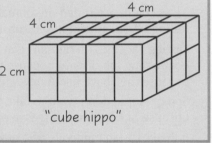

"cube hippo"

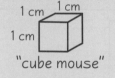

"cube mouse"

Compare this to a cube mouse measuring 1 cm × 1 cm × 1 cm.

Its **volume** is 1 x 1 x 1 = **1 cm³**

Its **surface area** is 6 x 1 x 1 = **6 cm²**

So the mouse has a **surface area : volume ratio** of **6 : 1**.

The cube mouse's surface area is six times its volume, but the cube hippo's surface area is only twice its volume. Smaller animals have a bigger surface area compared to their volume.

Multicellular Organisms need *Exchange Organs* and *Mass Transport Systems*

An organism needs to supply **every one of its cells** with substances like **glucose** and **oxygen** (for respiration). It also needs to **remove waste products** from every cell to avoid damaging itself.

1) In **single-celled** organisms, these substances can **diffuse directly** into (or out of) the cell across the cell surface membrane. The diffusion rate is quick because of the small distances the substances have to travel (see p. 102).

2) In **multicellular** animals, diffusion across the outer membrane is **too slow**, for three reasons:

- Some cells are **deep within the body** — there's a big distance between them and the **outside environment**.

- Larger animals have a **low surface area to volume ratio** — it's difficult to exchange **enough** substances to supply a **large volume of animal** through a relatively **small outer surface**.

- A lot of multicellular organisms (e.g. mammals) are also **very active**. This means that a **large number of cells** are all **respiring very quickly**, so they need a constant, rapid supply of glucose and oxygen.

So rather than using straightforward diffusion to absorb and excrete substances, multicellular animals need specialised **exchange organs** (like lungs — see p. 106).

They also need an efficient system to carry substances to and from their individual cells — this is **mass transport**. In mammals, 'mass transport' normally refers to the **circulatory system** (see p. 114), which uses **blood** to carry glucose and oxygen around the body. It also carries **hormones**, **antibodies** and **waste** like CO_2.

Size and Surface Area

This page is for AQA Unit 2 only. If you're doing OCR or Edexcel you can skip straight to the questions.

Body Size and Shape Affect Heat Exchange

As well as creating **waste products** that need to be transported away, the metabolic activity inside cells creates **heat**. Staying at the right temperature is difficult, and it's pretty heavily influenced by your **size** and **shape**...

Size

The **rate of heat loss** from an organism depends on its **surface area**. As you saw on the previous page, if an organism has a large volume, e.g. a hippo, its surface area is relatively **small**. This makes it **harder** for it to lose heat from its body. If an organism is small, e.g. a mouse, its relative surface area is **large**, so heat is lost more **easily**.

Shape

1) Animals with a **compact** shape have a **small surface area** relative to their volume — **minimising heat loss** from their surface.

2) Animals with a **less compact** shape (those that are a bit **gangly** or have **sticky outy** bits) have a **larger surface area** relative to their volume — this **increases heat loss** from their surface.

3) Whether an animal is compact or not depends on the **temperature** of its **environment**. Here's an example:

Arctic fox
Body temperature 37 °C
Average outside temperature 0 °C

The Arctic fox has **small ears** and a **round head** to **reduce** its SA : V ratio and heat loss.

African bat-eared fox
Body temperature 37 °C
Average outside temperature 25 °C

The African bat-eared fox has **large ears** and a more **pointed nose** to **increase** its SA : V ratio and heat loss.

European fox
Body temperature 37 °C
Average outside temperature 12 °C

The European fox is **intermediate** between the two, matching the temperature of its environment.

Organisms have Behavioural and Physiological Adaptations to Aid Exchange

Not all organisms have a body size or shape to suit their climate — some have **other adaptations** instead...

1) Animals with a high SA : volume ratio tend to **lose more water** as it evaporates from their surface. Some **small desert mammals** have **kidney structure adaptations** so that they produce **less urine** to compensate.

2) **Smaller animals** living in **colder regions** often have a much **higher metabolic rate** to compensate for their high SA : volume ratio — this helps to keep them warm by creating **more heat**. To do this they need to eat large amounts of **high energy foods** such as seeds and nuts.

3) Smaller mammals may have thick layers of **fur** or **hibernate** when the weather gets really cold.

4) **Larger organisms** living in **hot regions**, such as elephants and hippos, find it hard to keep cool as their heat loss is relatively slow. **Elephants** have developed **large flat ears** which **increase** their **surface area**, allowing them to lose more heat. **Hippos** spend much of the day in the **water** — a **behavioural adaptation** to help them lose heat.

Practice Questions

Q1 Give four things that organisms need to exchange with their environment.

Q2 Describe how body shape affects heat exchange.

Exam Question

Q1 Explain why diffusion is not an efficient transport system for large mammals. [4 marks]

Cube animals indeed — it's all gone a bit Picasso...

You need to understand why single-celled organisms and large multicellular organisms use different methods for exchange. Most multicellular organisms couldn't survive using diffusion alone — that's why they have exchange organs.

Gas Exchange

These pages are for AQA Unit 2, OCR Unit 1 and Edexcel Unit 1.

Lots of organisms have developed adaptations to improve gas exchange and you have to know all about them...

Gas Exchange Surfaces have **Two** Major **Adaptations**

Most gas exchange surfaces have two things in common:

1) They have a **large surface area**.

2) They're **thin** (often just one layer of epithelial cells) — this provides a **short diffusion pathway** across the gas exchange surface.

> All these features **increase** the **rate of diffusion**.

The organism also maintains a **steep concentration gradient** of gases across the exchange surface.

If you're doing Edexcel or OCR you can skip straight to the questions now, how nice — the rest is for AQA only.

Single-celled Organisms Exchange Gases across their **Body Surface**

1) Single-celled organisms absorb and release gases by **diffusion** through their **outer surface**.

2) They have a relatively **large surface area**, a **thin surface** and a **short diffusion pathway** (oxygen can take part in **biochemical reactions** as soon as it **diffuses** into the cell) — so there's **no need** for a gas exchange system.

Fish Use a **Counter-Current System** for Gas Exchange

There's a **lower concentration** of oxygen in water than in air. So **fish** have special **adaptations** to get enough of it.

1) Water, containing oxygen, enters the fish through its **mouth** and passes out through the gills.

2) Each gill is made of lots of **thin plates** called **gill filaments**, which give a **big surface area** for **exchange of gases**.

3) The gill filaments are covered in lots of tiny structures called **lamellae**, which **increase** the **surface area** even more.

4) The lamellae have lots of **blood capillaries** and a thin surface layer of cells to speed up diffusion.

vessels (oxygenated blood from the gill)

lamella (plural = lamellae)

artery (deoxygenated blood to gill)

gill filaments

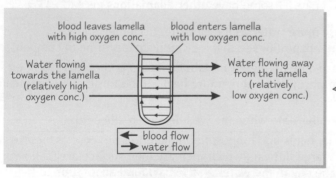

blood leaves lamella with high oxygen conc.

blood enters lamella with low oxygen conc.

Water flowing towards the lamella (relatively high oxygen conc.)

Water flowing away from the lamella (relatively low oxygen conc.)

← blood flow
→ water flow

5) **Blood** flows through the lamellae in one direction and **water** flows over in the opposite direction. This is called a **counter-current system**. It maintains a **large concentration gradient** between the water and the blood — so as much oxygen as possible diffuses from the water into the blood.

Insects use **Tracheae** to **Exchange Gases**

1) Insects have microscopic air-filled pipes called **tracheae** which they use for gas exchange.

2) Air moves into the tracheae through pores on the surface called **spiracles**.

3) **Oxygen** travels down the **concentration gradient** towards the **cells**. **Carbon dioxide** from the cells moves down its own concentration gradient towards the **spiracles** to be **released** into the atmosphere.

4) The tracheae branch off into smaller **tracheoles** which have **thin, permeable walls** and go to individual cells. This means that oxygen diffuses directly into the respiring cells (the insect's circulatory system doesn't transport O_2).

5) Insects use **rhythmic abdominal movements** to move air in and out of the spiracles.

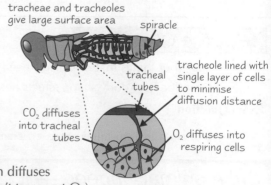

tracheae and tracheoles give large surface area

spiracle

tracheole lined with single layer of cells to minimise diffusion distance

tracheal tubes

CO_2 diffuses into tracheal tubes

O_2 diffuses into respiring cells

Gas Exchange

Dicotyledonous Plants Exchange Gases at the Surface of the Mesophyll Cells

1) Plants need CO_2 for **photosynthesis**, which produces O_2 as a waste gas. They need O_2 for **respiration**, which produces CO_2 as a waste gas.

2) The main gas exchange surface is the **surface of the mesophyll cells** in the leaf. They're well adapted for their function — they have a **large surface area**.

3) The mesophyll cells are inside the leaf. Gases move in and out through special pores in the **epidermis** called **stomata** (singular = stoma).

4) The stomata can **open** to allow exchange of gases, and **close** if the plant is losing too much water. **Guard cells** control the opening and closing of stomata.

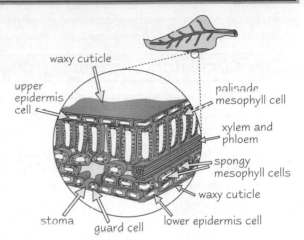

Insects and Plants can Control Water Loss

Exchanging gases tends to make you **lose water** — there's a sort of **trade-off** between the two. Luckily for plants and insects though, they've evolved **adaptations** to **minimise water loss** without reducing gas exchange too much.

1) If **insects** are losing too much water, they **close** their **spiracles** using muscles. They also have a **waterproof, waxy cuticle** all over their body and **tiny hairs** around their spiracles, both of which **reduce evaporation**.

2) Plants' stomata are usually kept **open** during the day to allow **gaseous exchange**. Water enters the guard cells, making them **turgid**, which **opens** the stomatal pore. If the plant starts to get **dehydrated**, the guard cells lose water and become **flaccid**, which **closes** the pore.

3) Some plants are specially adapted for life in **warm**, **dry** or **windy** habitats, where **water loss** is a problem. These plants are called **xerophytes**.

See p. 162 for more on water loss in plants.

Examples of xerophytic adaptations include:

- Stomata sunk in **pits** which trap moist air, reducing evaporation.

- **Curled** leaves with the stomata inside, protecting them from wind.

- A layer of 'hairs' on the epidermis to trap moist air round the stomata, reducing the concentration gradient of water.

- A **reduced number of stomata**, so there are fewer places for water to escape.

- **Waxy, waterproof cuticles** on leaves and stems to reduce evaporation.

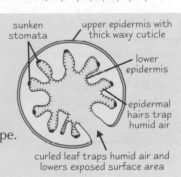

Practice Questions

Q1 How are single-celled organisms adapted for efficient gas exchange?

Q2 What is the advantage to fish of having a counter-current system in their gills?

Q3 What are an insect's spiracles?

Q4 Through which pores are gases exchanged in plants?

Exam Questions

Q1 Give three ways gas exchange organs are adapted to increase the rate of diffusion. [3 marks]

Q2 Explain why plants that live in the desert often have sunken stomata or stomata surrounded by hairs. [2 marks]

Keep revising and you'll be on the right trachea...

There's a pretty strong theme on these pages — whatever organism it is, to exchange gases efficiently it needs exchange organs with a large surface area, a thin exchange surface and a high concentration gradient. Don't forget that (or I'll hit you with a big stick).

Transport Systems

These pages are for AQA Unit 2, OCR Unit 1 and Edexcel Unit 1.

Right then, these two pages are all about blood and hearts and things, so if you're a bit squeamish it's not gonna float your boat. Unfortunately for you, it's all really important for the exams. And besides, without a circulatory system you'd probably have some issues when it comes to things like... ooh I dunno... living.

The **Circulatory System** is a **Mass Transport System**

1) All cells **need energy** — most cells get energy via **aerobic respiration**.

2) The raw materials for this are **glucose** and **oxygen**, so the body has to make sure it can deliver enough of these to all its cells.

3) **Mass transport systems** are used to **carry raw materials** from specialised **exchange organs** (e.g. the lungs and the digestive system) to the **body cells** and to **remove metabolic waste** (e.g. carbon dioxide).

4) In mammals, the mass transport system is the **circulatory system**, where **blood** is used to transport substances around the body.

5) Individual cells in tissues and organs get **nutrients** and **oxygen** from the blood and dispose of **metabolic waste** into the blood.

Richard had a different idea of mass transport from his biology teacher.

See Section 11 for more on the circulatory system.

This time AQA and Edexcel are the lucky ones and can skip straight to the questions — the rest is for OCR only.

Fish and **Mammals** have **Different** Circulatory Systems

Not all organisms have the same type of circulatory system
— **fish** have a **single circulatory system** and **mammals** have a **double circulatory system**.

1) In a **single** circulatory system, blood only passes through the heart **once** for each complete circuit of the body.

2) In a **double** circulatory system, the blood passes through the heart **twice** for each complete circuit of the body.

FISH

In **fish**, the **heart** pumps blood to the **gills** (to pick up oxygen) and then on through the **rest of the body** (to deliver the oxygen) in a single circuit.

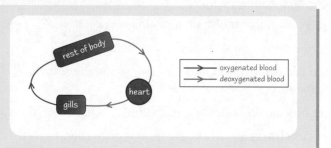

Single what now? Just pass me the tartar sauce.

MAMMALS

In **mammals**, the heart is **divided** down the middle, so it's really like **two** hearts joined together.

1) The **right side** of the heart pumps blood to the **lungs** (to pick up oxygen).

2) From the lungs it travels to the **left side** of the heart, which pumps it to the rest of the **body**.

3) When blood **returns** to the heart, it enters the right side again.

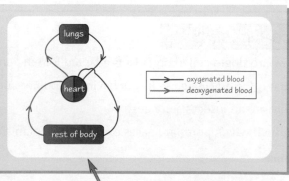

So, our circulatory system is really two linked loops. One sends blood to the lungs — this is called the **pulmonary** system, and the other sends blood to the rest of the body — this is called the **systemic** system.

The right and left sides of the heart are reversed in the diagram because it's the right and left of the person the heart belongs to.

The **advantage** of the mammalian double circulatory system is that the heart can give the blood an **extra push** between the lungs and the rest of the body. This makes the blood travel **faster**, so oxygen is delivered to the tissues **more quickly**.

Transport Systems

Circulatory Systems can be Open or Closed

All vertebrates (e.g. fish and mammals) have **closed circulatory systems** — the blood is **enclosed** inside **blood vessels**.

1) The heart pumps blood into **arteries**. These **branch out** into millions of **capillaries** (see p. 120).

2) Substances like oxygen and glucose **diffuse** from the blood in the capillaries into the body cells, but the blood **stays inside** the blood vessels as it circulates.

3) **Veins** take the blood back to the heart.

Some invertebrates (e.g. insects) have an **open circulatory system** — blood **isn't enclosed** in blood vessels all the time. Instead, it flows freely through the **body cavity**.

1) The heart is **segmented**. It **contracts** in a **wave**, starting from the back, pumping the blood into a **single main artery**.

2) That artery **opens up** into the body cavity.

3) The blood flows around the insect's **organs**, gradually making its way back into the heart segments through a series of **valves**.

The circulatory system supplies the insect's cell with nutrients, and transports things like hormones around the body. It **doesn't supply** the insect's cells with **oxygen** though — this is done by a system of tubes called the **tracheal system** (see p. 102 for more).

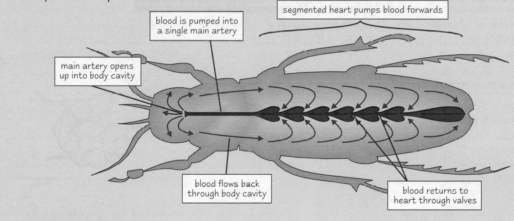

blood is pumped into a single main artery

segmented heart pumps blood forwards

main artery opens up into body cavity

blood flows back through body cavity

blood returns to heart through valves

Practice Questions

Q1 Give three things that cells need to exchange.

Q2 Explain why the mammalian circulatory system is described as a double circulatory system.

Q3 What is an open circulatory system?

Exam Questions

Q1 Explain why the circulatory system of a fish is described as being closed. [1 mark]

Q2 Briefly describe the circulatory system of an insect. [2 marks]

Q3 Describe one way in which the circulatory system of a fish is:

a) similar to that of a mammal. [1 mark]

b) different from that of a mammal. [1 mark]

OK, open circulatory systems are officially grim. Body cavities?! Bleurgh...

After reading this page, we can all finally put to rest the idea that the Earth will eventually be overrun by giant insects. Their circulatory system just isn't up to it you see... All the nutrients and stuff in their blood have to diffuse through the whole body cavity, so if they were giant they wouldn't be able to supply all their organs and bits and pieces properly. Phew.

Lung Function

This page is for AQA Unit 1, Edexcel Unit 1 and OCR Unit 1.

To the examiners, lung function is more than just breathing in and out — they love it (and don't even get them started on gas exchange in the alveoli). So unsurprisingly it's a good idea if you know a bit about the lungs... take a deep breath...

Lungs are Specialised Organs for Gas Exchange

Humans need to get **oxygen** into the blood (for respiration) and get rid of **carbon dioxide** (made by respiring cells). This is where **breathing** (or **ventilation** as it's sometimes called) and the **lungs** come in.

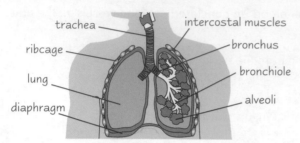

1) As you breathe in, air enters the **trachea** (windpipe).
2) The trachea splits into two **bronchi** — one **bronchus** leading to each lung.
3) Each bronchus then branches off into smaller tubes called **bronchioles**.
4) The bronchioles end in small 'air sacs' called **alveoli** — this is where gases are exchanged (see below).
5) The **ribcage**, **intercostal muscles** and **diaphragm** all work together to move air in and out (see page 108).

In Humans Gaseous Exchange Happens in the Alveoli

Lungs contain millions of **alveoli** — the gas **exchange surface**. Each alveolus is made from a single layer of thin, flat cells called **alveolar epithelium**.

1) Alveoli are arranged in **bunches** at the end of bronchioles.
2) They're surrounded by a network of **capillaries**, giving each alveolus its **own blood supply**.

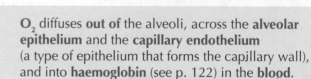

alveoli ('air sacs') covered in a network of capillaries

bronchiole

one alveolus

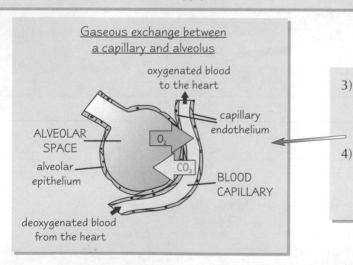

Gaseous exchange between a capillary and alveolus

oxygenated blood to the heart

capillary endothelium

ALVEOLAR SPACE

alveolar epithelium

O_2

CO_2

BLOOD CAPILLARY

deoxygenated blood from the heart

3) O_2 diffuses **out of** the alveoli, across the **alveolar epithelium** and the **capillary endothelium** (a type of epithelium that forms the capillary wall), and into **haemoglobin** (see p. 122) in the **blood**.

4) CO_2 diffuses **into** the alveoli from the blood, crossing the capillary endothelium then the alveolar epithelium. After entering the alveolar space, it's **breathed out**.

Epithelial tissue is pretty common in the body. It's usually found on exchange surfaces.

The Alveoli are Adapted for Gas Exchange

Alveoli have features that **speed up** the **rate of diffusion** so gases can be exchanged quickly:

1) **A thin exchange surface** — the **alveolar epithelium** is only **one cell thick**. This means there's a **short diffusion pathway** (which speeds up diffusion).

2) **A large surface area** — the **large number** of alveoli means there's a large surface area for gas exchange.

See p. 34 for more on diffusion.

There's also a **steep concentration gradient** of oxygen and carbon dioxide between the alveoli and the capillaries, which increases the rate of diffusion. This is constantly maintained by the **flow of blood** and **ventilation**.

Lung Function

This page is for OCR Unit 1 only. If you're doing AQA or Edexcel you can skip straight to the questions.

The Gaseous Exchange System has Different Parts with Different Functions

The respiratory system has **other parts** that help it to exchange gases **efficiently**.

1) **Goblet cells** secrete **mucus**. The mucus **traps** microorganisms and dust particles in the inhaled air, stopping them from reaching the alveoli.

2) **Cilia** on the surface of cells **beat** the mucus, which **moves** it (plus the trapped microorganisms and dust) upward away from the alveoli towards the throat, where it's swallowed. This helps **prevent lung infections**.

3) **Elastic fibres** in the walls of the trachea, bronchi, bronchioles and alveoli help the process of **breathing out** (see next page). On breathing in, the lungs inflate and the elastic fibres are **stretched**. Then, the fibres **recoil** to help push the air out when exhaling.

4) **Smooth muscle** in the walls of the trachea, bronchi and bronchioles allows their **diameter to be controlled**. During exercise the smooth muscle **relaxes**, making the tubes **wider**. This means there's **less resistance** to airflow and air can move in and out of the lungs more easily.

5) **Rings of cartilage** in the walls of the trachea and bronchi **provide support**. It's strong but flexible — it stops the trachea and bronchi **collapsing** when you breathe in and the pressure drops (see next page).

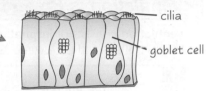

The Different Parts are Found in Different Places in the System

Part of the lung	Cartilage	Smooth muscle	Elastic fibres	Goblet cells	Epithelium
trachea	large C-shaped pieces	✓	✓	✓	ciliated
bronchi	smaller pieces	✓	✓	✓	ciliated
larger bronchiole	none	✓	✓	✓	ciliated
smaller bronchiole	none	✓	✓	✗	ciliated
smallest bronchiole	none	✗	✓	✗	no cilia
alveoli	none	✗	✓	✗	no cilia

smooth muscle
elastic fibres
c-shaped cartilage
ciliated epithelium

smooth muscle
small cartilage pieces
elastic fibres
ciliated epithelium

smooth muscle and elastic fibres
ciliated epithelium

blood capillary
elastic fibres
alveolar epithelium

Practice Questions

Q1 Describe the structure of the human gas exchange system.

Q2 Describe the movement of carbon dioxide and oxygen across the alveolar epithelium.

Exam Questions

Q1 Explain why there is a fast rate of gas exchange in the alveoli. [6 marks]

Q2 Name five tissues, cells or cell structures found in the mammalian gas exchange system and explain the function of each. [10 marks]

Alveoli — useful things... always make me think about pasta...

I know you've just got to the end of a page, but it'd be a pretty smart idea to have another look at diffusion on page 34. Not the most thrilling prospect I realise, but it'll help the stuff about gas exchange in the alveoli make more sense.

Breathing

These pages are for AQA Unit 1 and OCR Unit 1.

If you're in need of inspiration then there's plenty on this page... sadly I'm only talking about the kind of inspiration that gets air into your lungs — if you want the other sort head over to the Grand Canyon.

Ventilation is Breathing In and Out

Ventilation consists of **inspiration** (breathing in) and **expiration** (breathing out).
It's controlled by the movements of the **diaphragm**, **intercostal muscles** and **ribcage**.

Inspiration

1) The **intercostal** and **diaphragm muscles contract**.

2) This causes the **ribcage** to move **upwards and outwards** and the **diaphragm** to **flatten**, **increasing the volume** of the thorax (the space where the lungs are).

3) As the volume of the thorax increases the lung pressure **decreases** (to below atmospheric pressure).

4) This causes air to flow **into the lungs**.

5) Inspiration is an **active process** — it requires **energy**.

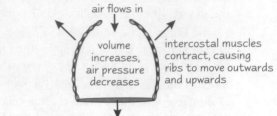

air flows in

volume increases, air pressure decreases

intercostal muscles contract, causing ribs to move outwards and upwards

diaphragm muscles contract, causing diaphragm to move downwards and flatten

Expiration

air is forced out

volume reduces, air pressure increases

intercostal muscles relax, causing ribs to move inwards and downwards

diaphragm muscles relax, causing diaphragm to become curved again

1) The **intercostal** and **diaphragm muscles relax**.

2) The **ribcage** moves **downwards and inwards** and the **diaphragm** becomes **curved** again.

3) The thorax volume **decreases**, causing the air pressure to **increase** (to above atmospheric pressure).

4) Air is forced **out of the lungs**.

5) Expiration is a **passive process** — it **doesn't** require energy.

Tidal Volume is the Volume of Air in a Normal Breath

dm³ is short for decimetres cubed — it's the same as litres.

Here are some terms you need to know about breathing:

1) **Tidal volume (TV)** is the volume of air in **each breath** — usually about **0.4 dm³**.

2) **Ventilation rate** (breathing rate) is the **number of breaths per minute**. For a person at rest it's about **15 breaths**.

3) You can figure out tidal volume and ventilation rate from the **graph** produced from a **spirometer** (see next page).

[Graph: volume of gas in lungs / dm³ (y-axis, 0 to 6) against time / seconds (x-axis, 0 to 60)]
deep breath in
deep breath out
residual air can't be expelled
tidal volume of normal breath
vital capacity of the lungs (OCR only)

If you're doing AQA you need to know about pulmonary ventilation:

Pulmonary ventilation is the product of **tidal volume** and **ventilation rate** — it's measured in dm³ min⁻¹. Here's the equation to calculate it:

> **Pulmonary Ventilation = Tidal volume × Ventilation rate**

So a normal person at rest would have a PV of about
0.4 dm³ × 15 min⁻¹ = **6 dm³ min⁻¹**.

If you're doing OCR you need to know these terms as well:

1) **Vital capacity** — the **maximum** volume of air that can be breathed **in** or **out**.

2) **Oxygen uptake** — the rate at which a person **uses up** oxygen (e.g. the number of dm³ used per minute).

Breathing

Those of you doing AQA can skip straight to the questions — the rest is for OCR only.

Spirometers Can be Used to Investigate Breathing

A spirometer is a machine that can give readings of **tidal volume**, **ventilation rate**, **vital capacity** and **oxygen uptake**.

1) A spirometer has an **oxygen-filled** chamber with a **movable lid**.

2) The person breathes through a **tube** connected to the oxygen chamber.

3) As the person breathes in and out, the lid of the chamber moves **up and down**.

4) These movements are recorded by a **pen** attached to the lid of the chamber — this writes on a **rotating drum**, creating a **spirometer trace**.

5) The **soda lime** in the tube the subject breathes into absorbs **carbon dioxide**.

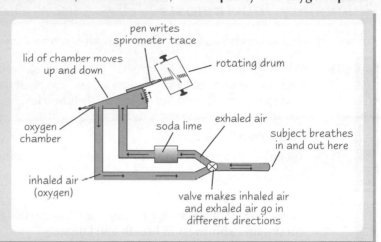

The **total volume of gas** in the chamber **decreases** over time. This is because the air that's breathed out is a **mixture** of oxygen and carbon dioxide. The carbon dioxide is absorbed by the **soda lime** — so there's **only oxygen** in the chamber which the subject inhales from. As this oxygen gets used up by respiration, the total volume decreases.

You Need to be Able to Analyse Data from a Spirometer

In the exam, you might have to work out **ventilation rate**, **tidal volume**, **vital capacity** and **oxygen consumption** from a spirometer trace. For example:

This graph looks different to the one on the previous page because it shows the volume of air in the spirometer, not in the lungs

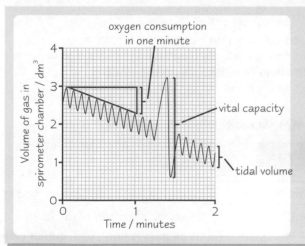

1) In this trace, the **ventilation rate** in the first minute is **10 breaths per minute** (there are 10 'peaks' in the first minute).

2) The **tidal volume** may change from time to time, but in this trace it's about **0.5 dm³**.

3) The graph shows a **vital capacity** of **2.65 dm³**.

4) **Oxygen consumption** is the **decrease** in the **volume of gas** in the **spirometer chamber**. It can be read from the graph by taking the **average slope** of the trace. In this case, it drops by 0.7 dm³ in the first minute — so, oxygen consumption is **0.7 dm³/min**.

Practice Questions

Q1 What is meant by: a) tidal volume, b) ventilation rate?

Q2 Describe how a spirometer can be used to measure oxygen uptake.

Exam Question

Q1 Describe the changes that take place in the human thorax during inspiration. [5 marks]

Investigate someone's breathing — make sure they've had a mint first...

I thought spirometers were those circular plastic things you draw crazy patterns with... apparently not. I know the graphs don't look that approachable, but it's important that you understand what the squiggly lines show, and the terms used when investigating breathing — I'd bet my right lung there'll be a question on spirometer graphs in the exam.

How Lung Disease Affects Function

These pages are for AQA Unit 1 and OCR Unit 2.

It's all very well when your lungs are working perfectly, but some pathogens (and even your lifestyle) can muck them up good and proper, reducing the rate of gas exchange. Not good.

Pulmonary Tuberculosis (TB) is a Lung Disease Caused by Bacteria

Pulmonary tuberculosis is caused by the bacterium **Mycobacterium tuberculosis**.

If you're doing OCR you only need to learn about the cause and transmission of TB.

Infection

1) When someone becomes infected with tuberculosis bacteria, immune system cells build a **wall** around the bacteria in the lungs. This forms small, hard lumps known as **tubercles**.

2) Infected tissue within the tubercles **dies**, the gaseous exchange surface is **damaged** so **tidal volume** is **decreased**.

3) Tuberculosis also causes **fibrosis** (see next page), which further reduces the tidal volume.

4) If the bacteria enter the **bloodstream**, they can **spread** to other parts of the body.

Symptoms

1) Common symptoms include a persistent **cough**, coughing up **blood** and **mucus**, **chest pains**, **shortness of breath** and **fatigue**.

2) Sufferers may also have a **fever**.

3) Many **lose weight** due to a reduction in appetite.

Transmission

1) TB is transmitted by **droplet infection** — when an infected person **coughs** or **sneezes**, tiny **droplets** of **saliva** and **mucus** containing the bacteria are released from their mouth and nose. If an uninfected person breathes in these droplets, the bacteria are **passed on**.

2) Tuberculosis tends to be much more widespread in areas where **hygiene** levels are **poor** and where people live in **crowded** conditions.

3) TB can be prevented with the BCG vaccine, and can be treated with antibiotics.

Many people with tuberculosis are **asymptomatic** — they're infected but they **don't show** any symptoms, because the infection is in an **inactive form**. People who are asymptomatic are unable to pass the infection on. But if they become **weakened**, for example by another disease or malnutrition, then the infection can become **active**. They'll show the symptoms and be able to pass on the infection.

Lung cancer and bronchitis are for OCR only, so if you're doing AQA skip to emphysema on the next page.

Some Lung Diseases are Caused by Smoking

Lung Cancer

1) Cigarette smoke contains many **carcinogens** (chemicals that can cause a cell to become cancerous).

2) These carcinogens may cause mutations in the **DNA** of **lung cells**, which could lead to **uncontrolled cell growth** and the **formation** of a **malignant** (cancerous) **tumour**.

3) Malignant tumours **grow uncontrollably**, **blocking air flow** to areas of the lung.

4) This **decreases gas exchange** and leads to a **shortness of breath** because the body is struggling to take in **enough oxygen**.

5) The tumour uses **lots** of **nutrients** and **energy** to grow, which causes **weight loss**.

Chronic Bronchitis

1) Chronic bronchitis is **inflammation** of the lungs.

2) The upper respiratory tract is lined with **goblet cells** that produce **mucus** to **trap microorganisms**. The tract is also lined with **cilia** that 'beat' to move the mucus towards the **throat** so it can be **removed**.

3) Cigarette smoke **damages** the **cilia** and causes the goblet cells to produce **more mucus**.

4) The mucus **accumulates** in the lungs, which causes **increased coughing** to try and remove the mucus.

5) **Microorganisms multiply** in the mucus and cause **lung infections** that lead to **inflammation**, which **decreases gas exchange**.

6) Chronic bronchitis is a type of **chronic obstructive pulmonary disease** (COPD). COPD is a group of diseases that involve permanent airflow reduction.

How Lung Disease Affects Function

Emphysema is for AQA and OCR.

OCR: Emphysema is also a type of COPD.

Emphysema

1) Emphysema is a lung disease caused by **smoking** or long-term exposure to **air pollution** — foreign particles in the smoke (or air) become **trapped** in the alveoli.

2) This causes **inflammation**, which encourages **phagocytes** to the area. The phagocytes produce an **enzyme** that breaks down **elastin** (an elastic protein found in the **walls** of the **alveoli**).

3) The alveolar walls are **destroyed** and the **elasticity** of the lungs is **lost**.

4) This **reduces** the **surface area** of the alveoli, so the **rate** of **gaseous exchange decreases**.

5) Symptoms of emphysema include **shortness of breath** and **wheezing**. People with emphysema have an **increased breathing rate** as they try to increase the amount of air (containing oxygen) reaching their lungs.

Fibrosis and *Asthma* Affect *Lung Function*

This bit is only for AQA, so if you're doing OCR, you can skip straight to the questions.

Fibrosis and asthma **reduce the rate of gas exchange** in the alveoli. Less oxygen is able to diffuse into the bloodstream, the body cells **receive less oxygen** and the rate of **aerobic respiration** is **reduced**. This means **less energy is released** and sufferers often feel **tired** and **weak**.

Fibrosis

1) Fibrosis is the formation of **scar tissue** in the lungs. This can be the result of an **infection** or exposure to substances like **asbestos** or **dust**.

2) Scar tissue is **thicker** and **less elastic** than normal lung tissue.

3) This means that the lungs are **less able to expand** and so **can't hold as much air** as normal — the tidal volume is **reduced**. It's also harder to **force air out** of the lungs due to the loss of elasticity.

4) There's a **reduction** in the rate of **gaseous exchange** — **diffusion** is **slower** across a **thicker** scarred membrane.

5) Symptoms of fibrosis include **shortness of breath**, a **dry cough**, **chest pain**, **fatigue** and **weakness**.

6) Fibrosis sufferers have a **faster breathing rate** than normal — to get enough air into their lungs to **oxygenate** their blood.

Asthma

1) Asthma is a respiratory condition where the airways become **inflamed** and **irritated**. The causes vary from case to case but it's usually because of an **allergic reaction** to substances such as **pollen** and **dust**.

2) During an asthma attack, the **smooth muscle** lining the **bronchioles contracts** and a large amount of **mucus** is produced.

3) This causes **constriction** of the airways, making it difficult for the sufferer to **breathe properly**. Air flow in and out of the lungs is **severely reduced**, so less oxygen enters the alveoli and moves into the blood.

4) Symptoms include **wheezing**, a **tight chest** and **shortness of breath**. During an attack the symptoms come on very suddenly. They can be relieved by **drugs** (often in **inhalers**) which cause the muscle in the bronchioles to **relax**, opening up the airways.

Practice Questions

Q1 What causes TB?

Q2 Describe how TB is transmitted from one person to another.

Q3 Give two lung diseases caused by smoking.

Exam Question

Q1 Explain why a person suffering from emphysema might hyperventilate (breathe quicker than normal). [7 marks]

Asthma, emphysema, fibrosis and bronchitis — what a wheeze...

Lung diseases can be pretty grim — all that coughing up blood and mucus. Whether they're inflicted on us by bacteria, or we've inflicted them on ourselves by smoking, they all inhibit the normal workings of the respiratory system in one way or another — and not being able to breathe properly ain't a good thing, I can tell you.

Interpreting Lung Disease Data

These pages are for AQA Unit 1 only.

It's very possible that you could be asked to interpret some data on lung disease in the exam. So, being my usual nice self, I've given you some examples to show you how to do it. I know it looks a bit dull but believe me, it'll really help.

You Need to be Able to **Interpret Data** on **Risk Factors** and **Lung Disease**

1) All diseases have factors which will **increase** a person's **chance** of getting that disease. These are called **risk factors**. For example, it's widely known that if you **smoke** you're more likely to get **lung cancer** (smoking is a risk factor for lung cancer).

2) This is an example of a **correlation** — a link between two things (see page 174). However, a correlation doesn't always mean that one thing **causes** the other. Smokers have an **increased risk** of getting cancer but that doesn't necessarily mean smoking **causes** the disease — there are lots of other factors to take into consideration.

3) You need to be able to describe and analyse data given to you in your exams. Here are two examples of the kind of thing you might get:

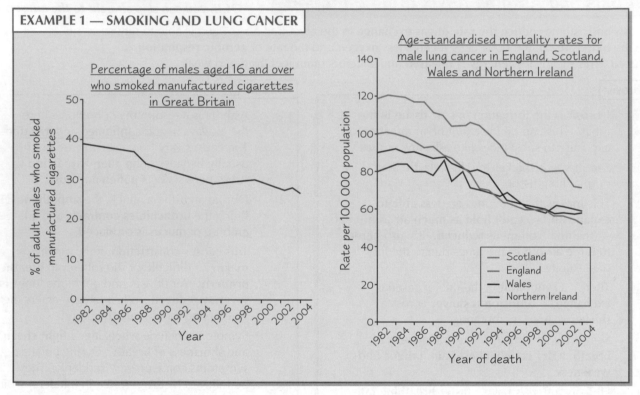

EXAMPLE 1 — SMOKING AND LUNG CANCER

Percentage of males aged 16 and over who smoked manufactured cigarettes in Great Britain

Age-standardised mortality rates for male lung cancer in England, Scotland, Wales and Northern Ireland

You might be asked to:

1) **Explain the data** — The graph on the left shows that the **number** of adult males in Great Britain (England, Wales and Scotland) who **smoke decreased** between 1982 and 2004. The graph on the right shows that the male lung cancer **mortality (death) rate decreased** between 1982 and 2004 for each of the countries shown. Easy enough so far.

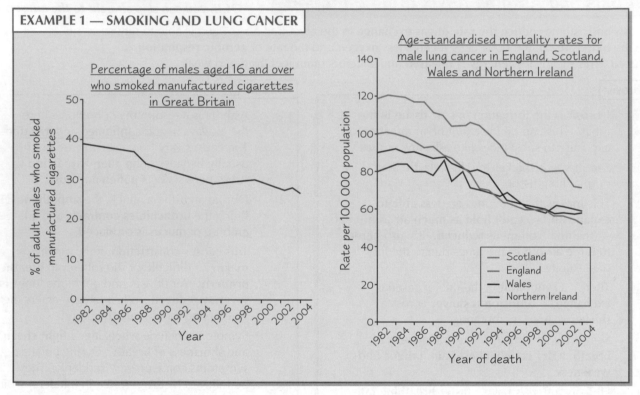
See pages 174-176 for more on interpreting data.

2) **Draw conclusions** — You need to be careful what you say here. There's a **correlation** (link) between the **number** of males **who smoked** and the **mortality rate** for male lung cancer. But you **can't** say that one **caused** the other. There could be **other reasons** for the trend, e.g. deaths due to lung cancer may have decreased because less asbestos was being used in homes (not because fewer people were smoking).

Other points to consider — The graph on the right shows mortality (**death**) rates. The rate of **cases** of lung cancer **may have been increasing** but medical advances may mean more people were **surviving** (so only mortality was decreasing). Some information about the **people involved** in the studies would be helpful. For example, we don't know whether both studies used similar groups — e.g. similar diet, occupation, alcohol consumption etc. If they didn't then the results might not be reliable.

Interpreting Lung Disease Data

EXAMPLE 2 — AIR POLLUTION AND ASTHMA

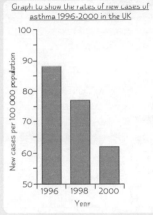

Graph to show the rates of new cases of asthma 1996-2000 in the UK

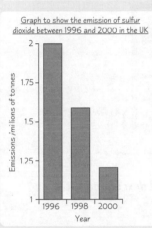

Graph to show the emission of sulfur dioxide between 1996 and 2000 in the UK

The **top graph** shows the number of **new cases of asthma** per 100 000 of the population diagnosed in the UK from 1996 to 2000. The **bottom graph** shows the **emissions** (in millions of tonnes) of **sulfur dioxide** (an **air pollutant**) from 1996 to 2000 in the UK.

You might be asked to explain the data...

1) The **top graph** shows that the number of **new cases of asthma** in the UK **fell** between 1996 and 2000, from 87 to 62 per 100 000 people.

2) The **bottom graph** shows that the **emissions of sulfur dioxide** in the UK **fell** between 1996 and 2000, from 2 to 1.2 million tonnes.

... or draw conclusions

1) Be careful what you say when drawing conclusions. Here there's a **link** between the **number** of new cases of **asthma** and **emissions of sulfur dioxide** in the **UK** — the rate of new cases of asthma has **fallen** as sulfur dioxide emissions have **fallen**. You **can't** say that one **causes** the other though because there could be **other reasons** for the trend, e.g. the number of new cases of asthma could be falling due to the **decrease** in the number of people **smoking**.

2) You can't say the **reduction** in asthma cases is **linked** to a **reduction in air pollution** (in general) either as **only** sulfur dioxide levels were studied.

Other points to consider:

1) The top graph shows **new cases** of asthma. The rate of new cases may be **decreasing** but existing cases may be becoming **more severe**.

2) The emissions were for the whole of the UK but air pollution **varies from area to area**, e.g. **cities** tend to be **more polluted**.

3) The asthma data doesn't take into account any **other factors** that may **increase** the risk of developing asthma, e.g. allergies, smoking, etc.

Practice Exam Question

Q1 In early December 1952, a dense layer of cold air trapped pollutants close to ground level in London. The graph opposite shows daily deaths and levels of sulfur dioxide and smoke between 1st and 15th December.

a) Describe the changes in the daily death rate and the levels of pollutants over the days shown. [3 marks]

b) What conclusions can be drawn from this graph? [1 mark]

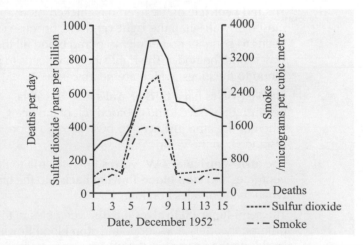

Drawing conclusions — you'll need your wax crayons and some paper...

These pages give examples to help you deal with what the examiners are sure to hurl at you — and boy, do they like throwing data around. There's some important advice here (even if I say so myself) — it's easy to leap to a conclusion that isn't really there — stick to your guns about the difference between correlation and cause and you'll blow 'em away.

The Heart

These pages are for AQA Units 1 and 2, Edexcel Unit 1 and OCR Unit 1.

The circulatory system circulates stuff (unsurprisingly) — blood, to be specific.

The **Circulatory System** Includes the **Heart** and **Blood Vessels**

1) The heart **pumps blood** through blood vessels (arteries, arterioles, capillaries and veins, see page 120) to reach different parts of the body.

2) Blood transports **respiratory gases**, products of **digestion**, **metabolic wastes** and **hormones** round the body — it's a mass transport system (see page 104)

3) There are **two circuits**. One circuit takes blood from the **heart** to the **lungs**, then **back to the heart**. The other loop takes blood around the **rest of the body**.

4) If you're doing **AQA Unit 2** you need to **know** the names of **all** the blood vessels **entering** and **leaving** the heart, **liver** and **kidneys** (bad luck). You also need to know that the heart has its own blood supply — the **coronary arteries**.

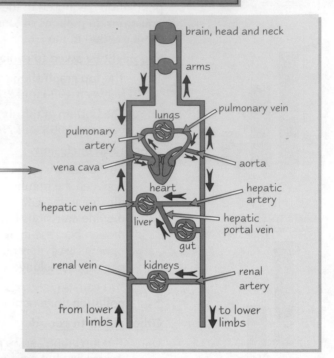

The **Heart Pumps** the Blood **Around** the Body

AQA Unit 1, Edexcel and OCR

The heart keeps the blood moving so that substances can get **to** and **from** individual cells. You need to learn the structure of the heart. The **right side** pumps **deoxygenated blood** to the **lungs** and the **left side** pumps **oxygenated blood** to the **whole body**. Note — the **left and right sides** are **reversed** on the diagram, cos it's the left and right of the person that the heart belongs to.

Each bit of the heart is adapted to do its job effectively.

1) The **left ventricle** of the heart has **thicker**, more muscular walls than the **right ventricle**, because it needs to contract powerfully to pump blood all the way round the body. The right side only needs to get blood to the lungs, which are nearby.

2) The **ventricles** have **thicker walls** than the **atria**, because they have to push blood out of the heart whereas the atria just need to push blood a short distance into the ventricles.

3) The **atrioventricular (AV) valves** link the atria to the ventricles and **stop blood flowing back** into the atria when the ventricles contract.

4) The **semi-lunar (SL) valves** link the ventricles to the pulmonary artery and aorta, and **stop blood flowing back** into the heart after the ventricles contract.

5) The **cords** attach the atrioventricular valves to the ventricles to stop them being forced up into the atria when the ventricles contract.

Internal Structure

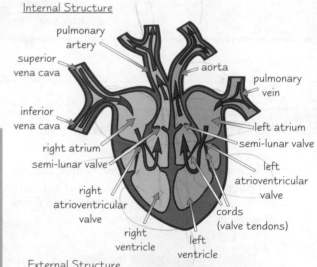

External Structure

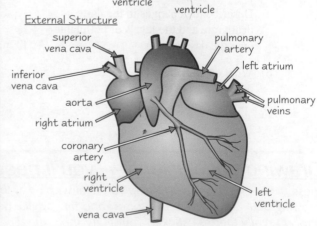

The Heart

AQA Unit 1, Edexcel and OCR

Valves *in the Heart* Prevent *Blood Flowing the* Wrong Way

1) The **valves** only open one way — whether they're open or closed depends on the **relative pressure** of the heart chambers.

2) If there's higher pressure **behind** a valve, it's **forced open**.

3) If pressure is higher **in front** of the valve, it's **forced shut**.

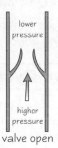
lower pressure / higher pressure

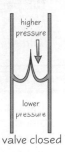
higher pressure / lower pressure

valve open   valve closed

This bit is just for AQA Unit 1 and OCR. If you're doing Edexcel, you can skip straight to the questions.

Cardiac Muscle *Controls the* Regular Beating *of the Heart*

Cardiac (heart) muscle is '**myogenic**' — this means that it can contract and relax without receiving signals from nerves. This pattern of contractions controls the **regular heartbeat**.

1) The process starts in the **sino-atrial node (SAN)**, which is in the wall of the **right atrium**.

2) The SAN is like a pacemaker — it sets the **rhythm** of the heartbeat by sending out regular **waves of electrical activity** to the atrial walls.

3) This causes the right and left **atria** to **contract at the same time**.

4) A band of non-conducting **collagen tissue** prevents the waves of electrical activity from being passed directly from the atria to the ventricles.

5) Instead, these waves of electrical activity are transferred from the SAN to the **atrioventricular node (AVN)**.

6) The AVN is responsible for passing the waves of electrical activity on to the bundle of His. But, there's a **slight delay** before the AVN reacts, to make sure the ventricles contract **after** the atria have emptied.

7) The **bundle of His** is a group of muscle fibres responsible for conducting the waves of electrical activity to the finer muscle fibres in the right and left ventricle walls, called the **Purkyne fibres**.

8) The Purkyne fibres carry the waves of electrical activity into the muscular walls of the right and left ventricles, causing them to **contract simultaneously**, from the bottom up.

waves of electrical activity — AVN — SAN — *non-conducting collagen tissue* — *bundle of His* — *Purkyne fibres* — *Purkyne fibres*

Purkyne fibres are sometimes called Purkyne tissue.

Practice Questions

Q1 Which side of the heart carries oxygenated blood?

Q2 Why is the left ventricle wall more muscular than the right ventricle wall?

Q3 Which valves link the ventricles to the pulmonary artery and aorta?

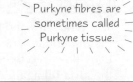

Exam Questions

Q1 Describe the passage of blood through the heart, staring with it entering the right atrium from the vena cava. [10 marks]

Q2 Explain how valves in the heart stop blood going back the wrong way. [6 marks]

Q3 What is the function of:

a) the sino-atrial node? [1 mark]

b) the Purkyne fibres? [1 mark]

Cardiac muscle controls the regular beating of the heart — that's a bit mean...

Your circulatory system's quite like the water plumbing in your house really — there are loads of connecting pipes, a pump and some valves. Don't get mixed up with waste plumbing though — that's a whole different pipe in humans...

The Cardiac Cycle

This page is for AQA Unit 1, Edexcel Unit 1 and OCR Unit 1.

Now it's time to see exactly what happens in your heart to make the blood flow — my heart's all of a flutter just thinking about it.

The **Cardiac Cycle** Pumps Blood Round the Body

The cardiac cycle is an ongoing sequence of **contraction** and **relaxation** of the atria and ventricles that keeps blood **continuously** circulating round the body. The **volume** of the atria and ventricles **changes** as they contract and relax. **Pressure** changes also occur, due to the changes in chamber volume (e.g. decreasing the volume of a chamber by contraction will increase the pressure of a chamber). The cardiac cycle can be simplified into three stages:

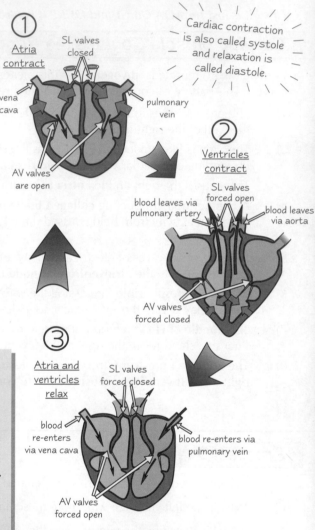

1 ⎡ Ventricles relax, atria contract ⎤

The **ventricles are relaxed**. The **atria contract**, decreasing the volume of the chamber and **increasing** the **pressure** inside the chamber. This **pushes** the blood into the ventricles. There's a slight **increase** in **ventricular pressure** and **chamber volume** as the **ventricles receive the ejected blood** from the contracting atria.

2 ⎡ Ventricles contract, atria relax ⎤

The **atria relax**. The **ventricles contract** (decreasing their volume), **increasing** their **pressure**. The pressure becomes **higher** in the ventricles than the atria, which forces the **AV valves shut** to prevent back-flow. The **pressure** in the **ventricles is also higher than in the aorta and pulmonary artery**, which forces **open** the **SL valves** and blood is forced out into these arteries.

3 ⎡ Ventricles relax, atria relax ⎤

The **ventricles and the atria both relax**. The higher pressure in the pulmonary artery and aorta closes the SL valves to prevent back-flow into the ventricles. Blood returns to the heart and the **atria fill again** due to the higher pressure in the vena cava and pulmonary vein. In turn this starts to **increase** the **pressure** of the atria. As the ventricles continue to **relax**, their **pressure falls below the pressure of the atria** and so the **AV valves open**. This allows blood to flow **passively** (without being pushed by atrial contraction) into the ventricles from the atria. The atria contract, and the whole process begins again.

Cardiac contraction is also called systole and relaxation is called diastole.

Learn the **Equation** for **Cardiac Output**   *AQA only*

Cardiac output is the **volume** of blood pumped by the **heart per minute** (measured in cm³ per minute). It's calculated using this **formula**:

$$\text{cardiac output} = \text{stroke volume} \times \text{heart rate}$$

1) **Heart rate** — the **number** of **heartbeats** per minute. You can measure your heart rate by feeling your pulse, which is basically surges of blood forced through the arteries by the heart contracting.

2) **Stroke volume** — the **volume** of blood pumped during **each heartbeat**, measured in cm³.

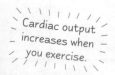

Cardiac output increases when you exercise.

The Cardiac Cycle

This page is for AQA Unit 1 only. If you're doing Edexcel or OCR, you can skip straight to the questions.

You Might be Asked to **Interpret Data** on the **Cardiac Cycle**

You may well be asked to analyse or interpret **data** about the changes in **pressure** and **volume** during the cardiac cycle. Here are two examples of the kind of things you might get:

Example 1

1 Ventricles relaxed Atria contract

pressure increase due to contraction

slight increase due to passive filling

2 Ventricles contract Atria relax

pressure increase due to contraction

pressure decrease as atria relax

3 Ventricles relax Atria relaxed

pressure decrease as ventricles relax

pressure increase as atria fill

pressure decrease as some blood passively moves from atria into ventricle

pressure increase as atria continue to fill

pressure increase as ventricles fill

KEY
— ventricles
— atria

A

C

Pressure / mmHg

ventricles stretch while filling

volume decrease due to contraction

atria expand as they relax and fill with blood

some blood passively moves from atria to ventricle as AV valves open

ventricles expand as they relax and fill with blood

B

Volume / ml

Time / s

If you get a graph you could be asked **questions** like this:

1) **When** does blood start flowing into the **aorta**? At **point A**, the ventricles are **contracting** (and the AV valves are shut), forcing blood into the aorta.

2) Why is **ventricular volume decreasing** at **point B**? The ventricles are **contracting**, **reducing** the volume of the chamber.

3) Are the **semi-lunar valves** open or closed at **point C**? **Closed**. The ventricles are **relaxed** and **refilling**, so the pressure is **higher** in the **pulmonary artery** and **aorta**, forcing the SL valves **closed**.

Example 2

You may have to describe the changes in pressure and volume shown by a **diagram**, like the one on the right. In this diagram the **AV valves** are **open**. So you know that the **pressure** in the **atria** is **higher** than in the **ventricles**. So you also know that the **atria are contracting** because that's what causes the **increase** in **pressure**.

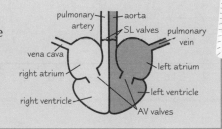

pulmonary artery — aorta
SL valves — pulmonary vein
vena cava
right atrium — left atrium
right ventricle — left ventricle
AV valves

The left ventricle has a thicker wall than the right ventricle and so it contracts more forcefully. This means the pressure is higher in the left ventricle (and in the aorta).

Practice Questions

Q1 During ventricular contraction, are the atrioventricular valves open or closed?

Q2 Why are the semi-lunar valves closed during ventricular and atrial relaxation?

Q3 What is the equation for cardiac output?

Exam Questions

Q1 Describe the events that take place in one complete cardiac cycle, beginning with when the heart muscle is completely relaxed. [8 marks]

Q2 The table opposite shows the blood pressure in two heart chambers at different times during part of the cardiac cycle. Between what times:
a) are the AV valves shut? [1 mark]
b) do the ventricles start to relax? [1 mark]

	Blood pressure / kPa	
Time / s	Left atrium	Left ventricle
0.0	0.6	0.5
0.1	1.3	0.8
0.2	0.4	6.9
0.3	0.5	16.5
0.4	0.9	7.0

My heart will go on... — well, I think I sound like Céline Dion anyway...

When you squeeze a bottle of washing-up liquid, the pressure inside increases and the liquid is forced out... it's no different in the heart — the muscles in the chamber walls contract and push the blood out into the next chamber or the arteries.

ECGs and Heart Rate

This page is for OCR Unit 1 only.

Doctors can use a groovy machine to make sure that your heart is beating in exactly the right way...

An **Electrocardiograph** Records the **Electrical Activity** of the Heart

A doctor can check someone's **heart function** using an **electrocardiograph** — a machine that **records** the **electrical activity** of the heart. The heart muscle **depolarises** (loses electrical charge) when it **contracts**, and **repolarises** (regains charge) when it **relaxes**. An electrocardiograph records these changes in electrical charge using **electrodes** placed on the chest.

The trace produced by an electrocardiograph is called an **electrocardiogram**, or **ECG**. A **normal** ECG looks like this:

1) The **P wave** is caused by **contraction** (depolarisation) of the **atria**.

2) The main peak of the heartbeat, together with the dips at either side, is called the **QRS complex** — it's caused by **contraction** (depolarisation) of the **ventricles**.

3) The **T wave** is due to **relaxation** (repolarisation) of the **ventricles**.

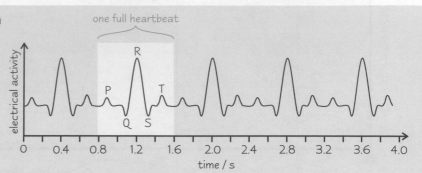

Doctors use ECGs to **Diagnose Heart Problems**

Doctors **compare** their patients' ECGs with a **normal trace**. This helps them to diagnose any heart problems.

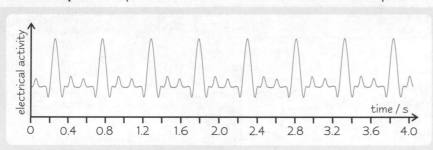

This heartbeat is **too fast** — around 120 beats per minute. That might be OK during **exercise**, but at **rest** it shows that the heart **isn't pumping blood efficiently**.

Here, the **atria** are contracting but sometimes the **ventricles** are **not** (some **P waves** aren't followed by a **QRS complex**). This might mean there's a problem with the **AVN** — impulses aren't travelling from the atria through to the ventricles.

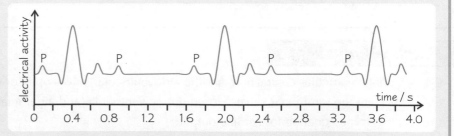

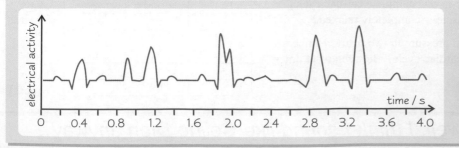

This is **fibrillation** — a really **irregular heartbeat**. The atria or ventricles completely **lose their rhythm** and **stop contracting properly**. It can result in anything from chest pain and fainting to lack of pulse and death.

ECGs and Heart Rate

This page is for Edexcel Unit 1 only. If you're doing OCR, you can skip straight to the questions.

You Can **Investigate** the Effect of **Caffeine** on the **Heart Rate** of **Daphnia**

Daphnia are tiny aquatic **invertebrates**. They're **transparent**, so you can see their internal organs. This means it's pretty easy to monitor their **heart rate** (the **number of heartbeats** in a **minute**) by observing them through a **microscope**. Here's how you could investigate the effect of caffeine on their heart rate:

There's more on controls on page 176.

1) Make up a **range** of caffeine solutions of **different concentrations** and a **control** solution that has no caffeine in it at all.

2) Transfer **one** *Daphnia* into the dimple on a **cavity slide** (a microscope slide with a rounded dip).

3) Place the slide onto the stage of a **light microscope** and **focus** it on the beating heart of the *Daphnia*.

4) Place a small drop of **caffeine solution** onto the *Daphnia*.

5) **Count** the number of **heartbeats** in **10 seconds** and multiply this by **six** to calculate beats per minute (**heart rate**).

6) **Repeat** this 10 times using the **same concentration** of caffeine but a **different** *Daphnia* individual each time.

7) Don't forget to keep **all other factors constant** (e.g. temperature and volume of caffeine solution).

8) Repeat the experiment using the **other concentrations** of caffeine solution.

9) Calculate the **average reading** for each concentration and draw a graph of the results. ⟹

10) The graph should show a **positive correlation** — as caffeine concentration **increases**, heart rate also **increases**.

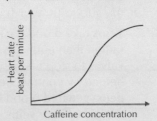

There are Some **Ethical Issues** Involved in Using **Invertebrates**

In the exam, you may have to discuss the **ethical issues** involved with using **invertebrates** in experiments. Here are some points to think about:

1) Experimenting on **animals** allows scientists to study things that would be **unethical** to study using humans.

2) But many people believe that using animals is **also unethical** — they can't give **consent** and they may be subjected to **painful procedures**.

3) Some people believe it's **more acceptable** to perform experiments on **invertebrates** (like *Daphnia*, spiders and insects) than on **vertebrates** (like dogs and monkeys).

4) This is because they're considered to be **simpler organisms** than vertebrates. For example, they have a much **less sophisticated nervous** system, which could mean that they feel less pain (or no pain). Also, invertebrates are more **distantly related** to humans than other vertebrates.

5) But there are still ethical issues to consider when experimenting with invertebrates. For example, some people believe it's unethical to cause **distress** or **suffering** to **any living organism** — e.g. by subjecting them to **extremes of temperature** or depriving them of **food**.

Practice Questions

Q1 What causes the QRS part of an ECG trace?

Q2 Describe the relationship between caffeine concentration and heart rate in Daphnia.

Exam Questions

Q1 Suggest the cause of an ECG which has a QRS complex that is smaller than normal. [2 marks]

Q2 Suggest two reasons why some people may feel it's more acceptable to carry out experiments on invertebrates, such as *Daphnia*, than on vertebrates. [2 marks]

I reckon there are some ethical issues involved with sitting exams...

When you're watching ER or Casualty they always show ECG traces on the patient's monitor. They're the ones that go beep, beep, beep, beep, beep, beep, beep, beep, beep, beep, beep, beep, beep, beep, beep, beeeeeeeeeeeeeeep. Uh oh.

Blood Vessels

This page is for AQA Unit 2, Edexcel Unit 1 and OCR Unit 1.

So, provided your heart is working properly, it'll be pumping out about a litre of blood every 15 seconds. You'll be needing some vessels or something to put that in, otherwise it'll be all over the place...

Different Blood Vessels are Adapted for Different Functions

Arteries, **arterioles** and **veins** have different **characteristics**, and you need to know **why**...

1) **Arteries** carry blood **from** the heart **to** the rest of the body. Their walls are thick and **muscular** and have elastic tissue to cope with the **high pressure** produced by the heartbeat. The inner lining (**endothelium**) is **folded**, allowing the artery to **expand** — this also helps it to cope with high pressure. All arteries carry **oxygenated** blood except for the **pulmonary arteries**, which take deoxygenated blood to the lungs.

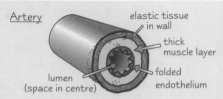

2) Arteries divide into smaller vessels called **arterioles**. These form a network throughout the body. Blood is directed to different **areas of demand** in the body by **muscles** inside the arterioles, which contract to restrict the blood flow or relax to allow full blood flow.

3) **Veins** take blood back **to the heart** under **low pressure**. They have a **wider** lumen than equivalent arteries, and little elastic or muscle tissue. Veins contain **valves** to stop the blood flowing backwards. Blood flow through the veins is helped by contraction of the **body muscles** surrounding them. All veins carry **deoxygenated** blood (because oxygen has been used up by body cells), except the **pulmonary veins**, which carry oxygenated blood to the heart from the lungs.

Substances are Exchanged between Blood and Body Tissues at Capillaries

Arterioles branch into **capillaries**, which are the **smallest** of the blood vessels. Substances (e.g. glucose and oxygen) are **exchanged** between cells and capillaries, so they're adapted for **efficient diffusion**.

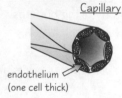

Capillary

endothelium (one cell thick)

1) They're always found very **near cells in exchange tissues** (e.g. alveoli in the lungs), so there's a **short diffusion pathway**.

2) Their walls are only **one cell thick**, which also shortens the diffusion pathway.

3) There are a large number of capillaries, to **increase surface area** for exchange. Networks of capillaries in tissue are called **capillary beds**.

Tissue Fluid is Formed from Blood   *AQA and OCR only*

Tissue fluid is the fluid that **surrounds cells** in tissues. It's made from substances that leave the blood, e.g. oxygen, water and nutrients. Cells take in oxygen and nutrients from the tissue fluid, and release metabolic waste into it. Substances move out of the capillaries, into the tissue fluid, by **pressure filtration**:

1) At the **start** of the capillary bed, nearest the arteries, the pressure inside the capillaries is **greater** than the pressure in the tissue fluid. This difference in pressure **forces fluid out** of the **capillaries** and into the **spaces** around the cells, forming tissue fluid.

2) As fluid leaves, the pressure reduces in the capillaries — so the pressure is much **lower** at the **end** of the capillary bed that's nearest to the veins.

3) Due to the fluid loss, the **water potential** at the end of the capillaries nearest the veins is **lower** than the water potential in the **tissue fluid** — so some **water re-enters** the capillaries from the tissue fluid at the vein end by **osmosis**.

Capillary Bed

from arteriole → ... → to vein

tissue

capillaries

blood flow

capillary containing blood

substances from blood plasma move out of capillary to form tissue fluid

tissue fluid

Unlike blood, tissue fluid **doesn't** contain **red blood cells** or **big proteins** — they're **too large** to be pushed through the capillary walls.

Blood Vessels

This page is for OCR Unit 1 only. If you're doing AQA or Edexcel, you can skip straight to the questions.

Excess Tissue Fluid Drains into the Lymph Vessels

Not all of the tissue fluid **re-enters** the capillaries at the vein end of the capillary bed — some **excess tissue fluid** is left over. This extra fluid eventually gets returned to the blood through the **lymphatic system** — a kind of **drainage** system, made up of **lymph vessels**.

The lymphatic system is also part of the immune system.

1) The smallest lymph vessels are the **lymph capillaries**.

2) Excess tissue fluid passes into lymph vessels. Once inside, it's called **lymph**.

3) **Valves** in the lymph vessels stop the lymph going **backwards**.

4) Lymph gradually moves towards the main lymph vessels in the **thorax**. Here, it's returned to the **blood**, near the **heart**.

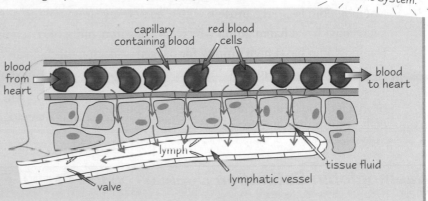

You Need to Know the Differences Between Blood, Tissue Fluid and Lymph

Blood, tissue fluid and lymph are all quite **similar** — tissue fluid is formed from **blood**, and **lymph** is formed from **tissue fluid**. The main differences are shown in the table.

	blood	tissue fluid	lymph	comment
red blood cells	✓	✗	✗	Red blood cells are too big to get through capillary walls into tissue fluid.
white blood cells	✓	very few	✓	Most white blood cells are in the lymph system. They only enter tissue fluid when there's an infection.
platelets	✓	✗	✗	Only present in tissue fluid if the capillaries are damaged.
proteins	✓	very few	only antibodies	Most plasma proteins are too big to get through capillary walls.
water	✓	✓	✓	Tissue fluid and lymph have a higher water potential than blood.
dissolved solutes	✓	✓	✓	Solutes (e.g. salt) can move freely between blood, tissue fluid and lymph.

Practice Questions

Q1 Which type of blood vessel contains valves?

Q2 Describe the structure of a vein.

Q3 Explain the differences between blood, tissue fluid and lymph.

Exam Questions

Q1	Describe the structure of an artery and explain how it relates to its function.	[6 marks]
Q2	Explain how the structure of capillaries enables them to carry out metabolic exchange efficiently.	[4 marks]
Q3	Explain how tissue fluid is formed and how it is returned to the circulation.	[4 marks]

Tissue fluid... Imagine draining the fluid out of a used tissue. Urrgh.

You may have noticed that biologists are obsessed with the relationship between structure and function (I can think of worse things to be obsessed by, like celebrity hairpieces, extreme ironing or beating your brother's lap time for Leguna Seca on Gran Turismo). So whenever you're learning the structure of something, make sure you know how it relates to its function.

Haemoglobin

These pages are for AQA Unit 2 and OCR Unit 1.

Aaagh, complicated topic alert. Don't worry though, just go through it slowly and all should become clear...

Oxygen is Carried Round the Body by Haemoglobin

> *'Affinity' for oxygen means tendency to combine with oxygen.*

1) **Red blood cells** contain **haemoglobin** (Hb).
2) Haemoglobin is a large **protein** with a **quaternary** structure (see p. 6) — it's made up of **four** polypeptide chains.
3) Each chain has a **haem group** which contains **iron** and gives haemoglobin its **red** colour.
4) Haemoglobin has a **high affinity for oxygen** — each molecule can carry **four oxygen molecules**.
5) in the lungs, oxygen **joins** to the **iron** in haemoglobin to form **oxyhaemoglobin**.
6) This is a **reversible reaction** — when oxygen leaves oxyhaemoglobin (**dissociates** from it) near the body cells, it turns back to haemoglobin.

$$Hb \ + \ 4O_2 \ \rightleftharpoons \ HbO_8$$
$$\text{haemoglobin} + \text{oxygen} \rightleftharpoons \text{oxyhaemoglobin}$$

Haemoglobin Saturation Depends on the Partial Pressure of Oxygen

1) The **partial pressure** of **oxygen** (pO_2) is a measure of **oxygen concentration**. The **greater** the concentration of dissolved oxygen in cells, the **higher** the partial pressure.
2) Similarly, the **partial pressure** of **carbon dioxide** (pCO_2) is a measure of the concentration of CO_2 in a cell.
3) Haemoglobin's **affinity** for oxygen **varies** depending on the **partial pressure** of **oxygen**:
4) Oxygen enters blood capillaries at the **alveoli** in the **lungs**. Alveoli have a **high pO_2** so oxygen **loads onto** haemoglobin to form oxyhaemoglobin.
5) **Respiring cells** use up oxygen — this **lowers the pO_2**. Red blood cells deliver oxyhaemoglobin to respiring tissues, where it unloads its oxygen.
6) The haemoglobin then returns to the lungs to pick up more oxygen.

> Oxygen **loads onto** haemoglobin to form oxyhaemoglobin where there's a **high pO_2**. Oxyhaemoglobin **unloads** its oxygen where there's a **lower pO_2**.

Dissociation Curves Show How Affinity for Oxygen Varies

A **dissociation curve** shows how **saturated** the haemoglobin (Hb) is with oxygen at any given partial pressure.

> 100% saturation means each Hb molecule is carrying 4 O_2 molecules. 0% saturation means none of the Hb molecules are carrying any O_2.

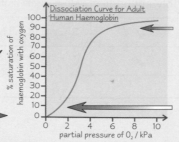

Dissociation Curve for Adult Human Haemoglobin

Where pO_2 is high (e.g. in the lungs), haemoglobin has a **high affinity** for O_2 (i.e. it will **readily combine** with O_2), so it has a **high saturation** of O_2.

Where pO_2 is low (e.g. in respiring tissues), haemoglobin has a **low affinity** for O_2, which means it **releases O_2** rather than combines with it. That's why it has a **low saturation** of O_2.

The graph is 'S-shaped' because when haemoglobin (Hb) combines with the **first O_2 molecule**, its **shape alters** in a way that makes it **easier** for other molecules to join too. But as the Hb starts to become saturated, it gets **harder** for more O_2 molecules to join. So the curve has a **steep** bit in the middle where it's really easy for O_2 molecules to join, and **shallow** bits at each end where it's harder. When the curve is steep, a **small change in pO_2** causes a **big change** in the **amount of O_2** carried by the Hb.

Fetal Haemoglobin has a High Affinity for Oxygen

OCR only

Fetal haemoglobin has a **higher affinity** for oxygen than **adult** haemoglobin.

1) The fetus gets oxygen from its **mother's blood** across the placenta.
2) By the time the mother's blood reaches the placenta, its oxygen saturation has **decreased** (because some has been used up by the mother's body).
3) For the fetus to get **enough oxygen** to survive, its haemoglobin has to have a **higher affinity** for oxygen (so it takes up enough).

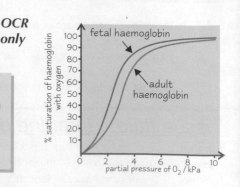

Haemoglobin

Carbon Dioxide Concentration Affects Oxygen Unloading

To complicate matters, haemoglobin gives up its oxygen **more readily** at **higher partial pressures of carbon dioxide** (pCO_2). It's a cunning way of getting more oxygen to cells during activity. When cells respire they produce carbon dioxide, which raises the pCO_2, increasing the rate of oxygen unloading. The reason for this is linked to how CO_2 affects blood pH.

1) Most of the CO_2 from respiring tissues diffuses into red blood cells and is converted to **carbonic acid** by the enzyme **carbonic anhydrase**. (The rest of the CO_2, around 10%, binds directly to haemoglobin and is carried to the lungs.)

2) The carbonic acid **splits up** to give **hydrogen ions** and **hydrogencarbonate ions**.

3) This increase in hydrogen ions causes oxyhaemoglobin to **unload** its oxygen so that haemoglobin can take up the hydrogen ions. This forms a compound called **haemoglobinic acid**. (This process also stops the hydrogen ions from increasing the cell's acidity).

4) The **hydrogencarbonate ions** diffuse out of the red blood cells and are **transported in the blood plasma**.

5) When the blood reaches the **lungs** the low pCO_2 causes the hydrogencarbonate and hydrogen ions to **recombine into CO_2**.

6) The CO_2 then diffuses into the **alveoli** and is breathed out.

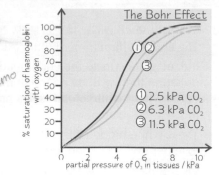

When carbon dioxide levels increase, the dissociation curve 'shifts' down, showing that more oxygen is released from the blood (because the lower the saturation of haemoglobin with O_2, the more O_2 is released). This is called the Bohr effect.

Haemoglobin is Different in Different Organisms

AQA only

Different organisms have different **types** of haemoglobin with different **oxygen transporting capacities**.

1) Organisms that live in environments with a **low concentration of oxygen** have haemoglobin with a **higher affinity** for oxygen than human haemoglobin — the dissociation curve is to the **left** of ours.

2) Organisms that are very **active** and have a **high oxygen demand** have haemoglobin with a **lower affinity** for oxygen than human haemoglobin — the curve is to the **right** of the human one.

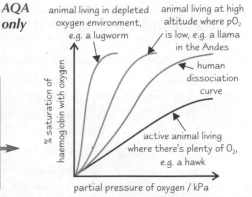

Practice Questions

Q1 How many oxygen molecules can each haemoglobin molecule carry?
Q2 Where in the body would you find a low partial pressure of oxygen?
Q3 Why are oxygen dissociation curves S-shaped?

Exam Questions

Q1 Explain why fetal haemoglobin is different from adult haemoglobin. [3 marks]

Q2 The graph on the right shows the oxygen dissociation curve for human haemoglobin.
On the graph, sketch the curve you would expect for a human in a high carbon dioxide environment.
Explain the position of your sketched curve. [2 marks]

Q3 Describe how carbon dioxide from respiring tissues is transported to the lungs. [6 marks]

There's more than partial pressure on you to learn this stuff...

Well, I don't know about you but after these two pages I need a sit-down. Most people get their knickers in a twist over partial pressure — it's not the easiest thing to get your head round. Whenever you see it written down just pretend it says concentration instead — cross it out and write concentration if you have to — and everything should become clearer. Honest.

Cardiovascular Disease

These pages are for AQA Unit 1, Edexcel Unit 1 and OCR Unit 2.

No, your heart won't break if HE/SHE (delete as appropriate) doesn't return your call... but there are diseases associated with the heart and blood vessels that you have to learn...

Most **Cardiovascular Disease (CVD)** starts with **Atheroma** Formation

1) The wall of an artery is made up of **several layers** (see page 120).

2) The **endothelium** (inner lining) is usually smooth and unbroken.

3) If **damage** occurs to the endothelium (e.g. by high blood pressure) there will be an **inflammatory response** — this is where **white blood cells** (mostly macrophages) move into the area.

4) These white blood cells and **lipids** (fats) from the blood clump together under the endothelium to form **fatty streaks**.

5) Over time, **more white blood cells**, **lipids** and **connective tissue** build up and harden to form a **fibrous plaque** called an **atheroma**.

6) This plaque **partially blocks** the lumen of the **artery** and **restricts blood flow**, which causes **blood pressure** to **increase**.

7) The **hardening** of arteries, caused by atheromas, is called **atherosclerosis**.

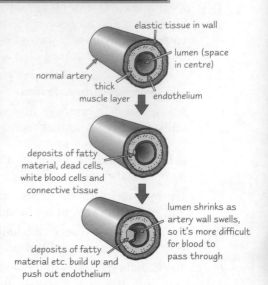

elastic tissue in wall
lumen (space in centre)
normal artery
thick muscle layer
endothelium

deposits of fatty material, dead cells, white blood cells and connective tissue

lumen shrinks as artery wall swells, so it's more difficult for blood to pass through

deposits of fatty material etc. build up and push out endothelium

Atheromas Increase the **Risk** of **Thrombosis** in Arteries

1) As you know, **atheromas** develop within the **walls** of **arteries** (see above).

2) An atheroma can **rupture** (burst through) the **endothelium** of an artery, **damaging** the artery wall and leaving a **rough** surface.

3) This triggers **thrombosis** (blood clotting) — a **blood clot** forms at the **site** of the rupture (see below).

4) This blood clot can cause a complete **blockage** of the artery, or it can become **dislodged** and block a blood vessel elsewhere in the body.

5) The **blood flow** to **tissues** supplied by the blocked blood vessel will be severely **restricted**, so **less oxygen** will reach those tissues, resulting in damage.

6) **Heart attack** and **stroke** are two forms of **cardiovascular disease** that can be caused by blood clots — these are explained in more detail on the next page.

You Need to Know **How** a Blood Clot Forms   *Edexcel only*

Thrombosis is used by the body to **prevent** lots of blood being **lost** when a **blood vessel** is **damaged**. A **series** of **reactions** occurs that leads to the formation of a **blood clot** (**thrombus**):

1) A **protein** called **thromboplastin** is **released** from the **damaged** blood vessel.

2) Thromboplastin triggers the **conversion** of **prothrombin** (a **soluble protein**) into **thrombin** (an **enzyme**).

3) Thrombin then catalyses the **conversion** of **fibrinogen** (a **soluble protein**) to **fibrin** (solid **insoluble fibres**).

4) The fibrin fibres **tangle together** and form a **mesh** in which **platelets** (**small fragments of cells** in the blood) and **red blood cells** get **trapped** — this forms the **blood clot**.

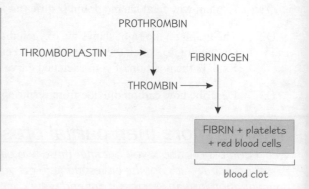

PROTHROMBIN
THROMBOPLASTIN →
FIBRINOGEN
THROMBIN →
FIBRIN + platelets + red blood cells
blood clot

Cardiovascular Disease

Blood Clots can Cause Myocardial Infarctions...

1) The **heart muscle** is supplied with **blood** by the **coronary arteries**.
2) This blood contains the **oxygen** needed by heart muscle cells to carry out **respiration**.
3) If a coronary artery becomes **completely blocked** (e.g. by a **blood clot**) an area of the heart muscle will be totally **cut off** from its blood supply, receiving **no oxygen**.
4) This causes a **myocardial infarction** — more commonly known as a **heart attack**.
5) A heart attack can cause **damage** and **death** of the **heart muscle**.
6) **Symptoms** include **pain** in the chest and upper body, **shortness of breath** and **sweating**.
7) If **large areas** of the heart are affected complete **heart failure** can occur, which is often **fatal**.

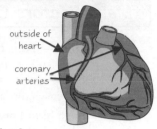

outside of heart

coronary arteries

...and Strokes   *Edexcel and OCR only*

1) A stroke is a **rapid loss of brain function**, due to a **disruption** in the **blood supply** to the **brain**.
2) This can be caused by a **blood clot** in an **artery** leading to the brain, which **reduces** the amount of blood, and therefore **oxygen**, that can reach the brain.

Coronary Heart Disease (CHD) is Another Type of Cardiovascular Disease

Coronary heart disease (CHD) is when the **coronary arteries** have lots of **atheromas** in them, which restricts blood flow to the heart. The atheromas also increase the risk of **blood clots** forming, leading to an increased risk of heart attack.

Atheromas also Increase the Risk of Aneurysm (a type of CVD)   *AQA only*

1) Atheroma plaques **damage** and **weaken arteries**. They also **narrow** arteries, **increasing blood pressure**.
2) When **blood** travels through a weakened artery at **high pressure**, it may **push** the **inner layers** of the artery **through the outer elastic layer** to form a **balloon-like swelling** — an **aneurysm**.
3) This aneurysm may **burst**, causing a **haemorrhage** (bleeding).

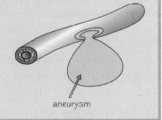

aneurysm

Practice Questions

Q1   Describe how an atheroma forms.

Q2   What is thrombosis?

Q3   What does CHD stand for?

Exam Questions

Q1   Sufferers of a disorder called hypoprothrombinaemia have a reduced amount of prothrombin in their blood. Explain the likely effect this will have on their blood clotting mechanism.   [3 marks]

Q2   Describe how atheromas can increase the risk of a person suffering from a myocardial infarction (heart attack).   [5 marks]

Q3   Describe how atheromas can increase the risk of a person suffering from an aneurysm.   [3 marks]

Atherosclerosis, thrombosis — more like a spelling test than biology...

I know there's a lot to take in on these pages... but make sure you understand the link between atheromas, thrombosis and some cardiovascular diseases. Basically an atheroma forms, which can cause thrombosis, which can lead to heart attacks and strokes. And make sure you don't get CVD and CHD mixed up, they're not the same thing — CHD is a type of CVD.

Risk Factors for Cardiovascular Disease

These pages are for AQA Unit 1, Edexcel Unit 1 and OCR Unit 2.

There are loads of factors that increase the risk of getting cardiovascular disease. And you need to learn them all...

Many Factors Can Increase the Risk of CVD (including CHD)

1) **Diet** — a diet **high** in **saturated fat** increases the risk of CVD. This is because it **increases blood cholesterol level** (see next page), which **increases atheroma formation**. Atheromas can lead to the formation of **blood clots**, which can cause a **heart attack** or stoke. A diet **high in salt** also increases the risk of CVD because it increases the risk of **high blood pressure** (see below).

2) **High blood pressure** — this **increases** the **risk** of **damage** to the **artery walls**, which **increases** the **risk** of **atheroma formation**, which can lead to CVD. **Excessive alcohol consumption, stress** and **diet** can **all** increase blood pressure.

   These factors increase the risk of CHD too because atheromas might form in the coronary arteries.

3) **Smoking** — **carbon monoxide** in cigarette smoke combines with **haemoglobin** (the protein that carries oxygen in the blood) and **reduces** the amount of **oxygen** transported in the **blood**. This **reduces** the amount of **oxygen available to tissues**. If the heart muscle doesn't receive enough oxygen it can lead to a **heart attack** and if the brain doesn't receive enough oxygen it can lead to a **stroke**. **Nicotine** in cigarette smoke makes **platelets sticky**, increasing the chance of **blood clots forming**, which increases the risk of CVD. Smoking also **decreases** the **amount of antioxidants** in the blood — these are important for **protecting cells** from damage. Fewer antioxidants means **cell damage** in the **artery walls** is more likely, and this can lead to **atheroma formation**, which increases the risk of CVD.

4) **Inactivity** — a **lack** of **exercise** increases the risk of CVD because it **increases blood pressure** (see above).

5) **Genetics** — some people inherit particular **alleles** (different versions of genes, see page 42) that make them **more likely** to have **high blood pressure** or **high blood cholesterol**, so they are **more likely** to suffer from CVD.

6) **Age** — the risk of developing CVD **increases with age**.

7) **Gender** — **men** are **three times more likely** to suffer from CVD than pre-menopausal women.

You Might Have to Interpret Data on Risk Factors and CHD

Here's an example I prepared earlier:

The graph shows the results of a study involving **34 439 male British doctors**. **Questionnaires** were used to find out the smoking habits of the doctors. The number of **deaths** among the participants from ischaemic heart disease (coronary heart disease) was counted, and **adjustments** were made to account for **differences in age**. Here are some of the things you might be asked to do:

1) <u>**Describe the data**</u> — The **number** of deaths from ischaemic heart disease **increased** as the number of cigarettes smoked per day **increased**. **Fewer former smokers** and **non-smokers** died of ischaemic heart disease than did smokers.

2) <u>**Draw conclusions**</u> — The **graph shows** a **positive correlation** between the number of cigarettes smoked per day by **male doctors** and the **mortality rate** from ischaemic heart disease.

3) <u>**Explain the link**</u> — You may get asked to **explain** the link between the risk factor under investigation (smoking) and CHD. E.g. **carbon monoxide** in **cigarette smoke** combines with **haemoglobin**, **reducing** the amount of **oxygen transported** in the **blood**. This **reduces** the amount of oxygen available to tissues, including **heart muscle**, which could lead to a **heart attack**. You would also talk about **antioxidants** (see above).

Mortality rate from ischaemic heart disease per 1000 men/year — bar chart with categories: Never smoked, Former smoker, 1-14, 15-24, Over 24 (Number of cigarettes smoked per day)

4) <u>**Check any conclusions are valid**</u> — Make sure the conclusions **match** the data, e.g. this study only looked at **male doctors** — no females were involved, so you can't say that this trend is true for **everyone**. Also, you couldn't say smoking more cigarettes causes an increased **risk** of heart disease. The data shows **deaths only** and **specifically** from ischaemic heart disease. It could be that the **morbidity rate** (the number who have heart disease) **decreases** with the number of cigarettes a day. But you can't tell that from this data.

5) <u>**Comment on the reliability of the results**</u> — For example:

   See pages 174-176 for more on interpreting data.

   • A **large sample size** was used — 34 439, which **increases** reliability.

   • People (even doctors) can tell **porkies** on questionnaires, **reducing** the **reliability** of results.

Risk Factors for Cardiovascular Disease

High Blood Cholesterol Increases the Risk of CVD *Edexcel and OCR*

1) **Cholesterol** is a **lipid** made in the body.
2) **Some** is **needed** for the body to **function normally**.
3) Cholesterol needs to be attached to **protein** to be moved around, so the body forms **lipoproteins** — substances composed of both **protein** and **lipid**. There are **two types** of lipoprotein:

> <u>High density lipoproteins</u> (HDLs) are mainly protein. They transport cholesterol from body tissues to the liver where it's **recycled** or **excreted**. Their function is to **reduce blood cholesterol** when the level is **too high**.
>
> <u>Low density lipoproteins</u> (LDLs) are **mainly lipid**. They transport cholesterol from the **liver** to the **blood**, where it circulates until needed by cells. Their function is to **increase blood cholesterol** when the level is **too low**.

4) **High total blood cholesterol level** (the level of HDL, LDL and other cholesterol) and **high LDL level** have both been linked to an **increased risk** of **CVD**.
5) A diet **high** in **saturated fat raises LDL** level — so more cholesterol is transported **to the blood**, increasing total blood cholesterol and **increasing** the risk of CVD.
6) A diet **high** in **polyunsaturated fat raises HDL** level — so more cholesterol is transported **from the blood** to the liver, decreasing total blood cholesterol and **decreasing** the risk of CVD.

You May Have to Interpret Data on the Link Between Cholesterol and CVD

Take a look at the following example of the sort of study you might see in your **exam**:

> The graph below shows the results of a study involving **27 939 American women**. The **LDL cholesterol level** was **measured** for each woman. They were then **followed** for an average of **8 years** and the **occurrence** of **cardiovascular events** (heart attack, stroke or surgery on coronary arteries) or **death** from cardiovascular diseases was **recorded**. The **relative risk** of a cardiovascular event, **adjusted** for **other factors** that can affect CVD, was then calculated. Here are some of the things you might be asked to do:
>
> 1) <u>Describe the data</u> — The **relative risk** of a cardiovascular event **increases** as the level of **LDL** cholesterol **increases**.
>
> 2) <u>Draw conclusions</u> — The graph shows a **positive correlation** between the relative **risk** of a cardiovascular event and the level of **LDL** cholesterol in the blood (as one factor **increases**, the other **increases**).
>
> 3) <u>Check any conclusions are valid</u> — Be careful that any conclusions **match** the data, e.g. this data only looked at **women** — no males were involved, so you can't say that this trend is true for **everyone**. Also, you **can't** say that a high LDL cholesterol level is **correlated with** an increased risk of **heart attacks**, because the data shows **all** first cardiovascular events, including stroke and surgery.

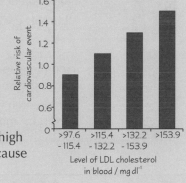

Sometimes studies come up with **conflicting evidence** — evidence that leads to a **different conclusion** than other studies. For example, one study may conclude that a factor **isn't a health risk**, whereas another study may conclude that the **same** factor **is a health risk**. If this happens, **more data** may be needed before you can say if the factor is a health risk or not.

Practice Question

Q1   Describe why high blood pressure increases the risk of CVD.

Exam Questions

Q1   Explain how smoking can increase the risk of developing CVD.   [11 marks]

Q2   Explain the difference between high density lipoproteins (HDLs) and low density lipoproteins (LDLs).   [6 marks]

Revision — a risk factor for headache, stress, boredom...

Questions involving interpreting data come up quite a lot at AS level. The examiners like to see that you can analyse the data and that you can pick out the good and bad bits of a study. Luckily, I'm giving you plenty of examples of these types of questions. Make sure you look at the section at the back of this book on how to interpret data — then you'll be sorted.

Prevention and Treatment of CVD

These pages are for Edexcel Unit 1 only.

It's not all doom and gloom though — there are some changes you can make to your lifestyle to reduce your risk of developing CVD. And even if you get CVD there are treatments available.

Lifestyle Advice to Reduce the Risk of CVD is Based on Scientific Research

There've been loads of **scientific studies** carried out to **identify risk factors** for CVD (see page 126 for risk factors). The **results** from these scientific studies are published in **scientific journals**.
Government organisations (like the **NHS**) and the **media** report the findings to the **general public**.
People can use this information to **make choices** about their **lifestyle**, so they can **reduce** their chance of developing CVD.

EXAMPLE: DIET

1) Scientific research has linked a **diet high in saturated fat** to an **increased risk** of CVD.
   - This information can be used to **educate people** about the risk of **certain diets** and to encourage them to **reduce** their saturated fat intake.
   - The **Food Standards Agency** encourages **food manufacturers** to label their products to show the amount of **saturated fat** in them, so people can make an **informed choice** about what they eat.
2) Scientific studies have also shown that **obese** people are **more likely** to develop CVD.
   - **Obesity indicators**, like BMI (**body mass index**), can be used to assess if people are **overweight** or **obese**. If someone is overweight or obese, then that person can make **choices** to reduce their **weight** and reduce their **risk of CVD** — e.g. they may go on a **diet** or **increase** their **activity level**. These obesity indicators can then be used to **monitor** the **effects** any **changes in lifestyle** have on the person's weight.

EXAMPLE: SMOKING

1) Scientific research has linked **smoking** to an **increased risk** of CVD.
2) This research has led to **TV adverts** and **warnings** on **cigarette packets** about the risks of smoking. The NHS encourages people to give up by giving **free advice** and prescribing **nicotine patches**.
3) All of this encourages people to **stop** smoking and so reduce their risk of CVD.

EXAMPLE: EXERCISE

1) Scientific research has linked **inactivity** to an **increased risk** of CVD.
2) This research has led to campaigns that encourage people to **exercise more frequently** to reduce their risk of CVD.

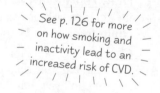

See p. 126 for more on how smoking and inactivity lead to an increased risk of CVD.

Perception of Risk Can be Different from Actual Risk

1) **Risk** can be defined as the **chance** of something **unfavourable** happening.
   E.g. if you **smoke** you **increase** your chance of developing CVD.
2) The **statistical chance** of something unfavourable happening is supported by **scientific research**. E.g. the actual risk of **dying** from **CVD** is **60%** higher for smokers than for non-smokers.
3) People's **perception** of risk may be very **different** from the actual risk:
   - People may **overestimate** the risk — they may believe things to be a **greater risk** than they actually are. E.g. they may have **known someone** who **smoked** and **died** from CVD, and therefore think that if you smoke you **will** die of CVD. Also, there are often **articles** in the **media** about health issues, e.g. articles that highlight the link between smoking and CVD. **Constant exposure** to information like this can make people **constantly worry** that they'll get CVD.
   - Some people may **underestimate** the risk — they may believe things to be a **lower risk** than they actually are. This could be due to a **lack of information** making them **unaware** of the **factors** that contribute to diseases like CVD.

Melvin underestimated the risk of letting his mum dress him...

Prevention and Treatment of CVD

There are **Four Types of Drug** That Can be Used to **Treat CVD**

① Antihypertensives Reduce High Blood Pressure

These drugs include **diuretics** (which increase **urine** production to **reduce blood volume**), **beta-blockers** (which **reduce** the **strength** of the **heartbeat**) and **vasodilators** (which **widen blood vessels**). They all **reduce blood pressure**, so there's **less damage** to artery walls, which reduces the risk of **atheromas** forming and **blood clots** developing.

1) **Benefits** — The **different types** of these drugs work in **different ways**, so they can be given in **combination** to reduce blood pressure. Also, blood pressure can be **monitored at home**, so the patient can see if the drugs are **working**.

2) **Risks** — Side effects include **palpitations** (rapid beating of the heart), **abnormal heart rhythms**, **fainting**, **headaches**, **drowsiness**, **allergic reactions** and **depression**.

② Plant Statins Reduce Cholesterol in the Blood

Plants contain chemicals called **stanols** and **sterols**. These **reduce blood cholesterol** in humans by **reducing** the amount of cholesterol **absorbed** from the **gut**. They're often referred to as **plant statins** (statins are a type of drug that lower cholesterol, but they work in a different way). A lower blood cholesterol level **reduces atheroma formation**, which reduces the risk of CVD. To consume enough plant statins to affect your blood cholesterol you'd have to eat **loads** of plants though. But, you can buy **foods** with **added plant statins** if you want, e.g. some margarines.

1) **Benefits** — Statins reduce the risk of **developing CVD**.

2) **Risks** — They can **reduce** the **absorbtion** of some **vitamins** from the gut.

③ Anticoagulants Reduce the Formation of Blood Clots

Anticoagulants (e.g. warfarin, heparin) **reduce blood clotting**. This means blood clots are **less likely** to form at sites of **damage** in artery walls. So there's **less chance** of one **blocking** a **blood vessel**, which reduces the risk of CVD.

1) **Benefits** — Anticoagulants can be used to treat people who **already have blood clots** or **CVD** — they **prevent** any existing blood clots from **growing any larger** and prevent any **new** blood clots from **forming**. However, anticoagulants **can't get rid** of existing blood clots.

2) **Risks** — If a person taking these drugs is badly **injured**, the reduction in blood clotting can cause **excessive bleeding**, leading to **fainting** (and in serious cases **death**). Other side effects include **allergic reactions**, **osteoporosis** and tissue **swelling**. These drugs may **damage** the **fetus** if they're taken during pregnancy.

④ Platelet Inhibitory Drugs Also Reduce the Formation of Blood Clots

Platelet inhibitory drugs (e.g. **aspirin**) are a type of **anticoagulant**. They work by **preventing platelets clumping together** to form a blood clot. So, they reduce the chance of a blood vessel becoming **blocked** by a clot.

1) **Benefits** — Like anticoagulants, these can be used to treat people who **already have blood clots** or **CVD**.

2) **Risks** — Side effects include **rashes**, **diarrhoea**, **nausea**, **liver function problems** and **excessive bleeding**.

Practice Question

Q1   Describe two risks involved in taking platelet inhibitory drugs.

Exam Question

Q1   A patient who is at risk of developing coronary heart disease (CHD) goes to see his doctor.
The patient is obese and suffers from high blood pressure.
a) Suggest a type of drug the doctor could prescribe to treat the patient's high blood pressure.
Explain how the drug reduces the risk of CHD and give one disadvantage of taking it. [4 marks]
b) Suggest two lifestyle changes that the doctor may recommend to his patient to reduce his
risk of developing CHD. [2 marks]

The only lifestyle advice I take is from Trinny & Susannah...

It's better to prevent CVD in the first place, rather than trying to treat it. That's 'cos the treatments don't cure the problem — they just prevent it from getting any worse. Right, so I'll meet you down at the park in about 10 mins for a quick sprint then...

Variation

These pages are for AQA Unit 2, Edexcel Unit 2 and OCR Unit 2.

Ever wondered why no two people are exactly alike? No, well nor have I actually, but it's time to start thinking about it. This variation is partly genetic and partly due to differences in the environment.

Variation Exists Between All Individuals

Variation is the **differences** that exist between **individuals**. Every individual organism is **unique** — even **clones** (such as identical twins) show some **variation**. It can occur:

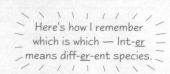
Here's how I remember which is which — Int-*er* means diff-*er*-ent species.

1) <u>Within species</u> — Variation within a species is called **intraspecific** variation. For example, **individual** European robins weigh **between** 16 g and 22 g and show some variation in many other characteristics including length, wingspan, colour and beak size.

2) <u>Between species</u> — The variation between **different species** is called **interspecific** variation. For example, the **lightest** species of bird is the bee hummingbird, which weighs around 1.6 g on average. The **heaviest** species of bird is the ostrich, which can weigh up to 160 kg (100 000 times as much).

No matter what anyone said, Malcolm knew size was important.

Variation can be Continuous...   *Edexcel and OCR only*

Continuous variation is when the **individuals** in a population vary **within a range** — there are **no distinct categories**, e.g. **humans** can be **any height** within a range (139 cm, 175 cm, 185.9 cm, etc.), **not just** tall or short. Here are some more examples:

Animals

1) **Milk yield** — e.g. cows can produce any volume of milk within a range.
2) **Mass** — e.g. humans can be any mass within a range.

Plants

1) **Number of leaves** — e.g. a tree can have any number of leaves within a range.
2) **Mass** — e.g. the mass of the seeds from a flower head varies within a range.

Microorganisms

1) **Width** — e.g. the width of *E. coli* bacteria varies within a range.
2) **Length** — e.g. the length of the flagellum (see p. 22) can vary within a range.

The categories are not distinct

Number of people

Height

...or Discontinuous   *Edexcel and OCR only*

Discontinuous variation is when there are two or more **distinct categories** — each individual falls into **only one** of these categories, there are **no intermediates**. Here are some examples:

Animals

1) **Sex** — e.g. humans can be either male or female.
2) **Blood group** — e.g. humans can be group A, B, AB or O.

Plants

1) **Colour** — e.g. courgettes are either yellow, dark green or light green.
2) **Seed shape** — e.g. some pea plants have smooth seeds and some have wrinkled seeds.

Microorganisms

1) **Antibiotic resistance** — e.g. bacteria are either resistant or not.
2) **Pigment production** — e.g. some types of bacteria can produce a coloured pigment, some can't.

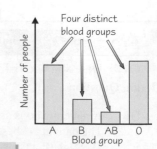
Four distinct blood groups

Number of people

A   B   AB   O
Blood group

Variation

Variation can be Caused by Genes, the Environment, or Both

Variation can be caused by **genetic factors**, **environmental factors** or a combination of **both**:

1) Genetic factors

1) **Different species** have **different genes**.

2) Individuals of the **same species** have the **same genes**, but **different versions** of them (called **alleles**).

3) **Different alleles** for the **same gene** are found in the same position on both **chromosomes**. This position is called the **locus**.

4) The genes and alleles an organism has make up its **genotype**.

5) The differences in **genotype** result in **variation** in **phenotype** — the **characteristics** displayed by an organism.

6) Characteristics controlled by only **one gene** are called **monogenic**. They tend to show **discontinuous variation**, e.g. courgette colour (see previous page).

7) Characteristics controlled by a **number of genes** at **different loci** are said to be **polygenic**. They usually show **continuous variation**, e.g. height (see previous page).

8) Examples of variation caused **only** by genetic factors include **blood group** in humans (O, A, B or AB) and **antibiotic resistance** in bacteria.

9) You **inherit** your genes from your parents. This means variation caused by genetic factors is **inherited**.

Two chromosomes

Allele for group A

Position (locus) of gene for blood group

Allele for group O

2) Environmental factors

1) Variation can also be caused by **differences in the environment**, e.g. climate, food, lifestyle.

2) Characteristics controlled by environmental factors can **change** over an organism's life.

3) Examples of variation caused **only** by environmental factors include **accents** and whether people have **pierced ears**.

3) Both

Genetic factors determine the characteristics an organism's **born with**, but **environmental factors** can **influence** how some characteristics **develop**. For example:

1) **Skin colour** — the amount of **melanin** (pigment) people have in their **skin** is partially controlled by **genes**, but skin colour is influenced by the **amount of sunlight** a person is exposed to.

2) **Flagellum** — **genes** determine if a microorganism **can grow** a flagellum, but some will only **start to grow** them in **certain environments**, e.g. if metal ions are present.

Practice Questions

Q1 What is variation?

Q2 Describe what is meant by continuous variation and give one example.

Q3 Briefly describe what is meant by variation caused by environmental factors.

Exam Question

Q1 The graph shows the results of an investigation into the effects of temperature on the length of time it took for ladybird larvae to emerge as adults. Two species of ladybird were investigated, species A and species B.

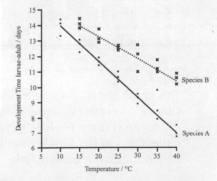

a) Describe the results of the study. [3 marks]

b) Explain what causes the variation between the species and within each species. [4 marks]

Environmental Factor — the search is on for the most talented environment...

It's amazing to think how many factors and genes influence the way we look and behave. It's the reason why every single organism is unique. My parents have often said they're glad they'll never have another child as 'unique' as me.

Variation

This page is for Edexcel Unit 2 only. If you're doing OCR you know all you need to know about variation, go to p. 136.

The variation in some characteristics is caused by a mixture of genetic factors and environmental factors. This makes it trickier than a Rubik's cube to work out which factors are influencing the characteristic the most.

You Need to Learn What **Causes Variation** in These **Four Phenotypes**

These four phenotypes (characteristics) are influenced by **both genetic** and **environmental factors**:

1) **Height** is **polygenic** and affected by **environmental factors**, especially nutrition. E.g. **tall parents** usually have **tall children**, but if the children are **undernourished** they **won't** have enough **food** and **nutrients** to grow to their **maximum height**.

2) **Monoamine Oxidase A** (**MAOA**) is an **enzyme** that breaks down **monoamines** (a type of **chemical**) in **humans**. **Low levels** of MAOA have been linked to **mental health problems**. MAOA production is controlled by a **single gene** (it's **monogenic**), but taking **anti-depressants** or **smoking tobacco** can **reduce** the amount produced.

3) **Cancer** is the **uncontrolled division of cells** that leads to lumps of cells (**tumours**) forming. The **risk of developing** some cancers is affected by **genes**, but **environmental factors** such as **diet** can also **influence** the risk.

4) **Animal hair colour** is **polygenic**, but the environment also plays a part in **some** animals. E.g. some **arctic animals** have **dark hair** in **summer** but **white hair** in **winter**. **Environmental factors** like decreasing temperature **trigger** this change but it **couldn't** happen if the animal **didn't** have the **genes** for it.

It's Difficult to **Interpret** the **Relative Contributions** of **Genes** and **Environment**

1) Data on variation can be very tricky to **interpret** because some characteristics can be affected by **many different genes** (they're polygenic) and **many environmental factors**.

2) It's difficult to know **which factors** (genes or environment) are having the **greatest effect**.

3) This makes it **hard** to **draw conclusions** about the **causes of variation**. Here's an example:

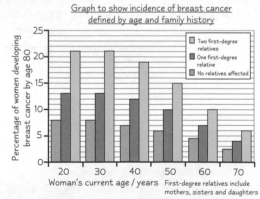

This graph shows that the **incidence** of **breast cancer** is affected by **age** and **family history**. A woman is **more likely** to develop breast cancer if **members of her family** have had the disease, which suggests a **genetic link**.

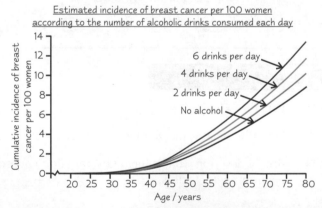

This graph shows that the **incidence** of **breast cancer** is linked to **age** and **alcohol consumption**. The incidence is **higher** in women who drink **more alcohol**. Alcohol consumption is an **environmental factor**.

1) If you only saw **one** of these graphs you may think **only genetics and age**, or **only alcohol consumption and age**, affect your **risk** of developing breast cancer.

2) When you look at **both sets of data** you can see that **all** these things affect the risk.

3) It's **difficult** to tell **which factor** (genes or alcohol) has the **largest effect**.

4) Also, there are other **environmental factors** that are thought to be involved in increasing the risk of developing breast cancer (e.g. **diet, exercise**, etc.) that aren't considered here.

Variation

This page is for AQA Unit 2 only. If you're doing Edexcel you can skip straight to the questions.

Be Careful When Drawing Conclusions About the Cause of Variation

In any **group of individuals** there's a lot of **variation** — think how different all your friends are. It's not always **clear** whether the variation is caused by **genes**, the **environment** or **both**. Scientists draw conclusions based on the information they have until **new evidence** comes along that **challenges** it — have a look at these two examples:

Example 1 — Overeating

1) **Overeating** was thought to be caused only by environmental factors, like an **increased availability of food** in developed countries.

2) It was later discovered that food consumption **increases** brain **dopamine** levels in animals.

3) Once enough dopamine was released, people would **stop** eating.

4) Researchers discovered that people with one particular **allele** had **30% fewer** dopamine receptors.

5) They found that people with this particular allele were **more likely** to overeat — they wouldn't stop eating when dopamine levels increased.

6) Based on this evidence, scientists now think that overeating has **both genetic** and **environmental** causes.

Example 2 — Antioxidants

1) Many foods in our diet contain **antioxidants** — compounds that are thought to play a role in **preventing chronic diseases**.

2) Foods such as **berries** contain **high levels** of antioxidants.

3) Scientists thought that the berries produced by different **species** of plant contained **different levels** of antioxidants because of **genetic factors**.

4) But experiments that were carried out to see if **environmental** conditions affected antioxidant levels found that environmental conditions caused a great deal of **variation**.

5) Scientists now believe that antioxidant levels in berries are due to **both genetic** and **environmental** factors.

Practice Questions

Q1 Is height a monogenic or a polygenic characteristic?

Q2 What factors affect variation in MAOA production?

Q3 What factors affect variation in animal hair colour?

Exam Question

Q1 A study was conducted into how smoking during pregnancy affects the birth mass of newborn babies, depending on the genotype of the mother. The results showed that women who smoked during the entire pregnancy had babies with a mean reduction in birth mass of 377 grams. But the reduction was as much as 1285 grams among women with certain genotypes.

a) Data on variation in child birth mass was also collected from a group of non-smokers. Suggest why this data was collected. [1 mark]

b) What can be concluded about the influence of genetic factors and environmental factors on birth mass? Give evidence from the study to support your answer. [4 marks]

c) Give two other factors that should be controlled in this experiment. [2 marks]

Jokes can show enormous variation — take the knock-knock jokes...

Knock, knock. Who's there? Dr. Dr Who? That's right. Knock, knock. Who's there? Boo. Boo who? No need to cry, it's only a joke. Knock, knock. Who's there? Isabelle. Isabelle who? Isabelle working? I've been here for hours... Lots of variation, but no humour. My dad knows loads of knock-knock jokes, so their variation is probably caused by genetic factors.

Investigating Variation

These pages are for AQA Unit 2 only.

It's a lot of work studying variation in an entire population (imagine studying all the ants in one nest) — so instead you can take a random sample and use this to give you a good idea of what's going on in the entire population.

To **Study** Variation You Have to **Sample** a **Population**

When studying variation you usually only look at a **sample** of the population, **not** the **whole thing**. For most species it would be too **time-consuming** or **impossible** to catch all the individuals in the group. So samples are used as **models** for the **whole population**.

The **Sample** has to be **Random**

Because sample data will be used to **draw conclusions** about the **whole population**, it's important that it **accurately represents** the whole population and that any patterns observed are tested to make sure they're not due to chance.

1) To make sure the sample isn't **biased**, it should be **random**. For example, if you were looking at plant species in a field you could pick random sample sites by dividing the field into a **grid** and using a **random number generator** to select coordinates.

2) To ensure any variation observed in the sample isn't just due to **chance**, it's important to analyse the results **statistically**. This allows you to be more **confident** that the results are true and therefore will reflect what's going on in the **whole population**.

You Need to be Able to **Analyse** and **Interpret Data** Relating to **Variation**

You might be asked to **analyse** and **interpret** data relating to **interspecific and intraspecific variation** in your exam. So here's a big **example** to give you an idea of what you might get:

The graph below shows the growth of two **different** species of plant in the **same environment**. You might be asked to:

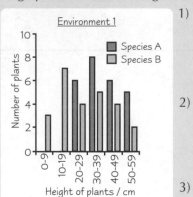

1) **Describe the data**...
   - The largest number of plants are **30-39 cm** tall for species **A** and **10-19 cm** tall for species **B**.
   - Species **A** plants **range in height** from **20-59 cm** but the range is **larger** for **species B** (**0-59 cm**).

2) ...or **draw conclusions**
   There is **interspecific variation** in plant height — Species **A** plants are **generally taller** than Species B. **Both species** show **intraspecific variation** — plant height varies for both species. There is **more intraspecific variation** in species **B** — the range of heights is bigger.

3) ...or **suggest a reason** for the differences
   A and B are **separate species**, grown in the same area. This means their **genes are different** but their **environment is the same**. So any **interspecific** variation in height is down to **genetic factors**, **not** the environment.

The graph below shows the **same** two species of plant but grown in a **different environment** than in the first graph.

1) You might be asked to **describe the data**...
   - E.g. the **largest number** of plants are **40-49 cm** tall for species **A** and **20-29 cm** tall for species **B**.

   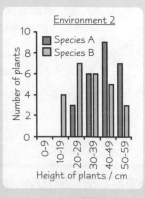

   - The **range in height** is **20-59 cm** for species **A** and **10-59 cm** for species **B**.
   - You may have to **compare** the data between the two graphs. E.g. for species **A**, the plants are generally **taller** in **environment 2**. The range in height has **stayed the same**. For species **B**, the plants are also generally **taller** in **environment 2**, but the range in height is **smaller**.

2) ...or **draw conclusions and suggest a reason** for the differences
   - Both species are **generally taller** in environment **2** than in environment **1**. So, variation in height is affected by **environmental factors**.
   - Species A shows **similar** height variation in **both environments**. The variation in species B **differs** between the two environments. This suggests that **environmental factors influence** height **more** in species **B**.

Investigating Variation

Standard Deviation Tells You About the Variation Within a Sample

1) The **mean value** tells you the **average** of the values collected in a **sample**.

2) It can be used to tell if there **is variation between samples**, e.g. the mean number of apples produced by species A = 26 and B = 32. So the **number** of apples produced by different tree species **does vary**.

3) Most samples give you a **bell-shaped graph** — this is called a **normal distribution**.

4) The **standard deviation** tells you **how much** the values in a **single sample vary**. It's a **measure** of the **spread of values about the mean**.

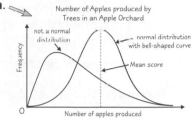

5) For example:
   - Species A: mean = 26, standard deviation = 3 — most of the trees in the sample produced between 23 and 29 apples (26 ± 3).
   - Species B: mean = 32, standard deviation = 9 — most of the trees in the sample produced between 23 and 41 apples (32 ± 9).
   - So species B generally produces **more apples** but shows a **greater variation** in the number produced, compared to species A.

6) A **large standard deviation** means the values in the sample **vary a lot**. A **small standard deviation** tells you most of the sample data is around the mean value, so **varies little**:

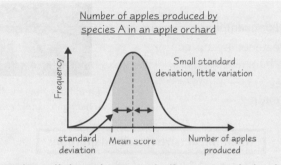

When all the values are **similar**, so vary little, the graph is **steep** and the standard deviation is **small**.

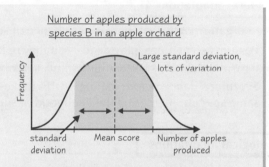

When all the values vary a lot, the graph is **fatter** and the standard deviation is **large**.

Practice Questions

Q1 Why does a population sample have to be chosen at random?

Q2 What does the standard deviation of a data set tell you?

Exam Question

Q1 A study was conducted to investigate the factors that influence the mass of children in the UK. The study involved identical and non-identical twins between the ages of 8 and 11 that live together. Measurements of mass, height and waist circumference were collected by questionnaire from a sample of 1813 pairs of identical twins and 3279 pairs of non-identical twins. The results showed that identical twin pairs were more likely to have a similar BMI (an obesity indicator measure) and waist circumference measurements than non-identical twin pairs.

a) Why do scientists look at a sample of a population, rather than the whole population? [1 mark]

b) Suggest why identical twins were included in the study. [1 mark]

c) What can be concluded from the study about the influence of genetic factors and environmental factors on childhood BMI and waist circumference? Explain your answer. [4 marks]

Investigating standards — say that to your teachers to scare them...

Bet you thought you'd finished with maths — 'fraid not. Thankfully you don't need to know how to work out standard deviation though. But you do need to know how to go about interpreting data — which is a bit more interesting than maths, and I can exclusively reveal it's what all the examiners dream about at night.

Adaptation and Evolution

These pages are for Edexcel Unit 2 and OCR Unit 2.

All the variation between and within species means that some organisms are better adapted to their environment than others...

Adaptations make Organisms **Well Suited** to Their **Environment**

1) Being **adapted** to an environment means an organism has features that **increase** its **chances of survival** and **reproduction**, and also the chances of its **offspring reproducing successfully**.

2) These features are called **adaptations** and can be behavioural, physiological and anatomical (see below).

3) Adaptations develop because of **evolution** by **natural selection** (see the next page).

4) In each generation, the **best-adapted individuals** are more likely to survive and reproduce — passing their adaptations on to their **offspring**. Individuals that are less well adapted are more likely to **die before reproducing**.

Adaptations can be **Behavioural**, **Physiological** and **Anatomical**

Behavioural adaptations

Ways an organism **acts** that increase its chance of survival. For example:

- **Possums** sometimes '**play dead**' — if they're being threatened by a **predator** they play dead to **escape attack**. This **increases** their chance of **survival**.

- **Scorpions dance** before **mating** — this makes sure they attract a mate of the **same species**, increasing the likelihood of **successful mating**.

Sid and Nancy were well adapted to hiding in candyfloss shops.

Physiological adaptations

Processes inside an organism's body that increase its chance of survival. For example:

- **Brown bears hibernate** — they **lower their metabolism** (all the chemical reactions taking place in their body) over **winter**. This **conserves energy**, so they don't need to look for **food** in the months when it's scarce — **increasing** their chance of **survival**.

- **Some bacteria** produce **antibiotics** — these **kill** other species of bacteria in the area. This means there's **less competition**, so they're **more likely** to **survive**.

Anatomical (structural) adaptations

Structural features of an organism's body that increase its chance of survival. For example:

- **Otters** have a **streamlined shape** — making it easier to **glide** through the **water**. This makes it easier for them to **catch prey** and **escape predators**, increasing their chance of **survival**.

- **Whales** have a **thick layer** of **blubber** (fat) — this helps to keep them **warm** in the cold sea. This increases their chance of survival in places where their **food** is found.

A **Niche** Describes the **Role** of a Species Within its Habitat   *Edexcel only*

1) The **niche** a species occupies within its habitat includes:

- Its **biotic** interactions — e.g. the organisms it **eats**, and those it's **eaten by**.
- Its **abiotic** interactions — e.g. the **oxygen** an organism breathes in, and the **carbon dioxide** it breathes out.

Don't get confused between habitat (where a species lives) and niche (what it does in its habitat).

2) Every species has its own **unique niche** — a niche can only be occupied by **one species**.

3) It may **look like** two species are filling the **same niche** (e.g. they're both eaten by the same species), but there'll be **slight differences** (e.g. variations in what they eat).

4) If **two species** try to occupy the **same niche**, they will **compete** with each other. One species will be **more successful** than the other, until **only one** of the species is **left**.

Adaptation and Evolution

Adaptations Become More Common by Evolution

1) Evolution is the slow and continual **change** of organisms from one generation to the next.

2) It explains how advantageous adaptations become **more common** within a population of organisms.

3) **Charles Darwin** came up with the Theory of Evolution by **Natural Selection**.

4) Scientists use **theories** to attempt to **explain** their **observations** — Charles Darwin was no exception. Darwin made **four** key observations about the world around him.

Natural selection is one process by which evolution occurs.

Observations:
1) Organisms produce **more offspring** than **survive**.
2) There's **variation** in the characteristics of members of the **same species**.
3) Some of these characteristics can be **passed on** from one generation to the next.
4) Individuals that are **best adapted** to their environment are more likely to **survive**.

5) Darwin wrote his theory of evolution by natural selection to **explain** his observations:

Theory:
1) Individuals within a population **show variation** in their **phenotypes** (their characteristics).
2) **Predation**, **disease** and **competition** create a **struggle for survival**.
3) Individuals with **better adaptations** (characteristics that give a selective advantage, e.g. being able to run away from predators faster) are **more likely** to **survive**, **reproduce** and **pass on** their advantageous adaptations to their **offspring**.
4) Over time, the **number** of individuals with the advantageous adaptations **increases**.
5) Over generations this leads to **evolution** as the favourable adaptations become **more common** in the population.

Evolution can Lead to Speciation   *OCR only*

Speciation is the **formation of a new species**:

1) A **species** is defined as a group of **similar organisms** that can **reproduce** to produce **fertile offspring** (see p. 140).
2) Species can exist as **one** or **more populations**.
3) Speciation happens when **populations** of the **same species** evolve to become so different that they can't breed with one another to produce **fertile** offspring.

Example: Darwin's finches   Darwin observed 14 species of finch on the **Galapagos Islands**. Each species of finch was unique to a single island. The finches were similar, except for the size and shape of their **beaks** — they were adapted to the **food sources** found on their specific island. Darwin theorised that:

1) All the species of finch had a **common ancestor**.
2) Different populations became **isolated** on different islands.
3) Each population **evolved adaptations** to their environment.
4) The populations evolved to become so different that they could no longer **breed** to produce **fertile offspring**.

Practice Questions

Q1 What is meant by the term adaptation?

Q2 What is a niche?

Exam Questions

Q1 Hedgehogs are commonly found in gardens across the UK. They are brown with long, spiky fur, small ears and claws. They hibernate over winter and can roll into a ball when alarmed. Give one behavioural, one physiological and two anatomical adaptations of hedgehogs, and suggest how each helps them to survive.   [8 marks]

Q2 Explain how natural selection can lead to adaptations becoming more common in a population.   [4 marks]

I'm perfectly adapted — for staying in bed...

Adaptations are features that make an organism more likely to survive and reproduce. Repetitive? Yes, but that's why it's so easy to learn. And don't forget — adaptations become more common because of evolution by natural selection. Simple...

Evolution

These pages are for OCR Unit 2 only.

Because there's so much evidence to support the theory of evolution it's pretty much considered scientific fact now...

There's **Plenty of Evidence** to **Support Evolution**

Fossil Record Evidence

Fossils are the **remains** of organisms **preserved in rocks**.
By arranging fossils in chronological (date) order, **gradual changes** in organisms can be observed that provide **evidence** of evolution.

Example — The fossil record of the **horse** shows a **gradual change** in characteristics, including increasing **size** and **hoof** development.

DNA Evidence

1) The theory of evolution suggests that all organisms have **evolved** from shared **common ancestors**.
2) Closely related species **diverged** (evolved to become different species) **more recently**.
3) Evolution is caused by **gradual changes** in the **base sequence** of organisms' DNA.
4) So, organisms that diverged away from each other more recently should have **more similar DNA**, as **less time** has passed for changes in the DNA sequence to occur. This is exactly what scientists have found.

See p. 38 for more on DNA.

Example — Humans, chimps and mice all evolved from a common ancestor. Humans and mice diverged a **long time ago**, but humans and chimps diverged **quite recently**. The **DNA base sequence** of humans and chimps is 94% the same, but human and mouse DNA is only 85% the same.

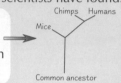

Molecular Evidence

In addition to DNA, the similarities in **other molecules** provide evidence.
Scientists compare the **sequence** of **amino acids** in **proteins** (see p. 40), and compare **antibodies**. Organisms that diverged away from each other **more recently** have **more similar molecules**, as **less time** has passed for changes in proteins and other molecules to occur.

Populations of **Bacteria** can **Evolve Resistance** to **Antibiotics**

Antibiotics are drugs that **kill or inhibit the growth** of bacteria. Scientists have observed the evolution of **antibiotic resistance** in many species of bacteria. For example, MRSA (methicillin-resistant *Staphylococcus aureus*) is a **strain** (type) of bacteria that's resistant to the antibiotic methicillin.

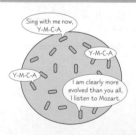

The **evolution** of antibiotic resistance can be explained by **natural selection**:
1) There is **variation** in a population of bacteria. **Genetic mutations** make some bacteria naturally **resistant** to an antibiotic.
2) If the population of bacteria is exposed to that antibiotic, only the individuals with resistance will **survive** to **reproduce**.
3) The **alleles** which cause the antibiotic resistance will be **passed on** to the next generation, and so the population will evolve to become resistant to the drug.

The Evolution of **Antibiotic Resistance** has **Implications** for **Humans**

1) **Infections** caused by antibiotic-resistant bacteria (such as MRSA) are **harder** to **treat** — some species of bacteria are resistant to **a lot of different antibiotics**. It takes doctors a while to figure out which antibiotics will get rid of the infection, and in that time the **patient** could become **very ill** or **die**.
2) There could come a point where a bacterium has developed resistance to **all known antibiotics**. To prevent this **new antibiotics** need to be **developed**. This takes **time** and costs a lot of **money**.

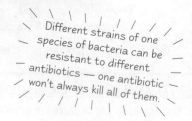

Different strains of one species of bacteria can be resistant to different antibiotics — one antibiotic won't always kill all of them.

Evolution

Populations of Insects can Evolve Resistance to Pesticides

Pesticides are chemicals that **kill pests** (e.g. insects that damage crops). Scientists have observed the evolution of **pesticide resistance** in many species of insect. For example, some populations of **mosquito** have **evolved resistance** to the pesticide **DDT**. Some populations of **pollen beetles** (which damage the crop oilseed rape) are resistant to **pyrethroid** pesticides.

Janet was resistant to DDT but not to Malcolm's smooth talking.

The evolution of **pesticide resistance** can be explained by **natural selection**:

1) There is **variation** in a population of insects. **Genetic mutations** make some insects naturally **resistant** to a pesticide.

2) If the population of insects is exposed to that pesticide, only the individuals with resistance will **survive** to **reproduce**.

3) The **alleles** which cause the pesticide resistance will be **passed on** to the next generation, and so the population will evolve to become more resistant to the chemical.

The Evolution of Pesticide Resistance has Implications for Humans

The implications for humans are pretty similar to those for antibiotic resistance:

1) **Crop infestations** with **pesticide-resistant** insects are **harder** to **control** — some insects are resistant to **lots of different pesticides**. It takes farmers a while to figure out which pesticide will kill the insect and in that time **all the crop could be destroyed**. If the insects are resistant to specific pesticides (ones that only kill that insect), farmers might have to use **broader pesticides** (those that kill a range of insects), which could kill beneficial insects.

2) If **disease-carrying** insects (e.g. mosquitoes) become pesticide-resistant, the **spread of disease** could **increase**.

3) A population of insects could **evolve resistance** to **all** pesticides in use. To prevent this **new pesticides** need to be **produced**. This takes **time** and costs **money**.

Practice Questions

Q1 Briefly describe how fossil evidence supports the theory of evolution.

Q2 Other than fossil evidence, describe two forms of evidence that support the theory of evolution.

Q3 Give two implications of the evolution of drug resistance in microorganisms.

Exam Question

Q1 The diamondback moth is a pest of many crops. In 1953 it became resistant to the pesticide DDT and by 1981 it had become resistant to 36 other pesticides.

a) Explain how the diamondback moth populations could have developed DDT resistance. [4 marks]

b) Describe two possible implications of the diamondback moth developing resistance to pesticides. [2 marks]

The fossil record — it rocks...

So there you have it — tonnes of evidence to back up the theory of evolution. As with any scientific theory, when all the evidence backs it up, it's generally thought of as scientific fact — for now. If any conflicting evidence comes along, the whole process starts again — and that's how science works (see p. 2).

Principles of Classification

These pages are for AQA Unit 2, Edexcel Unit 2 and OCR Unit 2.

Millions of different species have evolved over the few billion years since life began. All those species need names though, which is where classification comes in — it's about naming and organising species into groups — sounds thrilling...

Classification is All About Grouping Together Similar Organisms

Classification is the act of **arranging organisms** into **groups** based on their **similarities** and **differences**. This makes it **easier** for scientists to **identify** and **study** them. **Taxonomy** is the **study** of classification.

1) There are **seven** levels of groups (called taxonomic groups) used to classify organisms.

2) Organisms can only belong to **one group** at **each level** in the taxonomic hierarchy
   — there's **no overlap**.

3) **Similar organisms** are first sorted into **large groups** called **kingdoms**, e.g. all animals are in the animal kingdom.

4) **Similar** organisms from that kingdom are then grouped into a **phylum**. **Similar** organisms from each phylum are then grouped into a **class**, and **so on** down the seven levels of the hierarchy.

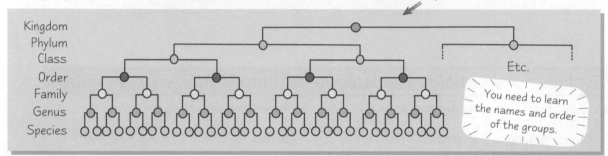

Kingdom
Phylum
Class
Order
Family
Genus
Species

Etc.

You need to learn the names and order of the groups.

If you're doing **OCR** you need to know a slightly different hierarchy — it's the same as the one above but it has an extra level at the start called a **domain**.

5) As you move **down** the hierarchy, there are **more groups** at each level but **fewer organisms** in each group.

6) The hierarchy **ends** with **species** — the groups that contain only **one type** of organism (e.g. humans, dogs, *E. coli*). You need to **learn** the definition of a **species**.

> **A species is a group of similar organisms able to reproduce to give fertile offspring.**

7) The **more similar** organisms are to each other the **more groups** they're in together as you go down the hierarchy. E.g. lions (*Panthera leo*) and tigers (*Panthera tigris*) are **different species** but they're in **all** the other, **higher** taxonomic groups together — same genus, same family, same order, etc.

8) Species in the **same genus** can be **very similar**, with similar **features** or **behaviours**, but they're **separate** species because they **can't breed together** to produce **fertile offspring** (e.g. lions and tigers can't produce fertile offspring).

9) Scientists constantly **update** classification systems because of **discoveries** about new species and new **evidence** about known organisms (e.g. **DNA sequence** data).

Phylogenetics Tells Us About an Organism's Evolutionary History

1) **Phylogenetics** is the study of the **evolutionary history** of groups of **organisms**.

2) All organisms have **evolved** from shared common ancestors (**relatives**). E.g. members of the Hominidae family (great apes and humans) evolved from a common ancestor. First orangutans **diverged** (evolved to become a **different species**) from this common ancestor. Next gorillas diverged, then humans, closely followed by bonobos and chimpanzees.

3) Phylogenetics tells us **who's related** to whom and how **closely related** they are.

4) Closely related species **diverged** away from each other **most recently**. E.g. the phylogenetic tree opposite shows the **Hominidae tree**. Humans and **chimpanzees** are **closely** related, as they diverged very **recently**. You can see this because their branches are **close** together. Humans and orangutans are more **distantly** related, as they diverged longer ago, so their branches are **further** apart.

5) **Molecular phylogenetics** looks at **molecules** (e.g. **DNA** and **proteins**) to see how **closely related** organisms are, e.g. **more closely related** organisms have **more similar molecules**.

Phylogenetics is sometimes called phylogeny.

Human
Chimpanzee
Bonobo
Orangutan
Gorilla
Common ancestor

Classification systems now take into account **phylogenetics** when arranging organisms into **groups**.

Principles of Classification

The Binomial Naming System is Used in Classification

1) The **nomenclature** (**naming system**) used for classification is called the **binomial system** — all organisms are given **one** internationally accepted scientific **name** in **Latin** that has **two parts**.

2) The **first part** of the name is the **genus** name and has a capital letter. The **second part** is the **species** name and begins with a lower case letter. E.g. using the binomial system humans are *Homo sapiens*. Names are always written in *italics* (or they're <u>underlined</u> if they're **handwritten**).

3) The binomial system helps to avoid the **confusion** of using **common names**. Scientists can **communicate** about organisms in a **standard** way that minimises confusion. E.g. Americans call a type of bird **cockatoos** and Australians call them **flaming galahs** (best said with an Australian accent), but it's the **same bird**. If the correct **scientific name** is used — *Eolophus roseicapillus* — there's no confusion.

Defining Organisms as Distinct Species Can be Quite Tricky   *AQA only*

1) Scientists can have problems when using the **definition** of a species on the previous page to decide which species an organism belongs to or if it's a new, **distinct species**.

2) This is because you can't always see their **reproductive behaviour** (you can't always tell if different organisms can reproduce to give **fertile offspring**).

3) Here are some of the **reasons** why you can't always see their reproductive behaviour:

> 1) They're **extinct**, so obviously you **can't** study their reproductive behaviour.
>
> 2) They **reproduce asexually** — they never **reproduce together** even if they belong to the same species, e.g. bacteria.
>
> 3) There are **practical** and **ethical issues** involved — you can't see if some organisms reproduce successfully in the wild (due to geography) and you can't study them in a lab (because it's unethical), e.g. humans and chimps are classed as separate species but has anyone ever tried mating them?

Evidence has been found of human/parrot reproduction.

4) Because of these problems some organisms are **classified** as one species or another using other **techniques**.

5) Scientists can now compare the **DNA** of organisms (see p. 144) to see **how related** they are, e.g. the **more** DNA they have in common the more **closely related** they are. But there's no strict cut-off to say **how much** shared DNA can be used to define a **species**. For example, **only** about 6% of human DNA **differs** from chimpanzee DNA but we are separate species.

Practice Questions

Q1 Define a species.

Q2 Describe the binomial naming system.

Exam Questions

		Phylum	Class	Order		Genus	
Humans	Animalia	Chordata	Mammalia	Primates	Hominidae	Homo	sapiens
Bonobos					Hominidae		

Q1 Define the following terms:
  a) classification   [1 mark]
  b) taxonomy   [1 mark]
  c) phylogenetics   [1 mark]

Q2 The table above shows the classification of humans. Complete the table to show the classification of the bonobo (*Pan paniscus*) — a small chimpanzee-like animal that's in the same family as humans.   [3 marks]

Q3 Give three reasons why it can be hard for scientists to define organisms as members of distinct species.   [3 marks]

Phylum — I thought that was the snot you get with a cold...

Remembering the order of the groups in the taxonomic hierarchy is about as easy as licking your elbow... try making up a mnemonic to help (like '<u>K</u>ing <u>P</u>rawns <u>C</u>an't <u>O</u>rder <u>F</u>ried <u>G</u>reen <u>S</u>ausages' for <u>K</u>ingdom, <u>P</u>hylum, <u>C</u>lass, <u>O</u>rder, <u>F</u>amily, etc.).

Classification Systems and Dichotomous Keys

These pages are for Edexcel Unit 2 and OCR Unit 2.

Classification systems and the groups organisms are placed in aren't set in stone. New technology and new evidence can lead to changes in these systems and the reclassification of organisms.

Remember — eukaryotic cells have DNA contained within a nucleus

Organisms *Can be Placed into One of* Five Kingdoms

All organisms can be placed into one of **five kingdoms** based on their **general features**:

KINGDOM	EXAMPLES	FEATURES
Prokaryotae (Monera)	bacteria	prokaryotes, single-celled, no nucleus, less than 5 µm
Protoctista	algae, protozoa	eukaryotic cells, usually live in water, single-celled or simple multicellular
Fungi	moulds, yeasts, mushrooms	eukaryotic, chitin cell wall, saprotrophic (absorb substances from dead or decaying organisms using enzymes)
Plantae	mosses, ferns, flowering plants	eukaryotic, multicellular, cell walls made of cellulose, can photosynthesise, contain chlorophyll, autotrophic (produce their own food)
Animalia	nematodes (roundworms), molluscs, insects, fish, reptiles, birds, mammals	eukaryotic, multicellular, no cell walls, heterotrophic (consume plants and animals)

Dichotomous Keys *can be used to* Identify Organisms   *OCR only*

1) **Dichotomous keys** provide a way to **identify organisms** based on **observable features** (e.g. colour, type of leaves).

2) They consist of a **series of questions**, each with **only two** possible answers. Each **answer** leads to the **name** of the organism or **another question**, and so on, until the organism is **identified**.

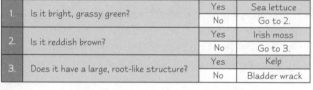

1.	Is it bright, grassy green?	Yes	Sea lettuce
		No	Go to 2.
2.	Is it reddish brown?	Yes	Irish moss
		No	Go to 3.
3.	Does it have a large, root-like structure?	Yes	Kelp
		No	Bladder wrack

3) In the **exam** you could be asked to **use** a dichotomous key to **identify** some organisms. For example, the dichotomous key shown can be used to identify seaweed.

 Using the **key** to identify this seaweed, the answer to Q1 is **yes** (it's **bright, grassy green**) — so it's **sea lettuce**.

Bright, grassy green? Yes. Sea lettuce? Not so sure.

 The answer to Q1 is **no**, but to Q2 is yes (it's **reddish brown**) — so it's **Irish moss**.

Classification Systems *are now Based on a* Range of Evidence

1) Early classification systems **only** used **observable features** (things you can see) to place organisms into groups, e.g. whether they lay eggs, can fly or can cook a mean chilli...

2) But this method has **problems**. Scientists don't always agree on the **relative importance** of different features and groups based **solely** on **physical features** may not show how **related** organisms are.

> For example, **sharks** and **whales look** quite similar and they both **live** in the **sea**. But they're **not** actually closely related.

3) Classification systems are **now** based on observable features **along** with **other evidence**.

4) The **more similar** organisms are, the **more related** they are. We now use a wide range of evidence to see **how similar**, and therefore how related, organisms are. For example:

> 1) <u>Molecular evidence</u> — the similarities in **proteins** and **DNA**. **More closely related** organisms will have **more similar** molecules. You can **compare** things like how **DNA** is **stored**, the **sequence** of DNA **bases** (see page 38) and the **sequence** of amino acids in **proteins** from different organisms. E.g. the **base sequence** for human and chimpanzee **DNA** is about 94% the **same**.
>
> 2) <u>Anatomical evidence</u> — the similarities in **structure** and **function** of different body parts.
>
> 3) <u>Behavioural evidence</u> — the similarities in **behaviour** and **social organisation** of organisms.

Classification Systems and Dichotomous Keys

New Scientific Data Can Lead to Changes in Classification Systems

1) New data about a species can influence the way that species and other species are **classified**.

2) This happens all the time as **more research** and **new technologies** (e.g. new **DNA** techniques, better **microscopes**) result in **new discoveries** being made.

3) New data has to be **evaluated** by other scientists though (to check it's **OK** — see page 2).

4) If scientists generally agree with the new data, it can lead to an **organism** being **reclassified** or lead to changes in the **classification system structure**.

EXAMPLE: Three Domains vs Five Kingdoms

A **new classification system** has been suggested because of **new evidence** (based on molecular phylogeny, see p. 140).

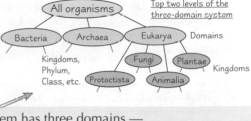

1) In the **five kingdom system** all organisms are placed into one of five kingdoms — the **largest groups** in this system.

2) In 1990, a **three domain system** was proposed. This new system has three domains — **large superkingdoms** that are **above** the kingdoms in the **taxonomic hierarchy** (see p. 140).

3) In the **three domain system**, organisms with cells that **contain a nucleus** are placed in the domain **Eukarya** (this includes four of the five kingdoms). Organisms that were in the kingdom **Prokaryotae** (which contains unicellular organisms **without a nucleus**) are separated into two domains — the **Archaea** and **Bacteria**.

4) The **lower** hierarchy stays the **same** — Domain, Kingdom, Phylum, Class, Order, Family, Genus, Species.

5) The three domain system was proposed because of **new evidence**, mainly molecular. E.g. the **Prokaryotae** were **reclassified** into **two domains** because new evidence showed **large differences** between the Archaea and Bacteria. The new evidence included:

- **Molecular evidence** — The enzyme **RNA polymerase** (needed to make RNA) is **different** in Bacteria and Archaea. **Archaea**, but **not Bacteria**, have similar **histones** (proteins that bind to DNA) to **Eukarya**.

- **Cell membrane evidence** — The **bonds** of the **lipids** (see p. 12) in the **cell membranes** of Bacteria and Archaea are **different**. The **development** and composition of **flagellae** (see p. 22) are also **different**.

6) Most scientists now **agree** that Archaea and Bacteria **evolved separately** and that Archaea are **more closely related** to Eukarya than Bacteria. The three-domain system reflects how **different** the Archaea and Bacteria are.

Practice Questions

Q1 Give two features of organisms in the kingdom Fungi.

Q2 Give two features of organisms in the kingdom Animalia.

Q3 Name three types of evidence that classification systems are based on.

Exam Questions

Q1 Use the key on the right to identify the organisms labelled A and B.
[2 marks]

		Yes	*Trichodesmium*
1.	Is it covered with hair-like filaments?	No	Go to 2.
2.	Is it unicellular and oval shaped?	Yes	*Synechococcus*
		No	Go to 3.
3.	Is it unicellular and rod shaped?	Yes	*Lyngbya*
		No	*Anabaena*

Q2 Members of the genus *Methanobacterium* are placed in the Prokaryotae kingdom in the five-kingdom classification system and in the Archaea domain in the three-domain classification system.

a) Describe three differences between organisms in the Bacteria and Archaea domains. [3 marks]

b) Describe two features that could be used to class *Methanobacterium* in the Prokaryotae kingdom. [2 marks]

Why did the starfish blush? — because the seaweed... (classic)

As soon as you've nailed down the changing world of classification systems you can run away to wherever you're imagination can take you... well, perhaps you can go and watch TV. I know that's what I'm going to do — Neighbours is on...

Classifying Species

These pages are for AQA Unit 2 only.

Early classification systems only used observable features to place organisms into groups, e.g. six heads, four toes, a love of Take That. But now a variety of evidence is used to classify organisms...

Species Can be Classified by Their DNA or Proteins

1) Species can be **classified** into different groups in the **taxonomic hierarchy** (see p. 140) based on **similarities** and **differences** in their **genes**.

2) This can be done by comparing their **DNA sequence** or by looking at their **proteins** (which are coded for by their DNA).

3) Organisms that are **more closely** related will have **more similar** DNA and proteins than distantly related organisms.

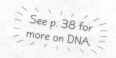 See p. 38 for more on DNA.

DNA Can be Compared Directly or by Using Hybridisation

DNA similarity can be measured by looking at the **sequence of bases** or by **DNA hybridisation**:

DNA sequencing

The **DNA** of organisms can be directly compared by looking at the **order of the bases** (As, Ts, Gs and Cs) in each. Closely related species will have a **higher percentage** of similarity in their DNA **base order**, e.g. humans and chimps share around 94%, humans and mice share about 85%.
DNA sequence comparison has led to **new classification systems** for **plants**, e.g. the classification system for flowering plants is based almost entirely on **similarities** between DNA sequences.

DNA Hybridisation

DNA Hybridisation is used to see how similar DNA is **without** sequencing it. Here's how it's done:

1) DNA from **two** different species is collected, separated into **single strands** and **mixed** together.

2) Where the **base sequences** of the DNA are the same on both strands, **hydrogen bonds** form between the base pairs by **specific base pairing**.
The more DNA bases that **hybridise** (bond) together, the more **alike** the DNA is.

3) The DNA is then **heated** to separate the strands again. **Similar DNA** will have **more hydrogen bonds** holding the two strands together so a **higher temperature** (i.e. **more energy**) will be needed to separate the strands.

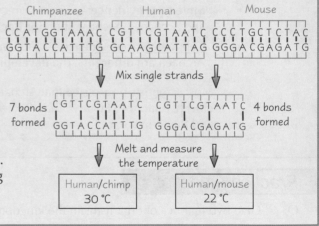

Proteins Can be Compared Directly or by Using Immunology

Similar organisms will have **similar proteins** in their cells. Proteins can be compared in **two** ways:

1) **Comparing amino acid sequence**
Proteins are made of **amino acids**. The **sequence** of amino acids in a protein is coded for by the **base sequence** in DNA (see p. 40). **Related organisms** have similar DNA sequences and so **similar amino acid sequences** in their proteins.

2) **Immunological comparisons** — Similar proteins will bind the same **antibodies** (see p. 91). E.g. if antibodies to a **human version** of a protein are added to isolated samples from some other **species**, any protein that's like the human version will also be **recognised** (bound) by that antibody.

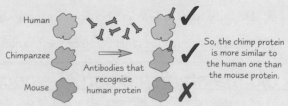

Classifying Species

You Need to be Able to **Interpret Data** on DNA and Protein **Similarities**

Here are two examples of the kind of thing you might get:

	Species A	Species B	Species C	Species D
Species A	100%	86%	42%	44%
Species B	86%	100%	51%	53%
Species C	42%	51%	100%	91%
Species D	44%	53%	91%	100%

The table on the left shows the **% similarity of DNA** using DNA sequence analysis between several species of bacteria.

The data shows that species **A** and **B** are **more closely related** to each other than they are to either C or D. Species **C** and **D** are also **more closely related** to each other than they are to either A or B.

The diagram on the right shows the **amino acid sequences** of a certain protein from three different species.

You can see that the amino acid sequences from species **A** and **B** are **very similar**. The sequence from species **C** is **very different** to any of the other sequences. This would suggest that species **A** and **B** are **more closely related**.

Courtship Behaviour can Also be Used to Classify Species

1) **Courtship behaviour** is carried out by organisms to **attract** a mate of the **right species**.

2) It can be fairly simple, e.g. **releasing chemicals**, or quite complex, e.g. a series of **displays**.

3) Courtship behaviour is **species specific** — only members of the same species will do and respond to that courtship behaviour. This prevents **interbreeding** and so makes reproduction **more successful** (as mating with the wrong species won't produce **fertile** offspring).

4) Because of this specificity, courtship behaviour can be used to **classify organisms**.

5) The more **closely related** species are, the **more similar** their courtship behaviour.

Some examples of courtship behaviour include:

1) **Fireflies** give off **pulses of light**. The pattern of flashes is specific to each species.

2) **Crickets** make **sounds** that are similar to Morse code, the code being different for different species.

3) **Male peacocks** show off their **colourful tails**. This tail pattern is only found in peacocks.

4) **Male butterflies** use **chemicals** to attract females. Only those of the correct species respond.

Geoff's jive never failed to attract a mate.

Practice Questions

Q1 Suggest two ways that DNA from two different species could be compared.

Q2 Suggest two ways that proteins from two different species could be compared.

Exam Questions

Q1 Explain how DNA hybridisation is used to analyse similarities between the DNA of two species. [5 marks]

Q2 The amino acid sequence of a specific protein was used to make comparisons between four species of animal. The results are shown on the right.

a) Which two species are the most closely related? [1 mark]

b) Which species is the most distantly related to the other three? [1 mark]

Species	Amino acid 1	Amino acid 2	Amino acid 3	Amino acid 4
Rabbit	His	Ala	Asp	Lys
Mouse	Thr	Ala	Asp	Val
Chicken	Ala	Thr	Arg	Arg
Rat	Thr	Ala	Asp	Phy

School discos — the perfect place to observe courtship behaviour...

It's important that you understand that the more similar the DNA and proteins, the more closely related (and hence the more recently diverged) two species are. This is because relatives have similar DNA, which codes for similar proteins, made of a similar sequence of amino acids. Just like you and your family — you're all alike because your DNA's similar.

Studying Biodiversity

These pages are for AQA Unit 2, Edexcel Unit 2 and OCR Unit 2.

Bet you've noticed how there are loads of different living things in the world — well that's biodiversity in a nutshell.

Biodiversity is the Variety of Organisms

Before you can sink your teeth into the real meat of biodiversity,
there are a few definitions you need to know:

1) **Biodiversity** — the **variety** of **living organisms** in an **area**.

2) **Species** — a group of **similar organisms** able to **reproduce** to give **fertile offspring**.

3) **Habitat** — the **area inhabited** by a species. It includes the **physical** factors, like the soil and temperature range, and the **living** (biotic) factors, like availability of food or the presence of predators.

Biodiversity is sometimes just called diversity.

Pete wasn't sure that the company's new increased biodiversity policy would be good for productivity.

Areas with a **high** biodiversity are those with lots of **different species**.

If you're doing Edexcel you also need to know the definition of endemism.

Endemism is when a species is **unique** to a **single place** (isn't naturally found anywhere else in the world), e.g. the **giant tortoise** is **endemic** to the Galapagos Islands — it can only be found there.

Biodiversity Can be Considered at Different Levels

1) **Species diversity** — the number of **different species** and the **abundance** of each species in an **area**. For example, a woodland could contain many different species of plants, insects, birds and mammals.

2) **Genetic diversity** — the variation of **alleles** within a species (or a population of a species). For example, human blood type is determined by a gene with four different alleles (see p. 42).

3) **Habitat diversity** — the number of **different habitats** in an **area**. For example, a coastal area could contain many different habitats — beaches, sand dunes, mudflats, salt marshes etc.

Alleles are different versions of genes.

Sampling Can be Used to Measure Species Diversity in a Habitat

Edexcel and OCR only

In most cases it'd be **too time-consuming** to count every individual organism in a **habitat**. Instead, a **sample** of the population is taken. **Estimates** about the whole habitat are based on the sample. Here's what sampling involves:

1) **Choose** an **area** to **sample** — a small area within the habitat being studied.

2) To avoid **bias** in your results, the sample should be **random** (see p. 134).
For example, if you were looking at the species in a field you could pick random sample sites by dividing the field into a **grid** and using a **random number generator** to select coordinates.

3) **Count** the number of individuals of **each species**. How you do this depends on **what** you're counting, for example:
   - For plants you'd use a **quadrat** (a frame that you place on the ground).
   - For flying insects you'd use a **sweepnet** (a net on a pole).
   - For ground insects you'd use a **pitfall trap** (a small pit that insects can't get out of).
   - For aquatic animals you'd use a **net**.

4) **Repeat** the process — take as many samples as possible. This gives a better indication of the **whole habitat**.

5) Use the results to **estimate** the total **number of individuals** or the total **number of different species** in the habitat being studied.

6) When sampling **different habitats** and comparing them, always use the **same sampling technique**.

Edexcel only
To measure **genetic diversity** (the variation of **alleles**) in a **population** you can look at two things:

1) The number of **different phenotypes** (different characteristics) in the population.

2) The **variation** in the **base sequences** of organisms' **DNA**.

Studying Biodiversity

Species Richness and Species Evenness Affect Biodiversity
Edexcel and OCR only

The **greater** the **species richness** and **species evenness** in an area, the **higher** the biodiversity.

1) **Species richness** is the number of **different species** in an area. The **higher** the number of species, the **greater** the species richness.

2) **Species evenness** is a measure of the **relative abundance** of each species in an area. The **more similar** the **population size** of each species, the **greater** the species evenness.

For Edexcel you only need to know what an index of diversity is, but for AQA or OCR you need to be able to calculate one.

Species Diversity is Measured using an Index of Diversity

1) The simplest way to measure species diversity is just to **count up** the number of **different species**.

2) But that **doesn't** take into account the **population size** of each species.

3) Species present in a habitat in very **small** numbers shouldn't be treated the same as those with **bigger** populations.

4) An **index of diversity** takes into account different population sizes (i.e. both **species richness** and **species evenness**).

5) The index of diversity in an area can be calculated using a formula:

If you're doing **AQA** you need to learn this formula for calculating the index of diversity (**d**):
$$d = \frac{N(N-1)}{\sum n(n-1)}$$
The **higher** the number, the **more diverse** the area is. If all the individuals are of the same species (i.e. no diversity) the diversity index is 1.

If you're doing **OCR** you need to learn **Simpson's Index of Diversity** (**D**):
$$D = 1 - \left(\sum \left(\frac{n}{N}\right)^2\right)$$
It always has a value **between 0 and 1**. The **closer to 1** the index is, the **more diverse** the habitat.

For both equations, n = **total number** of individuals of **one** species, N = **total number** of organisms of **all** species and $\sum$ = '**sum of**' (i.e. added together).

6) Here's a simple example of calculating the index of diversity and Simpson's Index of Diversity in a field:

- There are 3 different species of flower in this field — a red species, a white and a blue.
- There are 11 organisms altogether, so N = 11.
- There are 3 of the red species, 5 of the white and 3 of the blue.

So the index of diversity (**AQA**) for this field is:
$$d = \frac{11\,(11-1)}{3\,(3-1) + 5\,(5-1) + 3\,(3-1)} = \frac{110}{6 + 20 + 6} = 3.44$$
The field has an index of diversity of 3.44, which is fairly high.

Simpson's Index of Diversity (**OCR**) would be:
$$D = 1 - \left(\left(\frac{3}{11}\right)^2 + \left(\frac{5}{11}\right)^2 + \left(\frac{3}{11}\right)^2\right) = 1 - 0.36 = 0.64$$
The field has an index of diversity of 0.64, which is fairly high.

Practice Questions

Q1 What is endemism?

Q2 What is meant by species diversity and genetic diversity?

Exam Question

Q1 A group of students is investigating biodiversity by looking at the diversity of millipedes (small ground insects) in a habitat. They want to find out the species richness and species evenness in the area.

a) Give a definition of biodiversity. [1 mark]

b) Describe what is meant by species richness and species evenness. [2 marks]

Species richness — goldfish and money spiders top the list...

Be sure about all the definitions you need to know — there are a few similar terms here, like species richness and species evenness. As for using an index of diversity — well, sometimes I wish I was still a fresh-faced sixth-former, but this sure ain't one of them.

Factors Affecting Biodiversity

These pages are for AQA Unit 2 and OCR Unit 2. If you're doing Edexcel skip to page 156.

Human activity has an impact on local and global biodiversity — and I'm not just talking about stepping on bugs...

Current **Estimates** of **Global Biodiversity Vary**   OCR only

1) **Global biodiversity** is the **total number** of species on Earth.

2) This includes the species that have been **named** (between 1.5 and 1.75 million), and the species that are **unnamed** (many species are **undiscovered**, or are known but haven't been named).

3) Scientists **estimate** that the **total number** of species on Earth ranges from about 5 million to 100 million. Some of the most recent estimates are around 14 million. There are lots of reasons why scientists have such different ideas:

   - **Different scientists** have used **different techniques** to make their estimates.
   - Relatively **little is known** about some **groups** of organisms (e.g. bacteria and insects) — there could be **many more** than we think.
   - Biodiversity varies in **different parts** of the world — the greatest diversity is near the **equator** and it **decreases** towards the **poles**. Tropical rainforests are **largely unexplored** — this might mean current estimates of global biodiversity are **too low**.

   Scientific uncertainty makes biodiversity hard to measure.

4) Estimates of global biodiversity **change** as scientists find out new things — this is an example of the **tentative nature** of scientific knowledge.

Climate Change Affects Biodiversity...   OCR only

1) **Climate change** is the **variation** in the Earth's climate, e.g. things like changes in **temperature** and **rainfall patterns**.

2) It occurs **naturally**, but the **scientific consensus** is that the climate change we're **experiencing at the moment** is **caused** by **humans** increasing emissions of **greenhouse gases** (such as **carbon dioxide**).

3) Greenhouse gases cause **global warming** (**increasing global average temperature**), which causes **other types** of climate change, e.g. changing rainfall patterns.

4) Climate change will affect **different areas** of the world in **different ways** — some places will get **warmer**, some **colder**, some **wetter** and others **drier**. All of these are likely to **affect global biodiversity**:

   - Most species need a particular climate to survive.
   - A change in climate may mean that an area that was previously **inhabitable** becomes **uninhabitable** (and **vice versa**).
   - This may cause an **increase** or **decrease** in the **range** of some species (the area in which they live). This could increase or decrease biodiversity.
   - Some species may be forced to **migrate** to a more suitable area, causing a change in **species distribution**. Migrations usually **decrease** biodiversity in the areas the species migrate from, and **increase** biodiversity in the areas they migrate to.
   - If there isn't a suitable habitat to migrate to, the species is a plant and **can't migrate**, or if the change is **too fast**, the species may become **extinct**. This will **decrease** biodiversity.

   | Range change example |
   The southern **range** limit of the **Sooty Copper Butterfly** has **moved** 60 miles north in recent decades.

   | Extinction example |
   Corals die if water temperature **changes** by just one or two degrees. In 1998 a coral reef near Panama was badly damaged because the water **temperature** had **increased** — at least one species of coral became **extinct** as a result.

...the Spread of Disease...   OCR only

Changing climate may also contribute to the **spread of disease**, for example:

1) The **ranges** of some **insects** that **carry disease** might become **greater**. E.g. as areas become **warmer** and **wetter** insects like mosquitoes, which can carry **malaria**, will spread into areas that were **previously uninhabitable**, **bringing the disease** with them. This could lead to an increase in biodiversity, though the **spread of diseases** could **reduce biodiversity**.

2) Warmer and wetter conditions may also encourage the spread of **fungal diseases**. This could also lead to an increase or decrease in biodiversity.

Factors Affecting Biodiversity

...and *Agricultural Patterns*   OCR only

Changes in **temperature**, **rainfall**, the **timing of the seasons**, and the **frequency of flood** and **drought** will affect **patterns of agriculture**. This may also affect biodiversity:

1) Land that was **previously unsuitable** becomes **available** for agriculture — areas that were previously too hot or too dry to support much biodiversity can be farmed, **increasing** the biodiversity in an area.

2) **Different crops** need **different conditions** so, as the climate in an area changes, so will the **crops grown**. This could **disrupt food chains** — some **existing species** will be left **without** a source of food, and new food sources will be provided for **other species**. This could **increase** or **decrease** biodiversity in an area.

3) **Extreme weather events** and **unexpected conditions**, such as a **flood** or a **drought** or a change in the **timing of the seasons**, might result in **crop failure**. This could **disrupt food chains** and **decrease biodiversity**.

Deforestation and *Agriculture Decrease Biodiversity*   AQA only

DEFORESTATION

We cut down forests to get **wood** and **create land** for **farming** and **settlements**. Here are some reasons why this affects biodiversity:

1) Deforestation **directly** reduces the **number** of **trees** and sometimes the **number** of **different tree species**.

2) Deforestation also **destroys habitats**, so some species could lose their **shelter** and **food source**. This means that these species will **die** or be forced to **migrate** to another suitable area, further **reducing** biodiversity.

3) The migration of organisms into increasingly smaller areas of remaining forest may **temporarily increase biodiversity** in those areas.

AGRICULTURE

Farmers try to **maximise the amount of food** that they can produce from a given area of land. Many of the methods they use reduce biodiversity.

1) **Woodland clearance** — this is done to **increase** the **area** of farmland. This **reduces** biodiversity for the same reasons as **deforestation** (see left).

2) **Hedgerow removal** — this is also done to **increase** the **area** of farmland by turning **lots of small fields** into **fewer large fields**. This **reduces** biodiversity for the same reasons as **woodland clearance** and deforestation.

3) **Monoculture** — this is when farmers grow fields containing only **one type of plant**. A **single type** of plant will support **fewer species**, so biodiversity is **reduced**.

4) **Pesticides** — these are chemicals that **kill** organisms (**pests**) that feed on **crops**. This **reduces** biodiversity by **directly killing** the pests. Also, any species that feed on the pests will **lose** a food source.

5) **Herbicides** — these are chemicals that kill **unwanted plants** (**weeds**). This **reduces** plant diversity and could **reduce** the number of organisms that feed on the weeds.

Practice Questions

Q1 Suggest two ways a species might survive if the climate in an area changes.

Q2 Describe how climate change could affect the spread of disease.

Q3 Why does deforestation lead to reduced biodiversity?

Exam Questions

Q1 Suggest three reasons why current estimates of global biodiversity vary so widely.   [3 marks]

Q2 Give five agricultural practices that directly reduce biodiversity and for each one explain how it reduces it.   [5 marks]

Mosquitoes — coming soon to a climate near you...

All of this makes the future look a bit bleak — plagues of mosquitoes in places they never used to be, trees being cut down willy-nilly and farmers running riot — I bet you thought this section was going to be all about fluffy animals.

Interpreting Biodiversity Data

These pages are for AQA Unit 2.

Examiners are pretty fond of interpreting data, which means... wait for it... drum roll please... that you have to be pretty good at it too. Don't worry though — a bit of practice and a smidgen of common sense and you'll be fine.

Human Activity in an Area Has Benefits and Risks

Benefits

1) **Wood** and **land** for homes to be built.
2) Local areas become more **developed** by attracting businesses.

Deforestation

Risks

1) **Biodiversity** is **reduced** — species could become **extinct**.
2) Less **carbon dioxide** is stored because there are fewer plants and trees, which contributes to **climate change**.
3) Many **medicines** come from organisms found in rainforests — possible future discoveries are **lost**.
4) **Natural beauty** is **lost**.

Benefits

1) **More food** can be produced.
2) Food is **cheaper** to produce, so food **prices** are **lower**.
3) Local areas become more **developed** by attracting businesses.

Agriculture

Risks

1) **Biodiversity** is **reduced** — because of **monoculture**, **woodland and hedgerow clearance**, **herbicide** and **pesticide use** (see previous page).
2) **Natural beauty** is **lost**.

You Might Have to Interpret Data About How Human Activity Affects Biodiversity

You might have to interpret some data in the exam. Here are three examples of the kind of thing you might get:

Example 1 — Herbicides

Herbicides kill **unwanted plants** (weeds) whilst leaving **crops unharmed**.
The crops can then **grow better** because they're not **competing for resources** with weeds.
The graph below shows plant diversity in an **untreated** field and a field **treated annually** with **herbicide**.

Describe the data:

• Plant diversity in the **untreated field** showed a **slight increase** in the seven years. Plant diversity **decreased** a lot in the **treated field** when the **herbicide** was **first applied**. The diversity then **recovered** throughout each year, but was **reduced again** by **each** annual application of herbicide.

Explain the data:

• When the herbicide was applied, the weeds were **killed**, **reducing biodiversity**. **In between** applications, biodiversity **increased** as **new weeds** grew. These were then killed again by each annual application of herbicide.

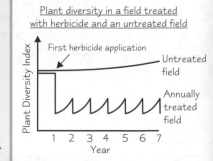

Plant diversity in a field treated with herbicide and an untreated field

Example 2 — Skylark Population

Since the 1970s, farmers have been planting many crops in the **winter** instead of the **spring** to **maximise production**. This means there are **fewer** fields left as **stubble** over the winter. This is a problem because **skylarks** like to **nest** in fields with **stubble**. The graph below shows how the skylark population has **changed** in the UK since 1970.

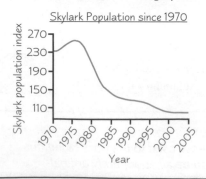

Describe the data:

• Skylark diversity showed a **small increase** from **1970** to the **late 1970s**. Since the late 1970s skylark diversity has **decreased** a lot. The skylark diversity has remained roughly **constant** from **2000** to **2005**.

Explain the data:

• With **fewer nesting sites** available, **fewer offspring** could be successfully raised, leading to a reduction in the number of skylarks.

Interpreting Biodiversity Data

Example 3 — Loss of Rainforest

The graph below shows the results of a study that **compared** the **biodiversity** in a **rainforest** with the biodiversity in a **deforested area** that had been **cleared** for agricultural use.

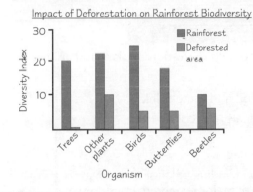

Impact of Deforestation on Rainforest Biodiversity

Describe the data:

- For **all types** of organism studied, **biodiversity** is **higher** in the **rainforest** than in the **deforested area**.
- **Deforestation** has **reduced** the species diversity of **trees** the most.

Explain the data:

- Many organisms **can't adapt** to the **change in habitat** and must **migrate** or **die** — **reducing** biodiversity in the area.
- Reduced **tree diversity** leads to a reduction in the diversity of **all other organisms**.

Society Uses Biodiversity Data to Make Decisions

Biodiversity data can be used to see which **species or areas** are being **affected** by **human activity**. This information can then be used by **society** to **make decisions** about human activities. For example:

Scientific Finding	Decision Made
Fewer hedgerows reduces biodiversity.	The UK government offers farmers money to encourage them to plant hedgerows, and to cover the cost of not growing crops on these areas.
Deforestation reduces biodiversity.	Some governments encourage sustainable logging (a few trees are taken from lots of different areas and young trees are planted to replace them).
Human development reduces biodiversity.	Many governments are setting up protected areas (e.g. national parks) where human development is restricted to help conserve biodiversity.
Some species are facing extinction.	Breeding programmes in zoos help to increase the numbers of endangered species in a safe environment before reintroducing them to the wild.

Practice Questions

Q1 Describe one risk associated with deforestation.

Q2 Describe one benefit of agricultural activities.

Exam Question

Q1 The graph on the right shows the results from a study conducted into wild bird populations in the UK between 1970 and 2006. It shows the pattern of change for woodland and farmland species.

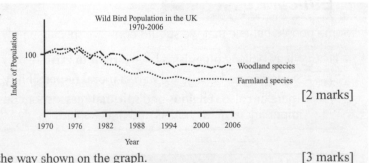

a) Describe the data. [2 marks]

b) Human activity has significantly affected wild bird populations. Suggest reasons why the woodland and farmland species have changed in the way shown on the graph. [3 marks]

c) Discuss the potential benefits of agriculture and deforestation and the associated risks to biodiversity. [8 marks]

Diver-city — it's a wonderful place where you get to jump off stuff...

Interpreting data is just about understanding what the graphs or tables are telling you. Describing it is simple — just say what you see. Then you've usually got to explain it — say what the reasons might be for what you've described. After that they might ask you to do a little song, or a little dance, or maybe jump through a couple of hoops...

Importance of Biodiversity

These pages are for OCR Unit 2 only. If you're doing AQA you know all you need to know about biodiversity. Put your feet up.

You're probably wondering what all this fuss about biodiversity is for. Well, biodiversity provides us with the means to make nice clothes and good food, so it's a pretty good idea not to reduce it.

Maintaining Biodiversity is Important for Economic Reasons...

Many species of animals and plants are important to the **global economy**. Products derived from plant and animal species are traded on a local and global scale, they include things like...

1) **Food** and **drink** — plants and animals are the source of almost all **food** and some **drinks**.

2) **Clothing** — a lot of **fibres** and **fabrics** are made from plants and animals (e.g. cotton from plants and leather from animals).

3) **Drugs** — many are made from compounds from plants (see the next page).

4) **Fuels** — we use a number of organisms to produce **renewable** fuels, including ethanol and biogas. Fossil fuels are **non-renewable** (they'll run out), so other sources are of **major economic importance**.

5) **Other industrial materials** — a huge variety of other materials are produced from plant and animal species, including **wood**, **paper**, **dyes**, **adhesives**, **oils**, **rubber** and chemicals such as **pesticides**.

It's important to conserve all the organisms we currently use to make products, as well as those we **don't currently use** — they may provide us with **new products** in the **future**, e.g. new drugs for diseases we can't yet cure.

...Ecological Reasons...

The ecological reasons for maintaining biodiversity are all down to the **complex relationships** between **organisms** and their **environments**. The loss of **just one species** can have pretty **drastic effects**, for example:

1) **Disruption** of **food chains**, e.g. some species of bear feed on salmon, which feed on herring. If the number of herring decline it can affect **both** the salmon and the bear populations.

2) **Disruption** of **nutrient cycles**, e.g. decomposers like worms improve the **quality of soil** by recycling nutrients. If worm numbers decline, soil quality will be affected. This will affect the **growth** of plants and the **amount of food** available to animals.

3) **Loss** of **habitats**, e.g. hedgerows are **wildlife corridors** — they enable organisms to move between different habitats **safely**. If they're removed species can become **isolated** and availability of **food** and **nesting sites** for many species will be **reduced**.

4) **Habitat destruction** can also affect **climate**, e.g. CO_2 is stored in trees and bogs — the destruction of forests and peat bogs is contributing to **climate change** (see p. 148).

All these ecological reasons also have knock-on economic effects.

...Ethical Reasons...

Some people believe that we should conserve species simply because it's the **right thing to do**.

1) Many believe organisms have a **right to exist** — they shouldn't become **extinct** as a result of our activities.

2) Some people believe we have a **moral responsibility** to conserve biodiversity for **future** human generations.

3) There are also **religious** and **spiritual** reasons for conservation — **harmony** with the **natural world** is important to many beliefs and philosophies.

...and Aesthetic Reasons

Others believe we should conserve biodiversity because it brings **joy** to millions of people.

1) Areas **rich** in biodiversity provide a pleasant, **attractive environment** that people can enjoy.

2) The more biodiversity in an area the more **visitors** the area is likely to **attract** — this also has economic advantages.

Importance of Biodiversity

Maintaining Biodiversity is Important to Agriculture...

In addition to all those economic, ecological, ethical and aesthetic reasons you now know all about, maintaining the biodiversity of wild plants and animals has some **benefits** for **agriculture**.

Pollinators
Many fruit and vegetable crops are **pollinated by insects** such as bees and butterflies. The higher the diversity of insects the more pollinators there are.

A source of food
Many species are used as **food sources** for humans and livestock. The more different species there are the more possible sources there are to **choose from**.

Protection against disasters
The majority of our food comes from **only a few species** of plants — if a disease or pest affects these few, our food supply is **at risk**. E.g. in 1845 **only two** varieties of potato were planted in Ireland. A **disease** destroyed both types of potato crop, causing **famine**. The **more** crop varieties that are used, the less chance there is that **all** the crops will be destroyed.

Maintaining biodiversity is important to **agriculture** because it provides:

Pest control
A number of animals like frogs, birds and hedgehogs are **natural predators** of crop pests like slugs. The more of these organisms there are the **less pests** there will be.

New varieties
Plant varieties are needed for **cross-breeding**. Wild plants can be bred with domesticated plants to produce **new varieties** with **improved characteristics**, e.g. increased disease resistance or faster growth. New varieties of crops can also be **bred** to cope with **climate change**. The more varieties of crop there are the **more characteristics** there are **to choose from**.

...and for Medical Science

Biodiversity should be preserved because **new medicines** can be derived from **living organisms**.

1) Many **medicinal drugs** are manufactured **using natural compounds** found in **plants**, **animals** or **microorganisms**. E.g. **penicillin** is obtained from a **fungus**.

2) Only a **small proportion** of organisms have been **investigated** so far, so it's possible that plants or microorganisms **exist** that contain compounds that could be used to treat **currently incurable** diseases, such as AIDS.

3) Possible **sources of drugs** need to be **protected** by **maintaining biodiversity**. If we **don't** protect them, some species could **die** out before their medicinal properties are **discovered**.

Practice Questions

Q1 Give an economic reason for the conservation of biodiversity.

Q2 Give an ethical reason for the conservation of biodiversity.

Q3 Give an aesthetic reason for the conservation of biodiversity.

Exam Question

Q1 Explain why decreasing biodiversity could have adverse ecological implications. [4 marks]

Q2 Briefly explain why maintaining biodiversity is important to the agricultural industry. [5 marks]

Hippy or not — better start hugging those trees...

So, it turns out biodiversity is pretty important. Without it, not only would your life lack its little luxuries (like toilet paper with aloe vera, and fancy designer clothes), just surviving would be tricky — there'd be nothing to eat and fewer drugs to treat you when you're ill. Make sure you learn all the reasons for maintaining biodiversity — they might just crop up in the exam.

Conservation and Biodiversity

These pages are for OCR Unit 2 only.

I'm sure no animals like being snatched from the African plains and taken to live in a safari park in Kidderminster, but sometimes they just don't know what's best for them...

In Situ Conservation Keeps Species in Their Natural Habitat

In situ conservation means **on site** — it involves protecting species in their **natural habitat**. Conservation is important to **ensure the survival** of **endangered species** — species which are at risk of **extinction** because of a **low** population, or a **threatened habitat**. Methods of *in situ* conservation include:

1) Establishing **protected areas** such as **national parks** and **nature reserves** — habitats and species are protected in these areas by **restricting urban development**, **industrial development** and **farming**.

2) **Controlling** or **preventing the introduction** of species that **threaten** local biodiversity. For example, grey squirrels are not native to Britain. They **compete** with the native red squirrel and have caused a population **decline**. So they're controlled in some areas.

3) **Protecting habitats** — e.g. controlling water levels to conserve wetlands and coppicing (trimming trees) to conserve woodlands. This allows organisms to **continue living** in their **natural habitat**.

4) **Restoring damaged areas** — such as a coastline polluted by an oil spill.

5) **Promoting** particular species — this could be by protecting **food sources** or **nesting sites**.

6) Giving **legal protection** to **endangered species**, e.g. making it illegal to kill them (see next page).

Jim reckoned he'd seen the last of those red squirrels — but he hadn't counted on their friends turning up.

The advantage of *in situ* conservation is that often both the **species** and their **habitat** are conserved. **Larger populations** can be protected and it's **less disruptive** than removing organisms from their habitats. The chances of the population **recovering** are **greater** than with *ex situ* methods (see below). But, it can be **difficult to control** some factors that are **threatening** a species (such as poaching, predators or climate change).

Ex Situ Conservation Removes Species from Their Natural Habitat

Ex situ conservation means **off site** — it involves protecting a species by **removing** part of the population from a **threatened habitat** and placing it in a **new location**. *Ex situ* conservation is often a **last resort**. Methods of *ex situ* conservation include:

1) **Relocating** an organism to a **safer area**, e.g. five white rhinos were recently relocated from the Congo to Kenya because they were in danger from **poachers** who kill them for their ivory.

2) **Breeding** organisms in **captivity** then **reintroducing** them to the wild when they are **strong enough**, e.g. sea eagles have been reintroduced to Britain through a captive breeding programme. Breeding is carried out in **animal sanctuaries** and **zoos**.

3) **Botanic gardens** are controlled environments used to grow a variety of **rare** plants for the purposes of **conservation**, **research**, **display** and **education**. **Endangered** plant species as well as species that are **extinct in the wild** can be grown and **reintroduced** into suitable habitats.

4) **Seed banks** — seeds can be frozen and stored in seed banks for over a century without losing their **fertility**. Seed banks provide a useful source of seeds if **natural reserves** are **destroyed**, for example by **disease** or other **natural disasters**.

The advantages of *ex situ* conservation are that it can be used to protect individual animals in a **controlled environment** — things like predation and hunting can be managed more easily. It can also be used to **reintroduce** species that have **left an area**. But, there are disadvantages — usually only a **small number** of individuals can be cared for. It can be **difficult** and **expensive** to create and **sustain** the **right environment**. *Ex situ* conservation is usually **less successful** than *in situ* methods — many species can't **breed successfully** in captivity, or don't **adapt** to their new environment when moved to a new location.

Conservation and Biodiversity

International Cooperation is Important in Species Conservation

Information about **threats** to biodiversity needs to be **shared** and countries need to decide on **conservation methods** and **implement them together**. Here are a couple of examples of successful international cooperation:

Rio Convention on Biodiversity

1) It aims to **develop international strategies** on the conservation of biodiversity and how to use animal and plant resources in a **sustainable** way.

2) The convention made it part of **international law** that conserving biodiversity is **everyone's responsibility**.

3) It also provides **guidance** to governments on how to conserve biodiversity.

CITES Agreement

1) CITES (**Convention** on **International Trade** in **Endangered Species**) is an agreement designed to increase **international cooperation** in **regulating trade** in wild animal and plant specimens.

2) The member countries all agreed to make it **illegal** to **kill** endangered species.

3) The agreement helps to **conserve** species by **limiting** trade through **licensing**, and by making it **illegal** to trade in products made from endangered animals (such as rhino ivory and leopard skins).

4) It's also designed to **raise awareness** of threats to biodiversity through **education**.

International cooperation is really **important** — it'd be pointless making hunting endangered species illegal in one country if poachers could just go and hunt them in another country.

Environmental Impact Assessments are Used to Inform Planning Decisions

An **Environmental Impact Assessment** (**EIA**) is an assessment of the **impact** a development project (such as building a new shopping centre or power station) might have on the environment. It involves:

1) **Estimating** biodiversity on the project site and **evaluating** how the development might **affect** biodiversity.

2) **Identifying** ways that biodiversity could be **conserved**.

3) Identifying threatened or **endangered species** on the project site and the **laws** relating to their conservation.

4) Deciding on **planning stipulations** — measures that will have to be implemented if the project proceeds, e.g. **relocating** or **protecting** endangered species.

Local authorities are often under pressure from **conservationists** who argue that developments **damage** the environment and **disturb** wildlife — they feel that habitats should be **left alone**.

Environmental impact assessments ensure that **decision makers** consider the **environmental impact** of development projects — they're used by local authorities to decide **if** and **how** projects will proceed.

Practice Questions

Q1 Describe how botanic gardens and seed banks help in the conservation of biodiversity.

Q2 What is CITES and how does it help to conserve endangered species?

Q3 Explain what environmental impact assessments are and describe how they are used.

Exam Question

Q1 The hawksbill turtle is an endangered species of sea turtle threatened by hunting and loss of nesting sites. They have slow reproductive, growth and development rates and their numbers are in rapid decline.

a) Suggest how the hawksbill turtle could be conserved by *in situ* and *ex situ* conservation methods. [5 marks]

b) Describe the disadvantages of using *ex situ* conservation methods. [4 marks]

c) Suggest why international cooperation is important to the conservation of the hawksbill turtle. [1 mark]

The path of true conservation ne'er did run smooth...

I'm sure the animals being forcibly removed from their homes are just as bemused as you are right now but I'm afraid it's another case of having to learn the facts. Plain and simple. Don't be put off by things like 'in' or 'ex' situ — that's just a way of saying 'on' or 'off' site that makes people feel clever when they say them. In fact, I'm feeling rather clever right now.

Conservation and Biodiversity

These pages are for Edexcel Unit 2 only.

Places like zoos and seedbanks help preserve biodiversity through conservation — they help species that are endangered get out of the woods, or back into the woods, depending on how you look at it...

Zoos and Seedbanks Help Conserve Endangered Species

1) The **extinction** of a **species**, or the loss of **genetic diversity** within a species (see p. 146), causes a **reduction** in **global biodiversity**.

2) Some species have **already become extinct** (e.g. the dodo) and there are lots of **endangered species** — species that are at **risk of extinction** because of a **low population** or a **threatened habitat**.

3) **Conservation** involves the **protection** and **management** of endangered species.

4) **Zoos** and **seedbanks** help to conserve endangered species and conserve genetic diversity.

Seedbanks Store Seeds from Plants That are Endangered

1) A **seedbank** is a **store** of lots of **seeds** from lots of **different species** of **plant**.

2) They help to conserve biodiversity by storing the seeds of **endangered** plants.

3) If the plants become extinct in the wild the stored seeds can be used to **grow new plants**.

4) Seedbanks also help to conserve **genetic diversity**. For some species they store a **range** of seeds from plants with **different characteristics** (and so **different alleles**), e.g. seeds from tall sunflowers and seeds from short sunflowers.

Polly had enough seeds in the bank for a fancy new perch.

5) The **work** of seedbanks involves:

- Creating the **cool**, **dry conditions** needed for storage. This means seeds can be stored for **a long time**.
- **Testing** seeds for **viability** (the **ability** to grow into a plant). Seeds don't last forever so periodically they are **planted**, **grown** and **new seeds** are harvested to put back into storage.

6) There are **advantages** and **disadvantages** to using seedbanks:

Advantages

1) It's **cheaper** to store seeds than to store **fully grown plants**.

2) **Larger numbers** of seeds **can be stored** than grown plants because they need **less space**.

3) **Less labour** is required to look after seeds than plants.

4) Seeds can be **stored anywhere**, as long as it's cool and dry. Plants would need the **conditions** from their **original habitat**.

5) Seeds are **less likely** to be damaged by **disease**, **natural disaster** or **vandalism** than plants.

Disadvantages

1) Testing the seeds for **viability** can be **expensive** and **time-consuming**.

2) It would be **too expensive** to store **all types** of seed and **regularly** test them all for viability.

3) It may be **difficult to collect** seeds from some plants as they may grow in **remote locations**.

Zoos have Captive Breeding Programmes to Help Endangered Species

1) Captive breeding programmes involve breeding animals in **controlled environments**.

2) Species that are **endangered**, or already **extinct in the wild**, can be **bred together** in zoos to help **increase their numbers**, e.g. pandas are bred in captivity because their numbers are **critically low** in the wild.

3) There are some problems with captive breeding programmes though.

1) Animals can have **problems breeding** outside their **natural habitat**, which can be hard to **recreate** in a zoo. For example, pandas do not reproduce as successfully in captivity as they do in the wild.

2) Many people think it's **cruel** to keep animals in captivity, even if it's done to prevent them becoming extinct.

Conservation and Biodiversity

Organisms from *Zoos* and *Seedbanks* can be *Reintroduced* to the *Wild*

1) The **reintroduction** of plants grown from seedbanks or animals bred in zoos can **increase** their **numbers in the wild**, helping to **conserve** their numbers or bring them **back** from the **brink of extinction**.

2) This could also help **organisms** that rely on these plants or animals for **food**, or as part of their **habitat**.

3) The reintroduction of plants and animals also contributes to **restoring habitats** that have been **lost**, e.g. rainforests that have been cut down.

4) Reintroducing organisms to the wild can cause problems though:

> **Example**
>
> The Californian condor was **nearly extinct** in the wild (only 22 birds were left). Thanks to **captive breeding programmes** there are now around 300, half of which have been **reintroduced** to the wild.

> 1) Reintroduced organisms could bring **new diseases** to habitats, **harming** other organisms **living there**.
>
> 2) Reintroduced animals may not **behave as they would** if they'd been **raised in the wild**. E.g. they may have problems **finding food** or **communicating** with wild members of their species.

Seedbanks and Zoos Contribute to Scientific Research

Seedbanks

1) Scientists can study how plant species can be **successfully grown** from seeds. This is useful for **reintroducing** them to the wild.

2) Seedbanks can be used to grow endangered plants for use in **medical research**, as **new crops** or for **new materials**. This means we don't have to **remove** endangered plants from the wild.

3) A **disadvantage** is that **only** studying plants from seeds in a seedbank limits the data to **small, interbred populations**. So the information gained may not be **representative** of wild plants.

Zoos

1) Research in zoos **increases knowledge** about the **behaviour**, **physiology** and **nutritional needs** of animals. This can **contribute** to conservation efforts in the wild.

2) Zoos can carry out research that's **not possible** for some species **in the wild**, e.g. **nutritional** or **reproductive studies**.

3) A **disadvantage** is that animals **in captivity** may **act differently** to those in the wild.

Zoos and Seedbanks Help to Educate People about Conserving Biodiversity

Educating people about endangered species and reduced biodiversity helps to **raise public awareness** and **interest** in conserving biodiversity:

1) Zoos let people get **close** to organisms, **increasing** their **enthusiasm** for conservation work.

2) Seedbanks contribute to education by **providing training** and setting up **local seedbanks** all round the world. For example, the **Millennium Seed Bank Project** aims to conserve seeds in their **original country**.

Practice Questions

Q1 What is conservation?

Q2 Suggest two advantages of storing seeds in a seedbank, rather than storing grown plants.

Exam Question

Q1 The sand lizard is a threatened species in the UK. Captive breeding and reintroduction programmes are being used to increase their numbers in the wild. Suggest four problems that could be involved with the captive breeding and reintroduction of sand lizards to the wild.

[4 marks]

The bank of seeds — high interest rates and 0% on branch transfers...

Zoos do a bit more than you thought — in fact they're just a front for all the covert operations to support conservation. Well, they're not that covert — there's a page here all about them actually. Sigh, I do try and make life more exciting...

Xylem and Phloem

This section is for AQA Unit 2 and OCR Unit 1 only. If you're doing AQA you can skip to page 160.

A whole section on transport in plants... just what I always dreamed of... you too? Oh good, because you need to learn it all for your exam.

Multicellular Plants Need Transport Systems

1) Plant cells need substances like **water**, **minerals** and **sugars** to live. They also need to **get rid of waste substances**.

2) Like animals, plants are **multicellular** so have a **small surface area : volume ratio** (see page 100).

3) Plants could exchange substances by **direct diffusion** (from the outer surface to the cells), but that would be **too slow**.

4) So plants **need transport systems** to move substances to and from individual cells **quickly**.

Plants also need <u>carbon dioxide</u>, but this enters at the leaves (where it's needed).

Two Types of Tissue are Involved in Transport in Plants

Xylem tissue transports **water** and **mineral ions**. Phloem tissue transports **dissolved substances**, like **sugars**. Xylem and phloem are found **throughout** a plant — they **transport materials** to all parts. **Where** they're found in each part is connected to the **xylem's** other function — **support**:

1) In a **root**, the xylem and phloem are in the **centre** to provide support for the root as it **pushes** through the soil.

2) In the **stems**, the xylem and phloem are **near the outside** to provide a sort of 'scaffolding' that reduces bending.

3) In a **leaf**, xylem and phloem make up a **network of veins** which support the thin leaves.

Emma had been through 12 rolls but she still couldn't find any phloem.

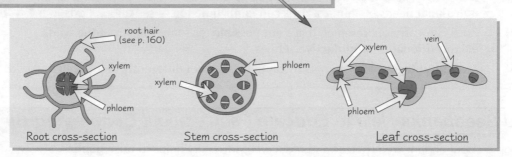

Root cross-section   Stem cross-section   Leaf cross-section

Xylem Vessels are Adapted for Transporting Water and Mineral Ions

Xylem is a **tissue** made from several **different cell types**.
You need to learn about **xylem vessels** — the part of xylem tissue that actually transports the water and ions. Xylem vessels are adapted for their **function**:

1) Xylem vessels are very **long**, **tube-like** structures formed from cells (**vessel elements**) joined end to end.

2) There are **no end walls** on these cells, making an **uninterrupted tube** that allows water to pass up through the middle easily.

3) The cells are **dead**, so they contain **no cytoplasm**.

4) Their walls are **thickened** with a **woody** substance called **lignin**, which helps to **support** the xylem vessels and stops them **collapsing inwards**.

5) The amount of lignin **increases** as the cell gets **older**.

6) **Water** and **ions** move **into** and **out of** the vessels through **small pits** in the walls where there's **no lignin**.

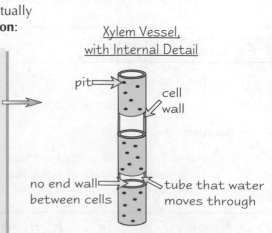

<u>Xylem Vessel, with Internal Detail</u>

pit

cell wall

no end wall between cells

tube that water moves through

Xylem and Phloem

Phloem Tissue *is Adapted for* Transporting Solutes

1) Phloem tissue transports **solutes** (dissolved substances), mainly sugars like sucrose, around plants.
2) Like xylem, phloem is formed from cells arranged in **tubes**.
3) But, unlike xylem, it's purely a **transport tissue** — it **isn't** used for support as well.
4) Phloem tissue contains **phloem fibres**, **phloem parenchyma**, **sieve tube elements** and **companion cells**.
5) **Sieve tube elements** and **companion cells** are the most important cell types in phloem for **transport**:

1 Sieve Tube Elements

1) These are **living cells** that form the tube for **transporting solutes** through the plant.
2) They are joined **end to end** to form **sieve tubes**.
3) The 'sieve' parts are the **end walls**, which have lots of **holes** in them to allow **solutes** to pass through.
4) Unusually for living cells, sieve tube elements have **no nucleus**, a **very thin** layer of **cytoplasm** and **few organelles**.
5) The cytoplasm of adjacent cells is **connected** through the holes in the sieve plates.

2 Companion Cells

1) The **lack** of a **nucleus** and **other organelles** in sieve tube elements means that they **can't survive** on their own.
2) So there's a **companion cell** for **every** sieve tube element.
3) Companion cells carry out the living functions for **both** themselves and their sieve cells. For example, they provide the **energy** for the **active transport** of solutes.

Phloem Tissue

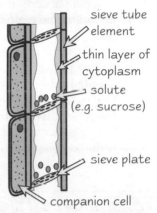

sieve tube element

thin layer of cytoplasm

solute (e.g. sucrose)

sieve plate

companion cell

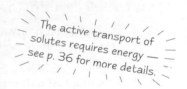

The active transport of solutes requires energy — see p. 36 for more details.

Practice Questions

Q1 Why do multicellular plants need transport systems?

Q2 State two functions of xylem vessels in plants.

Q3 What is the name of the substance that thickens the walls of xylem vessels?

Q4 What is the function of phloem tissue?

Q5 What is the function of companion cells?

Exam Questions

Q1 Describe the distribution of the xylem and phloem tissue in stems, roots and leaves.
Explain how this distribution is linked to the support function of the xylem. [6 marks]

Q2 Describe how the structure of xylem vessels relates to their function. [8 marks]

Sieve tube — WLTM like-minded cell for companionship and maybe more...

Sieve tube elements sound a bit feeble to me — not being able to survive on their own, and all that. Anyway, it's vital your mind doesn't wander on this page, because the structures and functions of some of these cell types are quite similar. It can be easy to get mixed up if you haven't learnt it properly, so take the time now to sort out which cell type does what.

Water Transport

These pages are for AQA Unit 2 and OCR Unit 1.

Water enters a plant through its roots and eventually, if it's not used, exits via the leaves. "Ah-ha", I hear you say, "but how does it flow upwards, against gravity?" Well that, my friends, is a mystery that's about to be explained...

Water Enters a Plant through its Root Hair Cells

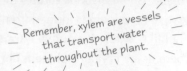
Remember, xylem are vessels that transport water throughout the plant.

1) Water has to get from the **soil**, through the **root** and into the **xylem** to be transported around the plant.

2) The bit of the root that absorbs water is covered in **root hairs**. These **increase** the root's **surface area**, speeding up water uptake.

3) Once it's absorbed, the water has to get through **the root cortex**, including the **endodermis**, to reach the xylem (see below).

4) Water is drawn into the roots down a **water potential gradient**:

<u>Cross-Section of a Root</u>

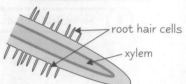
root hair cells
xylem

> Water always moves from areas of **higher water potential** to areas of **lower water potential** — it goes down a **water potential gradient**. The **soil** around roots generally has a **high water potential** (i.e. there's lots of water there) and **leaves** have a **lower water potential** (because water constantly **evaporates** from them). This creates a water potential gradient that keeps water moving through the plant in the right direction, **from roots to leaves**.

Water Moves Through the Root into the Xylem...

Water travels through the **roots** (via the **root cortex**) into the **xylem** by **two** different paths:

1) The **symplast pathway** — goes through the **living** parts of cells — the **cytoplasm**. The cytoplasm of neighbouring cells connect through **plasmodesmata** (small gaps in the cell walls).

2) The **apoplast pathway** — goes through the **non-living** parts of the cells — the **cell walls**. The walls are very absorbent and water can simply **diffuse** through them, as well as passing through the spaces between them.

The prison had been strangely quiet ever since plasmodesmata were installed.

> • When water in the **apoplast pathway** gets to the **endodermis** cells in the root, its path is blocked by a **waxy strip** in the cell walls, called the **Casparian strip**. Now the water has to take the **symplast pathway**.
>
> • This is useful, because it means the water has to go through a **cell membrane**. Cell membranes are able to control whether or not substances in the water get through (see p. 30).
>
> • Once past this barrier, the water moves into the **xylem**.

3) Both pathways are used, but the main one is the **apoplast pathway** because it provides the **least resistance**.

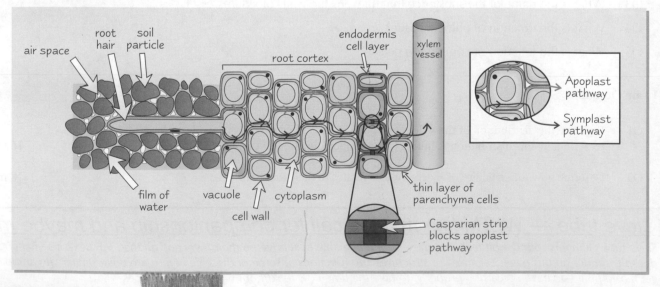

Water Transport

...then **Up** the **Xylem** and **Out** at the **Leaves**

1) **Xylem vessels** transport the water **all around** the plant.

2) At the **leaves**, water leaves the xylem and moves into the cells mainly by the **apoplast pathway**.

3) Water **evaporates** from the cell walls into the **spaces** between cells in the leaf.

4) When the **stomata** (tiny pores in the surface of the leaf) open, the water moves out of the leaf (down the **water potential gradient**) into the **surrounding air**.

5) The loss of water from a plant's surface is called **transpiration** (see next page).

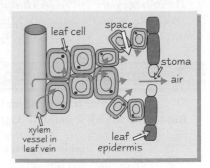

Water Moves **Up** a Plant **Against** the Force of **Gravity**

The movement of water from **roots to leaves** is called the **transpiration stream**. The **mechanisms** that **move** the water include **cohesion** and **tension**.

Cohesion and **tension** help water move up plants, from roots to leaves, **against** the force of gravity.

1) Water **evaporates** from the **leaves** at the 'top' of the xylem (**transpiration**).

2) This creates a **tension** (**suction**), which pulls more water into the leaf.

3) Water molecules are **cohesive** (they **stick together**) so when some are pulled into the leaf others follow. This means the whole **column** of water in the **xylem**, from the leaves down to the roots, **moves upwards**.

4) **Water** enters the stem through the **roots**.

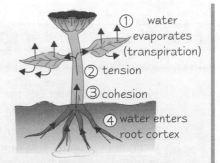

① water evaporates (transpiration)
② tension
③ cohesion
④ water enters root cortex

For OCR you need to know about adhesion.

Adhesion is also partly responsible for the **movement of water**.

1) As well as being attracted to each other, water molecules are **attracted to** the **walls** of the xylem vessels.

2) This helps water to **rise up** through the xylem vessels.

For AQA you need to know about root pressure.

Root pressure also helps move the water upwards. When water is transported into the xylem in the roots, it creates a **pressure** and **shoves** water already in the xylem **further upwards**. This pressure is **weak**, and couldn't move water to the top of bigger plants by itself. But it helps, especially in young, small plants where the leaves are still developing.

Practice Questions

Q1 In terms of water potential, why does water move into the roots from the soil?

Q2 What is the Casparian strip?

Q3 What is cohesion?

Q4 How does adhesion help to move water through a plant?

Exam Questions

Q1 Explain why the movement of water in the xylem stops if the leaves of a plant are removed. [4 marks]

Q2 Water can take two different paths through the roots of a plant.

a) Describe the symplast pathway through the roots of a plant. [2 marks]

b) Describe the apoplast pathway through the roots of a plant. [4 marks]

So many routes through the roots...

As you've probably noticed, there are lots of impressive biological words on this page, to amaze your friends and confound your enemies. Go through the page again, and whenever you see a word like plasmodesmata, just stop and check you know exactly what it means. (Personally I think they should just call them cell wall gaps, but nobody ever listens to me.)

Transpiration

These pages are for AQA Unit 2 and OCR Unit 1.

Plants can't sing, juggle or tap-dance (as you will hopefully be aware). But they can exchange gases — how exciting. What makes it all the more thrilling though is that they lose water vapour as they do it. Gripping stuff.

Transpiration is a Consequence of Gas Exchange

So you know that **transpiration** is the evaporation of **water** from a plant's surface, especially the **leaves**. But I bet you didn't know it happens as a result of **gas exchange**. Read on...

1) A plant needs to **open** its **stomata** to let in **carbon dioxide** so that it can produce **glucose** (by **photosynthesis**).

2) But this **also lets water out** — there's a **higher concentration** of water **inside** the leaf than in the air **outside**, so water moves **out** of the leaf down the **water potential gradient** when the stomata open.

3) So transpiration's really a **side effect** of the gas exchange needed for photosynthesis.

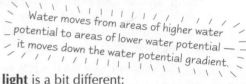
Water moves from areas of higher water potential to areas of lower water potential — it moves down the water potential gradient.

Four Main Factors Affect Transpiration Rate

Temperature, humidity and wind all alter the **water potential gradient**, but **light** is a bit different:

1) <u>Light</u> — the **lighter** it is the **faster** the **transpiration rate**. This is because the **stomata open** when it gets **light**. When it's **dark** the stomata are usually **closed**, so there's little transpiration.

2) <u>Temperature</u> — the **higher the temperature** the **faster** the **transpiration rate**. Warmer water molecules have more energy so they **evaporate** from the cells inside the leaf **faster**. This **increases** the **water potential gradient** between the inside and outside of the leaf, making water **diffuse** out of the leaf **faster**.

3) <u>Humidity</u> — the <u>lower</u> the **humidity**, the **faster** the **transpiration rate**. If the air around the plant is **dry**, the **water potential gradient** between the leaf and the air is **increased**, which increases transpiration.

4) <u>Wind</u> — the **windier** it is, the **faster** the **transpiration rate**. Lots of air movement **blows away** water molecules from around the stomata. This **increases** the water potential gradient, which increases the rate of transpiration.

A Potometer can be Used to Estimate Transpiration Rate

A **potometer** is a special piece of apparatus used to **estimate transpiration rates**. It actually measures **water uptake** by a plant, but it's **assumed** that water uptake by the plant is **directly related** to **water loss** by the **leaves**. You can use it to estimate how different factors **affect** the transpiration rate.

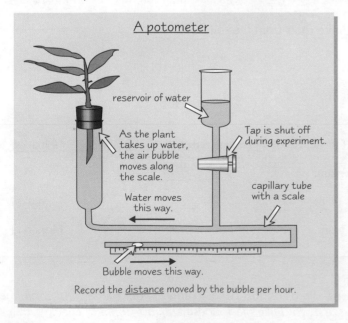

A potometer

reservoir of water

As the plant takes up water, the air bubble moves along the scale.

Water moves this way.

Tap is shut off during experiment.

capillary tube with a scale

Bubble moves this way.

Record the <u>distance</u> moved by the bubble per hour.

Here's what you'd do:

1) **Cut** a **shoot underwater** to prevent air from entering the xylem. Cut it at a **slant** to increase the surface area available for water uptake.

2) Check that the apparatus is **full of water** and that there are **no air bubbles**.

3) Insert the **shoot** into the apparatus **underwater**, so no air can enter.

4) Remove the potometer from the water and make sure it's **airtight** and **watertight**.

5) **Dry** the leaves, allow time for the shoot to **acclimatise** and then **shut the tap**.

6) Keep the **conditions constant** throughout the experiment, e.g. the temperature and the air humidity.

7) Record the **starting position** of the **air bubble**.

8) Start a **stopwatch** and record the **distance** moved by the bubble **per unit time**, e.g. per hour.

Transpiration

If you're doing AQA you can skip straight to the questions — the rest is for OCR only.

Xerophytic Plants are Adapted to Reduce Water Loss

Xerophytes are plants like **cacti**, **pine trees** and **prickly pears** (yes, the ones from the song).
They're **adapted** to live in **dry climates**. Their adaptations prevent them **losing too much water** by **transpiration**.
Examples of xerophytic adaptations include:

1) **Stomata** that are sunk in **pits** — so they're **sheltered from the wind**, which helps to slow transpiration down.

2) A layer of 'hairs' on the epidermis — this **traps moist air** round the stomata, which **reduces** the water potential gradient between the leaf and the air, **slowing** transpiration down.

3) **Curled leaves** — this **traps moist air**, slowing down transpiration. This also lowers the **exposed surface area** for losing water and protects the stomata from wind.

6) A reduced **number of stomata** — this means there are **fewer places** where water can be lost.

5) **Thick, waxy layer** on the epidermis — this **reduces** water loss by evaporation because the layer is **waterproof** (water can't move through it).

4) **Spines** instead of **leaves** (e.g. cactus) — this reduces the **surface area** for water loss.

Practice Questions

Q1 Explain why transpiration is a consequence of gaseous exchange.

Q2 What piece of apparatus is used to measure transpiration?

Q3 What is a xerophyte?

Q4 Suggest three ways that xerophyte leaves are adapted to reduce water loss by transpiration.

Exam Questions

Q1 Give four conditions that increase the rate of transpiration from a plant's leaves and explain how each one increases transpiration. [8 marks]

Q2 The diagram shows a section of a leaf of a xerophytic plant. Describe and explain two ways, visible in the picture, that this leaf is adapted to reduce water loss. [4 marks]

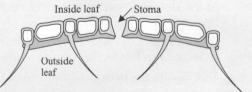

Inside leaf — Stoma

Outside leaf

Xerophytes — an exciting word for a boring subject...

Actually, that's unfair. It's taken millions of years for plants to evolve those adaptations, and here I am slagging them off. When I've managed to develop a thicker waxy cuticle on my leaves and stems, then I can comment, and not before. Oh, and learn the rest of the stuff on this page too. It may not be thrilling — but if you know it, it could earn you vital marks.

Translocation

These pages are for OCR Unit 1 only.

Translocation is the movement of dissolved solvents through a plant. Annoyingly, translocation sounds a lot like transpiration. Or is that just me? Make sure you don't get them confused.

Translocation *is the* Movement *of* Dissolved Substances

1) **Translocation** is the **movement** of dissolved substances (e.g. sugars like sucrose, and amino acids) to **where they're needed** in a plant. Dissolved substances are sometimes called **assimilates**.

2) It's an **energy-requiring** process that happens in the **phloem**.

See p. 159 for more on the phloem.

3) Translocation moves substances from **'sources'** to **'sinks'**.
The **source** of a substance is **where it's made** (so it's at a **high concentration** there). The **sink** is the area where it's **used up** (so it's at a **lower concentration** there).

> **EXAMPLE**
>
> The **source** for **sucrose** is the **leaves** (where it's made), and the **sinks** are the **other parts** of the plant, especially the **food storage organs** and the **meristems** (areas of growth) in the roots, stems and leaves.

4) **Enzymes** maintain a **concentration gradient** from the source to the sink by **changing** the dissolved substances at the **sink** (e.g. by breaking them down or making them into something else). This makes sure there's always a **lower concentration** at the sink than at the source.

> **EXAMPLE**
>
> In **potatoes**, **sucrose** is converted to **starch** in the **sink** areas, so there's always a **lower concentration** of sucrose **at the sink** than inside the phloem. This makes sure a **constant supply** of new sucrose reaches the sink from the phloem.

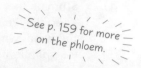

Howard liked a bit of translocation in his spare time.

The Mass Flow Hypothesis *Best Explains* Phloem Transport

Scientists still aren't certain **exactly how** the dissolved substances (solutes) are transported from source to sink by **translocation**. The best supported theory is the **mass flow hypothesis**:

①
1) Active transport (see p. 36) is used to **actively load** the dissolved solutes (e.g. sucrose from photosynthesis) into the **sieve tubes** of the phloem at the **source** (e.g. the **leaves**).

2) This **lowers the water potential** inside the sieve tubes, so water enters the tubes by **osmosis**.

3) This creates a **high pressure** inside the sieve tubes at the **source end** of the phloem.

②
1) At the **sink** end, **solutes** are removed from the phloem to be used up.

2) This **increases** the **water potential** inside the sieve tubes, so water also leaves the tubes by **osmosis**.

3) This **lowers the pressure** inside the sieve tubes.

③
1) The result is a **pressure gradient** from the **source** end to the **sink** end.

2) This gradient pushes solutes along the sieve tubes to where they're needed.

① SOURCE
low water potential, high pressure

companion cell

pressure gradient

③

solute (e.g. sucrose)

sieve plate

② SINK
high water potential low pressure

Translocation

There is **Evidence** Both For and Against **Mass Flow**

Supporting evidence

1) If you remove a **ring of bark** (which includes the phloem, but not the xylem) from a woody stem a **bulge forms above** the ring. If you analyse the fluid from the bulge, you'll find it has a **higher concentration** of **sugars** than the fluid from below the ring — this is evidence that there's a **downward flow** of sugars.

2) You can **investigate** pressure in the phloem using **aphids** (they pierce the phloem, then their bodies are removed leaving the mouthparts behind, which allows the sap to flow out... gruesome). The sap flows out **quicker nearer the leaves** than further down the stem — this is evidence that there's a **pressure gradient**.

3) If you put a **metabolic inhibitor** (which stops ATP production) into the **phloem** then **translocation stops** — this is evidence that **active transport** is involved.

4) There's an **experimental model** for mass flow (see below).

Objections

1) Sugar travels to **many different sinks**, not just to the one with the **highest water potential**, as the model would suggest.

2) The **sieve plates** would create a **barrier** to mass flow. A **lot of pressure** would be needed for the solutes to get through at a reasonable rate.

Mass Flow Hypothesis Can be **Demonstrated** in an **Experiment**

The hypothesis can be modelled in this experiment:

1) **A** and **B** are two containers, each lined with a **selectively permeable membrane** just like cells have.

2) The **top tube** connecting A and B represents the **phloem**, and the **bottom tube** represents the **xylem**.

3) **A** represents the **source** end and contains a **concentrated sugar solution**. **B** represents the **sink** end and contains a **weak sugar solution**.

4) Water enters **A** by **osmosis**, **increasing** the pressure, which causes the sugar solution to flow along the **top tube** (phloem).

5) **Pressure** increases in **B**, forcing water out and back through the **bottom tube** (xylem), which just transports water.

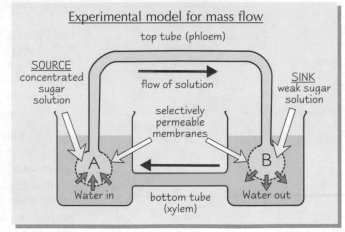

Experimental model for mass flow

Practice Questions

Q1 Explain the terms source and sink in connection with translocation.

Q2 State two pieces of evidence that support the mass flow hypothesis for translocation.

Exam Question

Q1 The mass flow hypothesis depends on a pressure difference in the phloem sieve tubes between the source and the sink. Explain how sugars cause the pressure to increase at the source end, according to the mass flow hypothesis.

[4 marks]

Human mass flow — running out of the hall at the end of an exam...

The mass flow hypothesis is just the best theory that scientists have come up with so far. If other evidence came along, a different theory could be developed based on the new findings (see p. 2). However, that doesn't mean that there's no point in learning about it — it could be in your exam. Don't look so sad — what else would you do with your time...

Plant Cell Structure and Plant Stems

This whole section is for Edexcel Unit 2 only.

Plants aren't everybody's cup of tea, but they should be — without them we'd be stuck. We get loads of useful stuff from plants, but before we delve into that there are a few important bits and pieces you need to know...

Plant Cells Have Different Organelles from Animal Cells

For more on animal organelles see p. 22.

You know all about the organelles in animal cells — well plant cells are a little bit different.
Plant cells contain all the organelles that animal cells do, **plus a few extras** that **animal cells don't have**:

ORGANELLE	DIAGRAM	DESCRIPTION	FUNCTION
Cell wall	cell membrane / cell wall / cytoplasm	A rigid structure that surrounds **plant cells**. It's made mainly of the carbohydrate **cellulose**.	**Supports** plant cells.
Middle lamella	middle lamella / cell A / cell B / cell wall	The **outermost layer** of the cell.	This layer acts as an **adhesive**, sticking adjacent plant cells together. It gives the plant **stability**.
Plasmodesmata	plasmodesma (plural = plasmodesmata) / cell A / cell wall / cell B	**Channels** in the cell walls that **link** adjacent cells together.	Allow **transport** of **substances** and **communication** between cells.
Pits	pits / cell A / cell B / cell wall	Regions of the cell wall where the wall is **very thin**. They're arranged in **pairs** — the pit in one cell is lined up with the pit in the adjacent cell.	Allow **transport** of **substances** between cells.
Chloroplast	stroma / two membranes / granum (plural = grana) / lamella (plural = lamellae)	A small, **flattened** structure. It's surrounded by a **double membrane**, and also has membranes inside called **thylakoid membranes**. These membranes are stacked up in some parts of the chloroplast to form **grana**. Grana are linked together by lamellae — thin, flat pieces of thylakoid membrane.	The **site** where **photosynthesis** takes place. Some parts of photosynthesis happen in the **grana**, and other parts happen in the **stroma** (a thick fluid found in chloroplasts).
Amyloplast	starch grain / membrane	A small organelle enclosed by a **membrane**. They contain **starch granules**.	**Storage** of **starch** (see p. 168). They also convert starch back to glucose for release when the plant requires it.
Vacuole and Tonoplast	vacuole / tonoplast / plant cell	The vacuole is a **compartment** surrounded by a **membrane** called the **tonoplast**.	The vacuole contains the **cell sap**, which is made up of water, enzymes, minerals and waste products. Vacuoles keep the cells **turgid** — this stops plants wilting. They're also involved in the **breakdown** and **isolation** of unwanted chemicals in the cell. The tonoplast controls what **enters** and **leaves** the vacuole.

Plant Cell Structure and Plant Stems

Different Parts of **Plant Stems** have **Different Functions**

Plant stems are made up of loads of different things — the only bits you need to worry about are **xylem vessels** and **sclerenchyma fibres**.

Xylem vessels

1) The function of xylem vessels is to **transport water** and **mineral ions** up the plant, and **provide support**.

2) They're very **long**, **tube-like** structures formed from **dead cells**, joined end to end. The tubes are found together in **bundles**.

3) The cells are **longer** than they are **wide**, they have a **hollow lumen** (they contain **no cytoplasm**) and have **no end walls**.

4) This makes an **uninterrupted tube**, allowing water and mineral ions to pass up through the middle easily.

5) Their walls are **thickened** with a **woody** substance called **lignin**, which helps to **support** the plant.

6) **Water** and **mineral ions** move **into** and **out of** the vessels through **pits** in the walls where there's **no lignin**.

7) Xylem vessels are found throughout the plant but particularly around the **centre of the stem**.

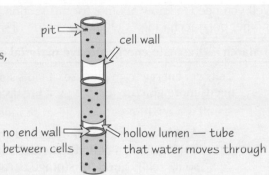

pit → cell wall

no end wall between cells → hollow lumen — tube that water moves through

Sclerenchyma fibres

1) The function of sclerenchyma fibres is to provide **support**.

2) Like xylem vessels, they're also made of bundles of **dead cells** that run vertically up the stem.

3) The cells are **longer** than they are **wide**, and also have a **hollow lumen** and **no end walls**.

4) Their cell walls are also **thickened** with **lignin**. They have more **cellulose** (see next page) than other plant cells.

5) They're found throughout the stems of plants but particularly around the **outer edge**.

<u>Stem cross-section</u>

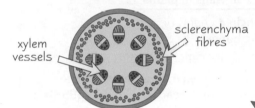

xylem vessels

sclerenchyma fibres

Practice Questions

Q1 Which two organelles allow transport of substances between plant cells?

Q2 What is the function of chloroplasts?

Q3 What is the function of amyloplasts?

Q4 Name the membrane that surrounds the vacuole.

Exam Question

Q1 a) The image on the right shows a cross-section of a plant stem as seen under a light microscope. Identify the structures labelled x and y.   [2 marks]

b) Compare the structure and function of the two structures you have named above.   [9 marks]

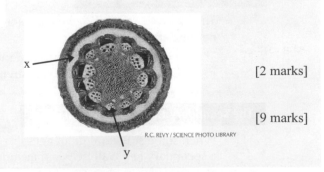

R.C. REVY / SCIENCE PHOTO LIBRARY

Esmerelda... the cells! the cells!

I know the table of organelles looks pretty daunting, but I'm afraid you've got to learn it — scribble down one diagram at a time and write out its description and function 'til you know it like the back of your hand. As for plant stems, they aren't too tricky — just make sure you can compare the structure and function of xylem vessels and sclerenchyma fibres.

Starch, Cellulose and Fibres

These pages are for Edexcel Unit 2 only.

I know these pages don't have the most stimulating title, but they're actually pretty interesting... honest...

The **Structures** of **Starch** and **Cellulose** Determine Their **Functions**

You might remember some stuff about the structure of **starch** from Section 1. Well you need to know about it for this section as well — but now you've got to **compare** it to **cellulose**, another polysaccharide. Cellulose is made of similar stuff, but has a **different function**.

① Starch — the main **energy storage material** in **plants**

1) Cells get **energy** from **glucose**. Plants **store** excess glucose as **starch** (when a plant **needs more glucose** for energy it **breaks down** starch to release the glucose).

2) Starch is a mixture of **two** polysaccharides of **alpha-glucose** — **amylose** and **amylopectin**:

- **Amylose** — a long, **unbranched chain** of α–glucose. The angles of the glycosidic bonds give it a **coiled structure**, almost like a cylinder. This makes it **compact**, so it's really **good for storage** because you can **fit more in** to a small space.

- **Amylopectin** — a long, **branched chain** of α–glucose. Its **side branches** allow the **enzymes** that break down the molecule to get at the **glycosidic bonds easily**. This means that the glucose can be **released quickly**.

3) Starch is **insoluble** in water, so it doesn't cause water to enter cells by **osmosis** (which would make them swell). This makes it good for **storage**.

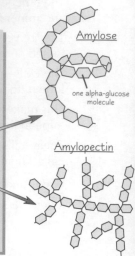

Amylose

one alpha-glucose molecule

Amylopectin

② Cellulose — the major component of **cell walls** in **plants**

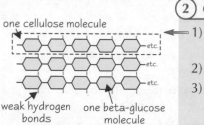

one cellulose molecule

weak hydrogen bonds   one beta-glucose molecule

1) Cellulose is made of **long**, **unbranched** chains of **beta-glucose**, joined by **glycosidic bonds**.

2) The glycosidic bonds are **straight**, so the cellulose chains are straight.

3) Between **50 and 80** cellulose chains are **linked together** by a large number of **hydrogen bonds** to form **strong threads** called **microfibrils**. The strong threads mean cellulose provides **structural support** for cells (e.g. they strengthen plant cell walls).

See page 9 for more on glycosidic bonds.

Plant Fibres are **Useful** to **Humans** Because They're **Strong**

1) Plant fibres are made up of **long tubes** of **plant cells**, e.g. sclerenchyma fibres are made of tubes of dead cells.

2) They're **strong**, which makes them useful for loads of things, e.g. **ropes** or **fabrics** like hemp.

3) They're strong for a **number of reasons**, but you only need to know **two**:

The arrangement of cellulose microfibrils in the cell wall

1) The cell wall contains **cellulose microfibrils** in a **net-like arrangement**.

2) The strength of the microfibrils and their arrangement in the cell wall gives plant fibres **strength**.

cell membrane   secondary cell wall   normal cell wall

layer of cellulose microfibrils in cell wall

The secondary thickening of cell walls

1) When some structural plant cells (like sclerenchyma) have finished growing, they produce a **secondary cell wall** between the normal cell wall and the cell membrane.

2) The secondary cell wall is **thicker** than the normal cell wall and usually has **more lignin**.

3) The growth of a secondary cell wall is called **secondary thickening**.

4) Secondary thickening makes plant fibres even **stronger**.

Starch, Cellulose and Fibres

You Can Measure the Tensile Strength of Plant Fibres

The **tensile strength** of a fibre is the **maximum load** it can take before it **breaks**. Knowing the tensile strength of plant fibres can be really important, especially if they're going to be used for things like ropes (e.g. a rock climber would want to know the rope they're using is going to hold their weight).
Here's how you'd find out the tensile strength of a plant fibre:

I don't know Dave, we usually use weights to test tensile strength...

1) Attach the fibre to a **clamp stand** and **hang** a **weight** from the other end.

2) Keep **adding weights**, one at a time, until the **fibre breaks**.

3) Record the **mass needed** to break the fibre — the **higher** the mass, the **higher** the tensile strength.

4) **Repeat** the experiment with different samples of the same fibre — this increases the **reliability**.

5) The fibres being tested should always be the **same length**.

6) Throughout the experiment all **other variables**, like temperature and humidity, must be kept **constant**.

7) You also need to take **safety measures** when doing this experiment, e.g. wear goggles to protect your eyes, and leave the area where the weights will fall clear so they don't squish your toes.

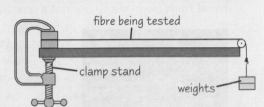

fibre being tested

clamp stand

weights

Practice Questions

Q1 Name the two polysaccharides that starch is made up from.

Q2 Compare the structure and function of starch and cellulose.

Q3 What is meant by tensile strength?

Exam Questions

Q1 The physical properties of plant fibres can make them useful to humans.

a) Describe the arrangement of cellulose microfibrils in a plant cell wall, and explain how this relates to the properties of plant fibres. [4 marks]

b) Describe secondary thickening of plant cell walls, and explain how this relates to the properties of plant fibres. [4 marks]

Q2 A group of students investigated the tensile strength of four different plant fibres. Their results are displayed in the table on the right.

	fibre A	fibre B	fibre C	fibre D
length of fibre / cm	60	60	60	60
mass which caused fibre to break / kg	3.5	220.0	52.7	17.2

a) Describe a method they could have used to obtain these results. [8 marks]

b) Based on this information, which fibre would be most suitable to make a climbing rope? Explain your answer. [2 marks]

The world's strongest plant — live from the Bahamas...

Well at least there are lots of pretty pictures on these pages to look at. Anyway, it's not so bad — basically plant fibres are really strong and there are lots of reasons, but you just need to know about how the cell walls are strong, which makes the plant fibres super strong. They're strong to the finish, 'cos they eats their spinach...

Sustainability and Plant Minerals

These pages are for Edexcel Unit 2 only.

So, you can use plants to make ropes and fabrics, but there are plenty of other groovy things you can make from plants, like plastics, fuel and castles of mashed potatoes. Making things from plants is also sustainable, which is nice...

Sustainable Practices Don't Deplete Resources

1) Sustainability is all about **using resources** in a way that meets the **needs** of the **present generation** without messing it up for **future generations** (i.e. not using something up so there's none left).

2) To **make products sustainably** you have to use **renewable resources**.

3) Renewable resources are resources that can be **used indefinitely** without **running out**, e.g. **plants** are a renewable resource because harvested plants can be **regrown** (so there'll be plenty for future generations). **Fossil fuels** (e.g. petrol) are **not** a renewable resource — once you've used it all there's no more.

If only Amy's sweets were a renewable resource...

4) An example of a **sustainable practice** is replacing trees after logging. Whenever a tree is cut down, a **new one** is planted in its place. When the tree is fully grown the process can **begin again** — the environment isn't **significantly damaged** in the long term.

5) **Unsustainable practices** can't continue indefinitely. The **resources** would eventually **run out**.

6) An example of an unsustainable practice is the use of **fossil fuels** to make oil-based plastics like polythene.

Using Plant Fibres and Starch can Contribute to Sustainability

Plant fibres

1) **Ropes** and **fabrics** can be made of **plastic**, which is made from **oil**. They can also be made from **plant fibres** (see page 168).

2) Making products from plant fibres is **more sustainable** than making them from oil — **less fossil fuel** is used up, and crops can be **regrown** to **maintain the supply** for future generations.

3) Products made from plant fibres are **biodegradable** — they can be broken down by **microbes**, unlike most oil-based plastics (which can't be broken down and remain in the environment for many years).

4) Plants are **easier to grow** and **process** (to extract the fibres) than extracting and processing oil. This makes them **cheaper** and it's easier to do in developing countries (as less technology and expertise is needed).

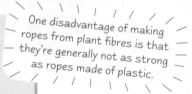

One disadvantage of making ropes from plant fibres is that they're generally not as strong as ropes made of plastic.

Starch

1) Starch is found in **all plants** — crops such as **potatoes** and **corn** are particularly rich in starch.

2) **Plastics** are usually made from **oil**, but some can be made from **plant-based** materials, like **starch**. These plastics are called **bioplastics**.

3) Making plastics from starch is **more sustainable** than making them from oil because less fossil fuel is used up and the **crops** from which the starch came from can be **regrown**.

4) **Vehicle fuel** is also usually made from **oil**, but you can make fuel from **starch**. E.g. **bioethanol** is a fuel that can be made from starch.

5) Making fuel from starch is **more sustainable** than making it from oil because, you guessed it, **less fossil fuel** is used up and the **crops** from which the starch came from can be **regrown**.

The potatoes were getting worried about all this talk of using more starch — you could see it in their eyes.

Sustainability and Plant Minerals

Plants Need Water and Inorganic Ions

Plants need **water** and **inorganic ions** (**minerals**) for a number of different functions. They're absorbed through the **roots** and travel through the plant in the xylem. If there isn't enough water or inorganic ions in the soil, the plant will show **deficiency symptoms**, like stunted growth. You need to know why plants need water and these three minerals:

- **Water** is needed for **photosynthesis**, to maintain **structural rigidity**, **transport minerals** and **regulate temperature**.
- **Magnesium ions** are needed for the production of **chlorophyll** — the **pigment** needed for **photosynthesis**.
- **Nitrate ions** are needed for the production of **DNA**, **proteins** (including enzymes) and **chlorophyll**. They're required for **plant growth**, **fruit production** and **seed production**.
- **Calcium ions** are important components in plant **cell walls**. They're required for **plant growth**.

You Can Investigate Plant Mineral Deficiencies in the Lab

Here's how to **investigate mineral deficiency** in a plant using calcium ions as an example (you could do the same experiment with any of the minerals mentioned above):

Method

1) Take 30 seedlings of the **same plant** (they should be the **same age** and **height**) and plant them in **separate pots**.
2) Make up three **nutrient broths** containing all the essential minerals, but vary the concentration of **calcium ions**. Make up one broth with a **high** concentration, one with a **medium** concentration and one with a **low** concentration of calcium.
3) Split the plants into three groups. Each group should be given **only one** of the three broths.
4) Record the **heights** of the plants after seven weeks. Calculate the **average height** of each group of plants.
5) During the experiment it's important to keep all other **variables the same**, e.g. the amount of sunlight and water the plants receive.

Results

1) The **greater** the concentration of calcium, the **more** the plants grew — average heights of 12, 18 and 23 cm were reached for plants given low, medium and high concentrations respectively.
2) This shows that when calcium is **deficient**, plant growth is **inhibited**.

Calcium ion concentration	Average height at start / cm	Average height after 7 weeks / cm
High	6	23
Medium	6	18
Low	6	12

Practice Questions

Q1 What does it mean if a product is made sustainably?

Q2 Suggest two advantages of using plant fibres rather than oil-based plastics to make rope.

Q3 Name two products, other than rope, that can be made from plants.

Exam Question

Q1 Describe an experiment you could carry out to investigate the effects of nitrate deficiency on a plant. [6 marks]

Potatoes, good for plastics and fuel — we'll be eating them next...

Renewable resources are great — they'll never run out (like my bad jokes — plenty more where they came from...). There's another experiment to learn here, but look at it like this — tonnes more cheap marks in the exam, 'cos when they ask you to describe an experiment you get loads for it. Now, doesn't that just make you want to copy it out a few times...

Drug Testing and Drugs from Plants

These pages are for Edexcel Unit 2 only.

A lot of drugs come from plants. Nowadays it's seen as a good idea to test drugs before we use them. But back in the olden days drug testing tended to be a bit hit and miss...

Testing Drugs Used to be Trial and Error

Before **new drugs** become available to the general public they need to be **tested** — to make sure they **work** and don't have any horrible **side effects**. In the past, drug testing was a lot **less scientific** than modern clinical trials (see below) and a bit more dangerous for the participants...

Example — William Withering's digitalis soup

1) **William Withering** was a scientist in the 1700s.

2) He discovered that an extract of **foxgloves** could be used to treat **dropsy** (swelling brought about by heart failure). This extract contained the drug **digitalis**.

3) Withering made a **chance observation** — a patient suffering from dropsy made a good recovery after being treated with a **traditional remedy** containing foxgloves. Withering knew foxgloves were **poisonous**, so he started testing **different versions** of the remedy with **different concentrations** of digitalis — this became known as his **digitalis soup**.

4) **Too much** digitalis **poisoned** his patients, while **too little** had **no effect**.

5) It was through this crude method of **trial and error** that he discovered the right amount to give to a patient.

Modern Drug Testing is More Rigorous

1) Nowadays **drug testing protocols** are much more **controlled**.

2) Before a drug is tried on any live subjects, computers are used to **model** the **potential effects**.

3) Tests are also carried out on **human tissues** in a **lab**, then they're tested on **live animals** before **clinical trials** are carried out on **humans**.

4) During clinical trials new drugs undergo **three phases of testing**. This involves three different stages, with more people at each stage:

Drugs that pass all three phases are considered for clinical use.

Phase 1 — This involves testing a new drug on a **small group** of **healthy individuals**. It's done to find out things like **safe dosage**, if there are any **side effects**, and how the body **reacts** to the drug.

Phase 2 — If a drug passes Phase 1 it will then be tested on a **larger group of people** (this time **patients**) to see **how well** the drug actually **works**.

Phase 3 — During this phase the drug is **compared** to **existing treatments**. It involves testing the drug on **hundreds**, or even **thousands**, of patients. Patients are randomly split into two groups — one group receives the **new treatment** and the other group receives the **existing treatment**. This allows scientists to tell if the new drug is **any better** than existing drugs.

Dirk carried on, blissfully unaware that drug testing was more rigorous these days.

Using **placebos** and a **double blind study design** make the results of clinical trials **more reliable**.

Placebos

In Phase 2 clinical trials the patients are split into **two groups**. One group is given the drug and the other is given a **placebo** — an **inactive substance** that looks exactly like the drug but doesn't actually do anything. Patients often show a **placebo effect** — where they show some improvement because they **believe** that they're receiving treatment. Giving half the patients a placebo allows researchers to see if the **drug actually works** (if it improves patients more than the placebo does).

Double blind study design

Phase 2 and 3 clinical trials are usually **double blind** — **neither** the **patients** nor the **doctors** know who's been given the new drug and who's been given the placebo (or old drug). This **reduces bias** in the results because the **attitudes** of the patients and doctors **can't affect the results**. E.g. if a doctor knows someone has received the real drug, they may think they've improved more than they actually have — but if they don't know this can't happen.

Drug Testing and Drugs from Plants

Some Plants Have Antimicrobial Properties

Some plants have **antimicrobial properties** — they **kill** or **inhibit the growth** of microorganisms.
You need to know how to investigate the antimicrobial properties of plants — here's an example:

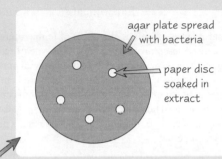

agar plate spread with bacteria

paper disc soaked in extract

1) Take **extracts** from the plants **you want to test**. To do this you need to **dry** and **grind** each plant, then soak them in **ethanol** (the ethanol acts as a solvent). The plants should all be the **same size**, so the amount of extract is the same.

2) **Filter off** the **liquid bit** (the ethanol containing the dissolved plant extract).

3) You need some **bacteria** to test the plant extract on — evenly spread a sample of bacteria onto an **agar** (nutrient) **plate**.

4) Dip discs of **absorbent paper** in the extracts. The discs of paper should all be the **same size** so they absorb the same volume of liquid.

5) You also need to do a **control disc** soaked only in ethanol (to make sure it isn't the ethanol or the paper that's inhibiting bacterial growth).

6) Place the paper discs on the agar plate — make sure they're spread out.

7) **Incubate** the plate to allow the bacteria to **grow**.

8) Where the bacteria **can't grow** there'll be a **clear patch** in the lawn of bacteria. This is called an **inhibition zone**.

9) The size of an **inhibition zone** tells you how well the antimicrobial plant extract is working. The **larger** the zone, the **more** effective the plant extract is.

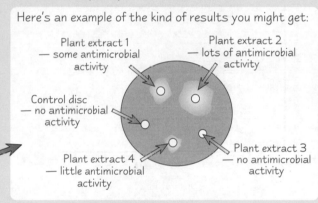

Here's an example of the kind of results you might get:

Plant extract 1 — some antimicrobial activity

Plant extract 2 — lots of antimicrobial activity

Control disc — no antimicrobial activity

Plant extract 3 — no antimicrobial activity

Plant extract 4 — little antimicrobial activity

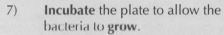

Practice Questions

Q1 Give one way that modern drug testing differs from historic drug testing.

Q2 What is a placebo?

Q3 What is a double blind trial?

Exam Questions

Q1 Describe how William Withering discovered and tested the drug digitalis. [5 marks]

Q2 Plant extracts have long been used to relieve symptoms of many diseases.

a) Describe how you could conduct an experiment to discover if a plant species had antibacterial properties. [10 marks]

b) A new drug made from a plant extract would have to go through clinical trials before it's made available to patients. Describe this process. [7 marks]

Digitalis soup — like Alphabetti Spaghetti with numbers...

Drug testing these days is really quite complicated, what with all this three-phase testing and placebos. Though if you ask me, anything that's double blind just sounds like a recipe for disaster. Anyway, make sure you can talk about the differences between past and present drug testing, and that you know how to test the antimicrobial properties of plants.

How to Interpret Experiment and Study Data

Science is all about getting good evidence to test your theories... so scientists need to be able to spot a badly designed experiment or study a mile off, and be able to interpret the results of an experiment or study properly. Being the cheeky little monkeys they are, your exam board will want to make sure you can do it too. Here's a quick reference section to show you how to go about interpreting data-style questions.

Here Are Some **Things** You Might be **Asked** to do...

For other examples check the interpreting data pages in the sections.

Here are two examples of the kind of data you could expect to get:

Experiment A

Experiment A examined the effect of temperature on the rate of an enzyme-controlled reaction. The rate of reaction for enzyme X was measured at six different temperatures (from 10 to 60 °C). All other variables were kept constant. A negative control containing all solutions except the enzyme was included. The rate of reaction for the negative control was zero at each temperature used. The results are shown in the graph below.

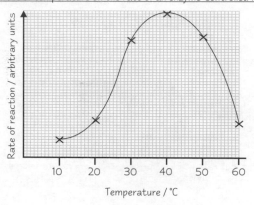

The effect of temperature on the rate of an enzyme-controlled reaction

Study B

Study B examined the effect of farm hedgerow length on the number of species in a given area. The number of species present during a single week on 12 farms was counted by placing ground-level traps. All the farms were a similar area. The traps were left out every day, at 6 am for two hours and once again at 6 pm for two hours. The data was plotted against hedgerow length. The results are shown in the scattergram below.

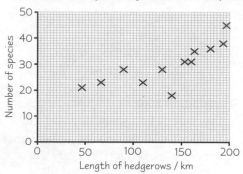

The effect of hedgerow length on number of species

1) Describe the Data

You need to be able to **describe** any data you're given. The level of **detail** in your answer should be appropriate for the **number of marks** given. Loads of marks = more detail, few marks = less detail.
For the two examples above:

Example — Experiment A

1) The data shows that the **rate of reaction increases** as **temperature increases** up to a **certain point**. The rate of reaction then **decreases** as temperature increases (2 marks).

2) The data shows that the rate of reaction **increases** as temperature increases from **10 °C up to 40 °C**. The rate of reaction then **decreases** as temperature increases from **40 °C to 60 °C** (4 marks).

Example — Study B

The data shows a **positive correlation** between the length of hedgerows and the number of species in the area (1 mark).

Correlation describes the **relationship** between two variables — the one that's been changed and the one that's been measured. Data can show **three** types of correlation:

1) **Positive** — as one variable **increases** the other **increases**.

2) **Negative** — as one variable **increases** the other **decreases**.

3) **None** — there is **no relationship** between the two variables.

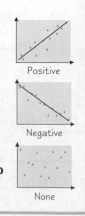

How to Interpret Experiment and Study Data

2) Draw or Check the Conclusions

1) Ideally, only **two** quantities would ever change in any experiment or study — everything else would be **constant**.

2) If you can keep everything else constant and the results show a correlation then you **can** conclude that the change in one variable **does cause** the change in the other. ➡

3) But usually all the variables **can't** be controlled, so other **factors** (that you **couldn't** keep constant) could be having an **effect**.

4) Because of this, scientists have to be very careful when **drawing conclusions**. Most results show a **link** (correlation) between the variables, but that **doesn't prove that a change in one causes the change in the other**. ➡

5) The **data** should always **support** the conclusion. This may sound obvious but it's easy to **jump** to conclusions. Conclusions have to be **precise** — not make sweeping generalisations. ➡

Example — Experiment A

All other variables were **kept constant**. E.g. pH, enzyme concentration and substrate concentration **stayed the same** each time, so these **couldn't** have influenced the change in the rate of reaction. So you **can say** that an increase in temperature **causes** an increase in the rate of reaction up to a certain point.

Example — Study B

The length of hedgerows shows a **positive correlation** with the number of species in that area. But you **can't** conclude that fewer hedgerows **causes** fewer species. **Other factors** may have been involved, e.g. the number of **predators** of the species studied may have increased in some areas, the farmers may have used **more pesticide** in one area, or something else you hadn't thought of could have caused the pattern...

Example — Experiment A

A science magazine **concluded** from this data that enzyme X works best at **40 °C**. The data **doesn't** support this. The enzyme **could** work best at 42 °C, or 47 °C but you can't tell from the data because **increases** of **10 °C** at a time were used. The rates of reaction at in-between temperatures **weren't** measured.

3) Comment on the Reliability of the Results

Reliable means the results can be **consistently reproduced** in independent experiments. And if the results are reproducible they're more likely to be **true**. If the data isn't reliable for whatever reason you **can't draw** a valid **conclusion**. Here are some of the things that affect the reliability of data:

1) **Size of the data set** — For experiments, the **more repeats** you do, the **more reliable** the data. If you get the **same result** twice, it could be the correct answer. But if you get the same result **20 times**, it's much more reliable. The general rule for **studies** is the **larger** the sample size, the more **reliable** the **data** is.

E.g. Study B is quite **small** — they only used 12 farms. The **trend** shown by the data may not appear if you studied **50 or 100 farms**, or studied them for a longer period of time.

Davina wasn't sure she'd got a large enough sample size.

2) **Variables** — The **more variables** you **control**, the **more reliable** your data is. In an experiment you would control all the variables, but when doing a study this isn't always possible. You try to control **as many as possible** or use **matched groups** (see page 3).

E.g. ideally, all the farms in Study B would have a similar **type** of land, similar **weather**, have the same **crops** growing, etc. Then you could be more sure that the one factor being **investigated** (hedgerows) is having an **effect** on the thing being **measured** (number of species). In Experiment A, **all** other variables were controlled, e.g. pH, concentrations, volumes, so you can be sure the temperature is causing the **change** in the **reaction rate**.

3) **Data collection** — think about all the **problems** with the **method** and see if **bias** has slipped in. For example, members of the public sometimes tell **little porkies**, so it's easy for studies involving **questionnaires** to be **biased**. E.g. people often underestimate how much alcohol they drink or how many cigarettes they smoke.

Jane rarely ate chocolate, honestly.

E.g. in Study B, the traps were placed on the **ground**, so species like birds weren't included. The traps weren't left overnight, so **nocturnal** animals wouldn't get counted, etc. This could have affected the results.

How to Interpret Experiment and Study Data

4) **Controls** — without controls, it's very difficult to **draw valid conclusions**. **Negative controls** are used to make sure that nothing you're doing in the experiment has an effect, **other than** what you're testing. But it's not always possible to have controls in studies (study controls usually involve a group where **nothing changes**, e.g. a group of patients aren't given a new long-term treatment to make sure any effects detected in the patients having the treatment aren't due to the fact that they've had two months to recover).

E.g. in Experiment A, the **negative control** contained everything from the experiment **except** the enzyme. This was used to show that the change in reaction rate was caused by the effect of **temperature** on the **enzyme**, and nothing else. If something else in the experiment (e.g. the water, or something in the test tube) was causing the change, you would get the **same results** in the negative control (and you'd know something was up).

5) **Repetition by other scientists** — for theories to become accepted as 'fact' other scientists need to **repeat** the work (see page 2). If **multiple studies** or **experiments** come to the same conclusion, then that conclusion is **more reliable**.

E.g. if a second group of scientists carried out the same experiment for enzyme X and got the same results, the results would be **more reliable**.

4) Analyse the Data

Sometimes it's easier to **compare data** by making a few calculations first, e.g. converting raw data into **ratios** or **percentages**.

Example Three UK hospitals have been trying out three **different methods** to **control the spread** of chest infections. A study investigated the number of people suffering from chest infections in those hospitals over a **three month period**. The table opposite shows the results. If you just look at the **number of cases** in the **last month** (March) then the method of hospital 3 appears to have worked **least well**, as they have the **highest number** of infections. But if you look at the **percentage increase** in infections you get a different picture: hospital 1 = 30%, hospital 2 = 293%, and hospital 3 = 18%. So hospital 3 has the lowest percentage increase, suggesting their method of control is **working the best**.

Number of cases per 6000 patients			
Hospital	Jan	Feb	March
1	60	65	78
2	14	24	55
3	93	96	110

Calculating percentage increase, hospital 1:

$$\frac{(78 - 60)}{60} \times 100 = \frac{18}{60} \times 100 = 30\%$$

There Are a Few Technical Terms You Need to Understand

I'm sure you probably know these all off by heart, but it's easy to get mixed up sometimes. So here's a quick recap of some words **commonly used** when assessing and analysing experiments and studies:

1) **Variable** — A variable is a **quantity** that has the **potential to change**, e.g. weight. There are two types of variable commonly referred to in experiments:
   - **Independent variable** — the thing that's **changed** in an experiment.
   - **Dependent variable** — the thing that you **measure** in an experiment.

When drawing graphs, the dependent variable should go on the y-axis (the vertical axis) and the independent on the x-axis (the horizontal axis).

2) **Accurate** — Accurate results are those that are **really close** to the **true** answer.

3) **Precise results** — These are results taken using **sensitive instruments** that measure in **small increments**, e.g. pH measured with a meter (pH 7.692) will be **more precise** than pH measured with paper (pH 8).

*It's possible for results to be precise **but not** accurate, e.g. a balance that weighs to 1/1000 th of a gram will give precise results, but if it's not **calibrated** properly the results won't be accurate.*

4) **Qualitative** — A **qualitative** test tells you **what's** present, e.g. an acid or an alkali.

5) **Quantitative** — A **quantitative** test tells you **how much** is present, e.g. an acid that's pH 2.46.

Controls — I think I prefer the remote kind...

*These pages should give you a fair idea of the points to think about when interpreting data. Just use your head and remember the three main points in the checklist — **d**escribe the **d**ata, **c**heck the **c**onclusions and make sure the **r**esults are **r**eliable.*

Answers

Section 1 — Biological Molecules

Page 5 — Water

1 Maximum of 6 marks.
In a water molecule, the shared electrons are pulled closer to the oxygen atom than the hydrogen atoms *[1 mark]*. This makes the molecule polar *[1 mark]*, which makes water a good solvent for other polar molecules *[1 mark]*. Substances can be transported more easily when dissolved in a solvent like water *[1 mark]*. Water is also cohesive due to its polar nature *[1 mark]*. This helps water to flow, which means it can transport substances *[1 mark]*.

Page 8 — Proteins

1 Maximum of 9 marks available.
Proteins are made from amino acids *[1 mark]*. The amino acids are joined together in a long (polypeptide) chain *[1 mark]*. The sequence of amino acids is the protein's primary structure *[1 mark]*. The amino acid chain/ polypeptide coils or folds in a certain way *[1 mark]*. The way it's coiled or folded is the protein's secondary structure *[1 mark]*. The coiled or folded chain is itself coiled or folded into a specific shape *[1 mark]*. This is the protein's tertiary structure *[1 mark]*. Different polypeptide chains can be joined together in the protein molecule *[1 mark]*. The way these chains are joined together is the quaternary structure of the protein *[1 mark]*.

2 Maximum of 6 marks available, from any of the 7 points below.
Collagen is a fibrous protein *[1 mark]*.
For this mark, including the word 'fibrous' is essential.
It forms supportive tissues in the body, so it needs to be strong *[1 mark]*. Collagen is made of three polypeptide chains *[1 mark]*, tightly coiled to form a triple helix *[1 mark]*. The chains are interlinked by covalent bonds *[1 mark]*, which makes it strong *[1 mark]*. Minerals can bind to the triple helix, increasing its rigidity *[1 mark]*.

Page 11 — Carbohydrates

1 Maximum of 7 marks available.
Glycosidic bonds are formed when a hydrogen atom *[1 mark]* from one monosaccharide combines with a hydroxyl/OH group *[1 mark]* from another monosaccharide. This releases a molecule of water *[1 mark]*. Glycosidic bonds are broken by hydrolysis *[1 mark]*. A molecule of water reacts with the glycosidic bond to split the monosaccharide molecules apart *[1 mark]*. The last two marks are given for a diagram showing a reversible reaction with correct reactants (e.g. two glucose molecules) *[1 mark]* and correct products (e.g. water and maltose) *[1 mark]*.

2 Maximum of 6 marks available, from any of the 8 points below.
Starch is made of two polysaccharides of alpha-glucose *[1 mark]*. Amylose is a long unbranched chain *[1 mark]* which forms a coiled shape *[1 mark]*. This coiled shape is very compact, making it good for storage *[1 mark]*. Amylopectin is a long, branched chain *[1 mark]*. Its side branches make it good for storage as the enzymes that break it down can reach the glycosidic bonds easily *[1 mark]*. Starch is insoluble in water *[1 mark]*. This means it can be stored in cells without causing water to enter by osmosis, which would cause them to swell *[1 mark]*.

Page 13 — Lipids

1 Maximum of 4 marks available.
Triglycerides are used as energy storage molecules *[1 mark]*. Their long hydrocarbon tails contain lots of chemical energy *[1 mark]*. The hydrophobic tails force them to clump together in the cytoplasm as insoluble droplets *[1 mark]*. This means they can be stored in cells without causing water to enter the cell by osmosis, which would cause them to swell *[1 mark]*.

2 Maximum of 2 marks available.
Saturated fatty acids don't have any double bonds between their carbon atoms *[1 mark]*. Unsaturated fatty acids have one or more double bonds between their carbon atoms *[1 mark]*.

3 Maximum of 3 marks available.
Two fatty acid molecules *[1 mark]* and a phosphate group *[1 mark]* attached to one glycerol molecule *[1 mark]*.
Don't get phospholipids mixed up with triglycerides — a triglyceride has three fatty acids attached to one glycerol molecule.

Page 15 — Biochemical Tests for Molecules

1 Maximum of 8 marks available
Add dilute hydrochloric acid to the solution *[1 mark]* and boil *[1 mark]*. Neutralise with sodium hydrogencarbonate *[1 mark]*. Add blue Benedict's reagent to the solution *[1 mark]* and heat without boiling *[1 mark]*. The formation of a green, yellow, orange or brick red precipitate indicates that a reducing sugar or non-reducing sugar is present *[1 mark]*. Repeat the last two stages with a fresh sample of the sugar *[1 mark]*. If this test is negative the sugar is non-reducing *[1 mark]*.
The question asks to describe a test for a non-reducing sugar. Remember, there are a couple more steps involved in the test for a non-reducing sugar than in the test for a reducing sugar (and you have to double check that you haven't got a reducing sugar by doing the reducing test too).

2 a) Maximum of 1 mark available.
Solution C *[1 mark]*
Solution C has the lowest absorbance. It therefore has the least amount of Benedict's reagent left — so it had the most reducing sugar before the Benedict's test.
  b) Maximum of 1 mark available.
The colorimeter measures the amount of Benedict's reagent left after reacting with glucose. You therefore need to use an excessive amount of Benedict's reagent to make sure there's some left behind *[1 mark]*.
  c) Maximum of 2 marks available.
The concentration of Benedict's reagent used *[1 mark]*. The length of time each solution is left for *[1 mark]*.

Section 2 — Enzymes

Page 17 — Enzyme Action

1 Maximum of 7 marks available.
In the 'lock and key' model the enzyme and the substrate have to fit together at the active site of the enzyme *[1 mark]*. This creates an enzyme-substrate complex *[1 mark]*. The active site then causes changes in the substrate *[1 mark]*. This mark could also be gained by explaining the change (e.g. bringing molecules closer together, or putting a strain on bonds). The change results in the substrate being broken down/joined together *[1 mark]*. The 'induced fit' model has the same basic mechanism as the 'lock and key' model *[1 mark]*. The difference is that the substrate is thought to cause a change in the enzyme's active site shape *[1 mark]*, which enables a better fit *[1 mark]*.

Page 19 — Factors Affecting Enzyme Activity

1 Maximum of 8 marks available, from any of the 10 points below.
If the solution is too cold, the enzyme will work very slowly *[1 mark]*. This is because, at low temperatures, the molecules have little kinetic energy, so move slowly, making collisions between enzyme and substrate molecules less likely *[1 mark]*. Also, fewer of the collisions will have enough energy to result in a reaction *[1 mark]*.
The marks above could also be obtained by giving the reverse argument — a higher temperature is best to use because the molecules will move fast enough to give a reasonable chance of collisions and those collisions will have more energy, so more will result in a reaction.
If the temperature gets too high, the reaction will stop *[1 mark]*. This is because the enzyme is denatured *[1 mark]* — the active site changes shape and will no longer fit the substrate *[1 mark]*. Denaturation is caused by increased vibration breaking bonds in the enzyme *[1 mark]*. Enzymes have an optimum pH *[1 mark]*. pH values too far from the optimum cause denaturation *[1 mark]*.
Explanation of denaturation here will get a mark only if it hasn't been explained earlier.
Denaturation by pH is caused by disruption of ionic and hydrogen bonds, which alters the enzyme's tertiary structure *[1 mark]*.

2 Maximum of 4 marks available.
As the enzyme concentration is increased, the initial rate of reaction will increase *[1 mark]* up to a point *[1 mark]*. This is because the more enzyme molecules there are in a solution, the more likely a substrate molecule is to collide with one of them and form an enzyme-substrate complex *[1 mark]*. But if the amount of substrate is limited, increasing the concentration of enzyme will have no further effect above a certain point *[1 mark]*.
You can tell by the number of marks for this question that four points are needed. So, make sure you go into enough detail to get all those marks.

Answers

Page 21 — Factors Affecting Enzyme Activity

1 a) Maximum of 3 marks available.
Competitive inhibitor molecules have a similar shape to the substrate molecules [1 mark]. They compete with the substrate molecules to bind to the active site of an enzyme [1 mark]. When an inhibitor molecule is bound to the active site it stops the substrate molecule from binding [1 mark].

b) Maximum of 2 marks available.
Non-competitive inhibitor molecules bind to enzymes away from their active site [1 mark]. This causes the active site to change shape so the substrate molecule can no longer fit [1 mark].

Section 3 — Cell Structure

Page 25 — Cells and Organelles

1 Maximum of 4 marks available.
cell wall [1 mark], plasmodesmata [1 mark], vacuole [1 mark], chloroplasts [1 mark].

2 a) i) Maximum of 1 mark available.
mitochondrion [1 mark]
ii) Maximum of 1 mark available.
Golgi apparatus [1 mark]

b) Maximum of 2 marks available.
Mitochondria are the site of aerobic respiration [1 mark].
The Golgi apparatus processes and packages new lipids and proteins / makes lysosomes [1 mark].

3 Maximum of 2 marks available.
Ciliated epithelial cells have lots of mitochondria [1 mark] because they need lots of energy [1 mark].

Page 27 — Organelles

1 a) Maximum of 2 marks available
Ribosomes [1 mark] because this is where protein synthesis occurs [1 mark].

b) Maximum of 3 mark available
The rough endoplasmic reticulum [1 mark], ribosomes [1 mark] and some vesicles [1 mark].

2 Maximum of 8 marks available.
First, the cell sample is homogenised [1 mark] to break up the plasma membranes and release the organelles into solution [1 mark]. The cell solution is then filtered [1 mark] to remove any large cell debris or tissue debris [1 mark]. Next the solution is ultracentrifuged [1 mark] to separate out the different types of organelles [1 mark]. The organelles are separated according to mass, with the heaviest being separated first [1 mark]. Centrifugation is repeated at higher and higher speeds to separate out the lighter and lighter organelles [1 mark].
Make sure you remember to explain each step otherwise you won't be able to get full marks.

Page 29 — Analysis of Cell Components

1 Maximum of 2 marks available
Magnification = length of image ÷ length of object
= 80 mm ÷ 0.5 mm [1 mark]
= × 160 [1 mark]
Always remember to convert everything to the same units first — the insect is 0.5 mm long, so the length of the image needs to be changed from 8 cm to 80 mm.

2 Maximum of 6 marks available.
TEMs use electromagnets to focus a beam of electrons, which is transmitted through the specimen [1 mark]. Denser parts of the specimen absorb more electrons and appear darker [1 mark]. SEMs scan a beam of electrons across the specimen [1 mark]. This knocks off electrons from the specimen, which are gathered in a cathode ray tube, to form an image [1 mark]. TEMs can only be used on thin specimens [1 mark]. SEMs produce lower resolution images than TEMs [1 mark].

3 a) Maximum of 3 marks available
mitochondrion [1 mark] and nucleus [1 mark]
The resolution of light microscopes is not good enough to show objects smaller than 0.2 µm [1 mark].

b) Maximum of 2 marks available
All of the organelles in the table would be visible [1 mark].
SEMs can resolve objects down to about 5 nm (0.005 µm) [1 mark].

Page 31 — Cell Membranes

1 Maximum of 2 marks available.
The membrane is described as fluid because the phospholipids are constantly moving [1 mark]. It is described as a mosaic because the proteins are scattered throughout the membrane like tiles in a mosaic [1 mark].

2 Maximum of 5 marks available.
The hydrophobic tails [1 mark] of the phospholipid bilayer prevent water-soluble molecules from diffusing through the membrane [1 mark]. Channel proteins [1 mark] and carrier proteins [1 mark] control which of these water-soluble substances can enter and leave the cell [1 mark].

Page 33 — Cell Membranes

1 a) Maximum of 4 marks available.
There is a higher concentration of beetroot pigment in tube 3 than in tube 2 [1 mark]. This is because the high temperature tube 3 was exposed to caused the membranes of the beetroot cells to break down [1 mark], increasing their permeability [1 mark] and causing more pigment to move out of the cells into the water [1 mark].
For questions like this try to work out what the data in the table is telling you, using your own knowledge, before you attempt to answer the question.
The table shows that the pieces of beetroot exposed to highest temperatures have released the most pigment. From your knowledge you know that very high temperatures damage cell membranes. If the cell membranes are damaged the cells become leaky, so they lose pigment.

b) Maximum of 4 marks available
The absorbance reading would have been high [1 mark].
At temperatures below 0 °C, channel proteins and carrier proteins denature [1 mark] and ice crystals form, which pierce the membrane [1 mark]. This makes the membrane highly permeable, so a lot of pigment would leak out into the solution [1 mark].

2 Maximum of 3 marks available.
Nicotine only binds to receptors with a complementary shape [1 mark]. Different cells have different membrane-bound receptors [1 mark]. Nicotine only affects nerve cells because only they have the correct receptor for nicotine [1 mark].

Page 35 — Exchange Across Cell Membranes

1 a) Maximum of 3 marks available.
The water potential of the sucrose solution was higher than the water potential of the potato [1 mark]. Water moves by osmosis from a solution of higher water potential to a solution of lower water potential [1 mark]. So water moved into the potato, increasing its mass [1 mark].

b) Maximum of 1 mark available.
The water potential of the potato and the water potential of the solution were the same [1 mark].

c) Maximum of 4 marks available.
– 0.4 g [1 mark]. The potato has a higher water potential than the solution [1 mark] so net movement of water is out of the potato [1 mark]. The difference in water potential between the solution and the potato is the same as with the 1% solution, so the mass difference should be about the same [1 mark].

Page 37 — Exchange Across Cell Membranes

1 Maximum of 6 marks available.
Facilitated diffusion involves channel proteins [1 mark], which transport charged molecules across the membrane [1 mark] down their concentration gradient [1 mark]. It also involves carrier proteins [1 mark], which transport large molecules across the membrane [1 mark] down their concentration gradient [1 mark].

2 Maximum of 4 marks available.
Endocytosis takes in substances from outside the cell [1 mark] via vesicles formed from the cell membrane [1 mark]. Exocytosis secretes substances from the cell [1 mark] via vesicles made from the Golgi apparatus [1 mark].
Make sure you don't get these two processes mixed up — try to remember endo for 'in' and exo for 'out'.

Answers

Section 4 — Genetics

Page 39 — DNA

1   Maximum of 1 mark available.

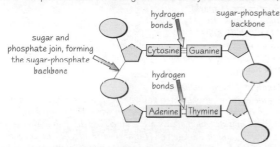

2   Maximum of 4 marks available, from any of the 5 points below.
Nucleotides are joined between the phosphate group of one nucleotide
and the sugar of the next [1 mark], forming the sugar-phosphate backbone
[1 mark]. The two polynucleotide strands join through hydrogen bonds
[1 mark] between the base pairs [1 mark]. The final mark is given for at
least one accurate diagram showing at least one of the above points
[1 mark].
As the question asks for a diagram make sure you do at least one, e.g.:

Page 41 — Genes and Protein Synthesis

1   Maximum of 1 mark available.
Tryptophan, proline, proline, glutamic acid [1 mark].

2   Maximum of 10 marks available, from any of the 12 points below.
Transcription happens inside the nucleus and translation happens in the
cytoplasm [1 mark]. The hydrogen bonds between the two DNA strands
of a gene break [1 mark], and the DNA molecule uncoils at that point
[1 mark]. One of the strands (antisense strand) is used as a template to
make an mRNA (messenger RNA) copy [1 mark] using specific base
pairing [1 mark]. The mRNA moves out of the nucleus and attaches to a
ribosome in the cytoplasm [1 mark]. tRNA molecules carry amino acids
to the ribosome [1 mark]. tRNA molecules with complementary bases to
the triplets on the mRNA attach themselves to the molecule using specific
base pairing [1 mark]. The amino acids attached to the tRNA molecules
are joined together by peptide bonds [1 mark], forming a polypeptide
chain [1 mark], and the tRNA molecules move away [1 mark].
This process continues until there's a stop signal on the mRNA [1 mark].

Page 43 — Genes and Development

1   Maximum of 4 marks available.
The DNA sequence codes for the sequences of amino acids in proteins
[1 mark]. Enzymes are proteins, so DNA codes for all enzymes [1 mark].
Enzymes control metabolic pathways [1 mark]. Metabolic pathways help
to determine nature and development [1 mark].

Page 45 — Genetic Diversity

1   Maximum of 3 marks available.
An event that causes a big reduction in a population, e.g. many members
of a population die [1 mark]. A small number of members survive and
reproduce [1 mark]. Because there are fewer members, there are fewer
alleles in the new population, so the genetic diversity is reduced [1 mark].

2   Maximum of 3 marks available.
Selective breeding involves humans selecting which organisms to breed
until they produce one with the desired characteristics [1 mark].
Only organisms with similar traits and therefore similar alleles are bred
together [1 mark]. So, the number of alleles in the population is reduced,
resulting in reduced genetic diversity [1 mark].

Page 47 — Mutations and Inheritance

1 a) Maximum of 2 marks available.
genotype — Yy [1 mark], phenotype — yellow [1 mark].

b) Maximum of 3 marks available.

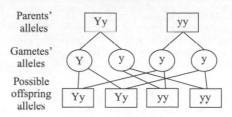

c) Maximum of 1 mark available.
1:1 [1 mark]

Page 49 — Inheritance of Genetic Disorders

1 a) Maximum of 2 marks available.
Emma is homozygous for the CF allele [1 mark]. Martha/James is a carrier
[1 mark].

b) Maximum of 3 marks available. 2 marks for the working, 1 for correct
answer.
E.g.

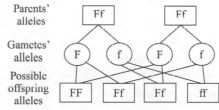

1 in 4/25% [1 mark]

c) Maximum of 8 marks available.
Cystic fibrosis leads to the production of abnormally thick and sticky
mucus [1 mark]. The thick mucus can block the tubes connecting the
pancreas to the small intestine [1 mark], preventing digestive enzymes
from reaching the small intestine [1 mark]. The mucus can also cause
cysts/growths to form in the pancreas [1 mark], which inhibits the
production of digestive enzymes [1 mark]. These both reduce the
sufferer's ability to digest food and so fewer nutrients can be absorbed
[1 mark]. The mucus lining the small intestine is very thick [1 mark],
which inhibits the absorption of nutrients [1 mark].

Page 51 — Genetic Screening and Gene Therapy

1 a) Maximum of 2 marks available.
To see if they're a carrier [1 mark]. If they are, this will affect the chance
of any children they have suffering from the disorder [1 mark].

b) i) Maximum of 1 mark available.
Screening embryos produced by IVF for genetic disorders before
they're implanted into the uterus [1 mark].

ii) Maximum of 1 mark available, from any of the 2 points below.
It reduces the chance of having a baby with a genetic disorder as
only 'healthy' embryos will be implanted [1 mark]. Because it's
performed before implantation, it avoids any issues about abortion
raised by prenatal testing [1 mark].

iii) Maximum of 2 marks available.
It can be used to find out about other characteristics, leading to
concerns about designer babies [1 mark]. Decisions could be made
based on incorrect information (false positives and false negatives)
[1 mark].

c) Maximum of 2 marks available, 1 mark for method and 1 mark for stating
that the change occurs in muscle cells.
A normal, dominant allele could be added [1 mark] to muscle cells
[1 mark].

Section 5 — Cell Division, Differentiation and Organisation

Page 53 — The Cell Cycle and DNA Replication

1 a) Maximum of 1 mark available.

 [1 mark]

b) *Maximum of 2 marks available. 1 mark for each new correct molecule with correct labels.*

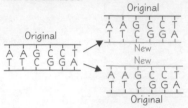

Page 56 — Cell Division — Mitosis

1 a) *Maximum of 6 marks available.*
A = Metaphase [1 mark], because the chromosomes are lined up at the middle of the cell [1 mark].
B = Telophase [1 mark], because there are now two nuclei and the cytoplasm is dividing to form two new cells [1 mark].
C = Anaphase [1 mark], because the centromeres have divided and the chromatids are moving to opposite ends of the cell [1 mark].
If you've learned the diagrams of what happens at each stage of mitosis, this should be a breeze. That's why it'd be a total disaster if you lost three marks for forgetting to give reasons for your answers. Always read the question properly and do exactly what it tells you to do.

b) *Maximum of 3 marks available:*
X = Chromatid [1 mark].
Y = Centromere [1 mark].
Z = Spindle fibre [1 mark].

2 *Maximum of 8 marks available.*
Cut a root tip from a growing root [1 mark]. Place it on a watch glass and add a few drops of hydrochloric acid to the root tip [1 mark], followed by an appropriate stain (e.g. toluidine blue, acetic orcein, Schiff's reagent, Feulgen's reagent) [1 mark]. Warm the watch glass [1 mark]. Place the root tip on a microscope slide and use a mounted needle to break it open and spread the cells out [1 mark]. Add a few more drops of stain and place a cover slip over the root tip [1 mark]. Gently squash the cover slip down [1 mark]. Warm the slide to intensify the stain [1 mark].

Page 59 — Cell Division — Meiosis

1 *Maximum of 3 marks available.*
Sperm have flagella/tails, which allow them to swim/move towards the egg cell [1 mark]. They contain lots of mitochondria to provide the energy needed for swimming/movement [1 mark]. The acrosome in the sperm head contains digestive enzymes that break down the egg cell's zona pellucida, enabling the sperm to penetrate the egg [1 mark].

2 *Maximum of 2 marks available, from any of the 3 points below.*
Normal body cells have two copies of each chromosome [1 mark]. Gametes have to have half the number of chromosomes so that when fertilisation takes place, the resulting embryo will have the correct diploid number [1 mark]. If the gametes had a diploid number, the resulting offspring would have twice the number of chromosomes that it should have [1 mark].

3 *Maximum of 6 marks available, from any of the 7 points below.*
The DNA unravels and replicates [1 mark]. The DNA condenses to form double-armed chromosomes [1 mark]. The chromosomes arrange themselves into homologous pairs [1 mark]. The pairs separate [1 mark]. The pairs of sister chromatids then separate [1 mark]. Four haploid, genetically different cells are produced [1 mark]. The final mark is given for at least one accurate diagram showing at least one of the above points [1 mark].

As the question asks for a diagram make sure you do at least one, e.g.:

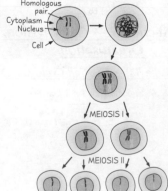

4 a) *Maximum of 4 marks available.*
During meiosis I, homologous pairs of chromosomes come together [1 mark]. The chromatids twist around each other and bits swap over [1 mark]. The chromatids now contain different combinations of alleles [1 mark]. This means each of the four daughter cells will contain chromatids with different combinations of alleles [1 mark].

b) *Maximum of 2 marks available.*
Independent segregation means the chromosome pairs can split up in any way [1 mark]. So, the daughter cells produced can contain any combination of maternal and paternal chromosomes with different alleles [1 mark].

Page 61 — Fertilisation

1 a) *Maximum of 4 marks available.*
A = Pollen tube [1 mark].
B = Embryo sac [1 mark].
C = Tube nucleus [1 mark].
D = Micropyle [1 mark].

b) *Maximum of 2 marks available.*
The enzymes digest surrounding cells [1 mark], providing a path to the ovary [1 mark].

2 *Maximum of 9 marks available.*
During the acrosome reaction, digestive enzymes are released from the acrosome of the sperm [1 mark]. These enzymes digest the zona pellucida [1 mark], which allows a sperm to pass through and fuse with the cell membrane of the egg cell [1 mark]. This triggers the cortical reaction [1 mark] where the contents of the cortical granules are released from the egg cell [1 mark]. The chemicals from the cortical granules make the zona pellucida thick and impenetrable to other sperm [1 mark], so that only one sperm can fertilise the egg cell [1 mark]. The sperm nucleus enters the egg cell [1 mark] and fuses with the egg cell nucleus — this is fertilisation [1 mark].
This question asks you to start by describing the acrosome reaction, so you won't get any marks for describing anything before this, e.g. the sperm swimming towards the egg cell in the oviduct.

Page 63 — Stem Cells and Differentiation

1 *Maximum of 4 marks available.*
Stem cells divide to make new, specialised cells [1 mark]. In animal embryos stem cells differentiate into cells needed to form a fetus [1 mark]. In adult animals, adult stem cells are used to replace damaged cells [1 mark], e.g. stem cells in the bone marrow differentiate into erythrocytes/red blood cells/neutrophils/white blood cells [1 mark].

2 *Maximum of 6 marks available, from any of the 8 points below.*
All stem cells contain the same genes but not all of them are expressed/active [1 mark]. Under the right conditions, some genes are activated and others are inactivated [1 mark]. mRNA is only transcribed from the active genes [1 mark]. mRNA from the active genes is translated into proteins [1 mark]. These proteins modify the cell by changing the cell structure [1 mark] and controlling the cell's processes [1 mark]. The changes cause the cell to become specialised [1 mark], and they're hard to reverse [1 mark].

Page 65 — Stem Cells in Medicine

1 a) *Maximum of 1 mark available, from any of the 2 points below.*
Stem cells could be used to save lives [1 mark]. Stem cells could be used to improve a person's quality of life [1 mark]. Accept a description of stem cells being used to cure a specific disease [1 mark].

b) i) *Maximum of 3 marks available, from any of the 4 points below.*
Embryos are created in a laboratory using in vitro fertilisation [1 mark]. Egg cells are fertilised by sperm outside the womb [1 mark]. Once the embryos are approximately 4 to 5 days old, stem cells are removed from them [1 mark]. The rest of the embryo is destroyed [1 mark].

ii) *Maximum of 2 marks available.*
Some people believe that fertilised embryos have a right to life from the moment of fertilisation [1 mark]. Some people believe it is wrong to destroy (viable) embryos [1 mark].

Answers

Page 67 — Cell Organisation

1   Maximum of 4 marks available.
    The cell contains many microvilli/folds *[1 mark]* which increase the surface area for absorption *[1 mark]*. The cells form a layer just one cell thick *[1 mark]*, forming a short pathway for the nutrients to cross *[1 mark]*.

2   Maximum of 2 marks available.
    It's best described as an organ *[1 mark]* as it is made of many tissues working together to perform a particular function *[1 mark]*.

Section 6 — Diet, Food Production and Digestion

Page 69 — Diet and Energy

1 a) Maximum 2 marks available
      0.2 mg/cm³ *[2 marks]*.
      Incorrect answer but correct working *[1 mark]*.
      E.g.

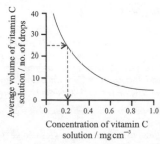

      Always show your working — you could get marks for it even if you get the final answer wrong.

  b) Maximum 3 marks available, from any of the 5 points below.
      Volume of DCPIP *[1 mark]*. Concentration of DCPIP *[1 mark]*. Time taken to shake the vitamin C and DCPIP solution *[1 mark]*. Temperature *[1 mark]*. Time between each drop of solution being added *[1 mark]*.

2 a) Maximum 3 marks available
      Energy input – energy output = energy budget,
      2000 – 1200 – (2 x 513) – (2 x 328) = –882 *[1 mark]*.
      The woman's energy output is greater than her energy input *[1 mark]*, so she will lose weight *[1 mark]*.

  b) The woman may become (severely) underweight *[1 mark]*.

Page 71 — Balanced Diet

1   Maximum of 6 marks available. 1 mark for each correct box.

NUTRIENTS	FUNCTIONS
Carbohydrates	Provide energy.
Fats (lipids)	Act as an energy store, provide insulation, make up cell membranes, physically protect organs.
Proteins	Needed for growth, the repair of tissues and to make enzymes.
Vitamins	Different vitamins have different functions, e.g. vitamin D is needed for calcium absorption, vitamin K is needed for blood clotting.
Mineral salts	Different mineral salts have different functions, e.g. iron is needed to make haemoglobin in the blood, calcium is needed for bone formation.
Fibre	Aids movement of food through gut.
Water	It is used in chemical reactions. We need a constant supply to replace water lost through urinating, breathing and sweating.

2   Maximum of 5 marks available.
    Not having enough food can cause malnutrition *[1 mark]* because you get too little of every nutrient *[1 mark]*. Having an unbalanced diet can lead to malnutrition *[1 mark]* because you get too much or too little of some nutrients *[1 mark]*. Malnutrition can also be caused by not being able to absorb the nutrients from digestion into your bloodstream properly *[1 mark]*.

Page 73 — Food Production

1 a) Maximum of 3 marks available.
      Plants with large grains were bred together *[1 mark]*. Then the offspring with the largest grains were bred together *[1 mark]*. This was repeated over generations *[1 mark]* to make the grains of modern wheat plants larger.

  b) Maximum of 3 marks available.
      Hessian fly infestation would reduce the crop yield by damaging the crops *[1 mark]*. A short-term solution would be to use a pesticide to kill the flies *[1 mark]*. A long-term solution would be to use selective breeding to create a wheat strain resistant to the fly *[1 mark]*.
      A lot of exam questions will be like this one — you have to use your knowledge and apply it to a real-life situation to show you've understood the principles. Make sure you refer to the situation the question has described.

Page 75 — Microorganisms and Food

1 a) Maximum of 2 marks available.
      It's heat-treated to kill any microorganisms *[1 mark]*, which extends its shelf life *[1 mark]*.

  b) Maximum of 3 marks available, from any of the 4 points below.
      The fungus can be grown faster than cows *[1 mark]*. The environment for growth of fungus can be more easily controlled, so they can potentially be grown anywhere *[1 mark]* and at any time of year *[1 mark]*. It's easier to create the right conditions for fungus to grow *[1 mark]*.

Page 77 — The Digestive System

1 a) Maximum of 6 marks available.
      The pancreas releases pancreatic juice into the small intestine/duodenum *[1 mark]*. Pancreatic juice contains amylase, trypsin, chymotrypsin and lipase *[1 mark]*. Amylase breaks down starch into maltose *[1 mark]*. Chymotrypsin and trypsin break down proteins into peptides *[1 mark]*. Lipase breaks down lipids into fatty acids and glycerol *[1 mark]*. Pancreatic juice also neutralises acid from the stomach *[1 mark]*.

  b) Maximum of 1 mark available.
      E.g. salivary glands *[1 mark]*

2   Maximum of 4 marks available, 1 mark for each correct label.
    w — duodenum
    x — stomach
    y — ileum
    z — colon

Page 79 — Enzymes and Carbohydrate Digestion

1   Maximum of 10 marks available.
    Some glucose moves across the intestinal epithelial cells and into the blood by diffusion *[1 mark]*. This is because initially there is a higher concentration of glucose in the lumen of the small intestine than in the blood *[1 mark]*. The rest of the glucose moves into the blood by co-transport with sodium ions *[1 mark]*. There is a higher concentration of sodium ions in the lumen of the small intestine than inside the intestinal epithelial cell *[1 mark]*. This is because sodium ions are actively transported out of the cell into the blood by a sodium-potassium pump *[1 mark]*. So sodium ions diffuse from the small intestine lumen into the cell *[1 mark]* through sodium-glucose co-transporter proteins *[1 mark]*. These co-transporter proteins carry glucose into the cell along with the sodium *[1 mark]*. The concentration of glucose inside the cell increases *[1 mark]* and glucose diffuses out of the cell, into the blood *[1 mark]*.
    To answer this question it may help if you remember the diagram and then work through it step by step in your head, writing down each point. Also you need to remember the two methods of glucose transport (diffusion and co-transport) to get full marks.

2   Maximum of 4 marks available
    Lactose intolerance is caused by a lack of the enzyme lactase *[1 mark]*. Sufferers don't have enough lactase to break down lactose, a sugar found in milk/milk products *[1 mark]*. Undigested lactose is fermented by bacteria *[1 mark]*. This can lead to intestinal complaints such as stomach cramps, flatulence and diarrhoea *[1 mark]*.

Answers

Section 7 — Disease

Page 81 — Health and Disease

1 a) Maximum of 1 mark available.
An organism that can cause damage to the organism it infects (the host) *[1 mark]*.
b) Maximum of 2 marks available.
E.g. some fungi *[1 mark]*, all viruses *[1 mark]*.

Page 83 — Cholera

1 Maximum of 3 marks available.
A pathogen may rupture the host cells *[1 mark]*. It may break down and use nutrients in the host cells, so that the host cells starve *[1 mark]*. Or a pathogen may replicate inside host cells and burst them as it leaves *[1 mark]*.

2 Maximum of 5 marks available.
The bacterium produces a toxin *[1 mark]* that causes chloride channels in the lining of the small intestine to open *[1 mark]*. Chloride ions diffuse into the small intestine *[1 mark]*. The small intestine now has a lower water potential than the blood *[1 mark]*, so water moves from the blood into the small intestine, causing diarrhoea and dehydration *[1 mark]*.

3 Maximum of 2 marks available.
Against: e.g. children can't make their own decision to be part of the trial *[1 mark]*. For: e.g. scientists believe treatment for a disease that mainly affects children must be tested on children *[1 mark]*.

Page 85 — Antibiotic Action and Resistance

1 a) Maximum of 3 marks available.
A mutation occurs in the DNA of a bacterium *[1 mark]*. If the mutation occurs in a gene it may alter the protein that gene codes for *[1 mark]*, which may make the bacteria resistant to an antibiotic *[1 mark]*.
b) Maximum of 3 marks available.
Resistance to antibiotics is spread between two bacteria by horizontal gene transmission *[1 mark]*. The two bacteria join together by a process called conjugation *[1 mark]* and a copy of a plasmid carrying a gene for antibiotic resistance is transferred from one cell to the other *[1 mark]*.
c) Maximum of 4 marks available.
Penicillin inhibits an enzyme involved in making the bacterial cell wall *[1 mark]*. This prevents cell wall formation in growing bacteria and weakens the wall *[1 mark]*. Water moves into the cell by osmosis *[1 mark]*. The weakened cell wall can't withstand the increased pressure so bursts (lyses), killing the bacterium *[1 mark]*.

Page 87 — Antibiotic Resistance

1 Maximum of 6 marks available.
As the use of the pesticide increased, the number of aphids fell *[1 mark]* as they were being killed by the pesticide *[1 mark]*. Random mutations may have occurred in the aphid DNA, resulting in pesticide resistance *[1 mark]*. Any aphids resistant to the pesticide were more likely to survive and pass on their alleles *[1 mark]*. Over time, the number of aphids increased *[1 mark]* as those carrying pesticide-resistant alleles became more common *[1 mark]*.

2 Maximum of 3 marks available.
Some bats in the population will carry a mutation for a longer tongue *[1 mark]*. The bats with longer tongues will be able to feed from the flowers and so will be more likely to survive, reproduce and pass on their alleles *[1 mark]*. Over time, this feature will become common in the population *[1 mark]*.

Page 89 — Evaluating Resistance Data

1 Maximum of 2 marks available.
Argument for: E.g. if a person has an infection that can be treated they should not be denied treatment. / If the person is not treated they may become very ill *[1 mark]*.
Argument against: E.g. a person suffering with dementia may forget to take their medication and so increase the risk of antibiotic resistant bacteria developing *[1 mark]*.

2 a) Maximum of 2 marks available.
E.g. the chest infection is mild *[1 mark]*. Prescribing antibiotics for non-life-threatening illnesses contributes to increased antibiotic resistance *[1 mark]*.
b) Maximum of 2 marks available.
E.g. not prescribing antibiotics could reduce her son's quality of life *[1 mark]*. He may take longer to get better without antibiotics, so she may have to take longer off work *[1 mark]*.

3 Maximum of 3 marks available, from any of the 4 points below.
E.g. getting information from one area (East Anglia) would not show national trends *[1 mark]*. It's a relatively small study (only 300 patients), which decreases its reliability *[1 mark]*. Patients don't always tell the truth on questionnaires, which reduces its reliability *[1 mark]*. Patients may not return the questionnaire *[1 mark]*.

Section 8 — The Immune System

Page 93 — The Immune Response

1 Maximum of 6 marks available
A phagocyte recognises the antigens on a pathogen *[1 mark]*. The phagocyte engulfs the pathogen *[1 mark]*. The pathogen is now contained in a phagocytic vacuole *[1 mark]*. A lysosome fuses with the phagocytic vacuole *[1 mark]* and lysosomal enzymes break down the pathogen *[1 mark]*. The phagocyte presents the antigens to T cells *[1 mark]*.

2 Maximum of 3 marks available.
Antibodies agglutinate pathogens, so that phagocytes can get rid of a lot of the pathogens at once *[1 mark]*. Antibodies neutralise toxins produced by pathogens *[1 mark]*. Antibodies bind to pathogens to prevent them from binding to and infecting human cells *[1 mark]*.
There are three marks available for this question so you need to think of three different functions.

3 Maximum of 10 marks available.
When Emily caught chickenpox the first time *[1 mark]* her B- and T-cells produced memory cells *[1 mark]*, giving her immunological memory against the virus antigens *[1 mark]*. When exposed a second time *[1 mark]* the memory B-cells divided into plasma cells *[1 mark]* to produce the right antibody to the virus *[1 mark]*. The memory T-cells divided into the correct type of T-cell *[1 mark]* to kill the virus *[1 mark]*. The secondary response was quicker and stronger *[1 mark]* and so got rid of the pathogen before she showed any symptoms *[1 mark]*.
This question is asking about the secondary response and the immune system memory, so no detail is needed about how the primary response got rid of the infection.

Page 95 — Immunity and Vaccinations

1 Maximum of 4 marks available.
The flu virus is able to change its surface antigens/shows antigenic variation *[1 mark]*. This means that when you're infected for a second time with a different strain, the memory cells produced from the first infection will not recognise the new/different antigens *[1 mark]*. The immune system has to carry out a primary response against these new antigens *[1 mark]*. This takes time and means you become ill *[1 mark]*.

Page 97 — Antibodies in Medicine

1 Maximum of 3 marks available.
Antibodies are proteins that have specific tertiary structures *[1 mark]*. This gives them specific binding sites *[1 mark]* that only molecules with a complementary shape will fit into *[1 mark]*.

2 Maximum of 4 marks available.
Monoclonal antibodies are made against antigens specific to cancer cells *[1 mark]*. An anti-cancer drug is attached to the antibodies *[1 mark]*. The antibodies bind to tumour markers on cancer cells because their binding sites have a complementary shape *[1 mark]*. This delivers the anti-cancer drug to the cells *[1 mark]*.

Page 99 — Interpreting Vaccine and Antibody Data

1 a) Maximum of 2 marks available.
Because people were immunised against Hib *[1 mark]* and also had the protection of herd immunity *[1 mark]*.

Answers

b) Maximum of 1 mark available.
The number of cases of Hib increased [1 mark].

Section 9 — Exchange and Transport Systems

Page 101 — Size and Surface Area

1 Maximum of 4 marks available.
Large mammals have a high demand for oxygen and glucose, which cannot be met by diffusion alone [1 mark]. This is because they have a small surface area : volume ratio [1 mark], there is a large number of cells deep inside the body [1 mark] and they are very active so they need a constant, rapid supply of glucose and oxygen [1 mark].

Page 103 — Gas Exchange

1 Maximum of 3 marks available.
Gaseous exchange surfaces have a large surface area [1 mark]. They are thin, which provides a short diffusion pathway [1 mark]. There is a steep concentration gradient, which is constantly maintained [1 mark].

2 Maximum of 2 marks available.
Sunken stomata and hairs help to trap any water vapour that does evaporate [1 mark], reducing the concentration gradient from leaf to air, which reduces water loss [1 mark].

Page 105 — Transport Systems

1 Maximum of 1 mark available.
The blood flows through the body in vessels [1 mark].

2 Maximum of 2 marks available.
Insects have an open circulatory system [1 mark]. The blood is pumped into the body cavity where it circulates freely [1 mark].

3 a) It is a closed system [1 mark].
  b) It is a single circulatory system, not a double one [1 mark].

Section 10 — The Respiratory System

Page 107 — Lung Function

1 Maximum of 6 marks available.
There's a thin exchange surface [1 mark] as the alveolar epithelium is only one cell thick [1 mark]. This means there's a short diffusion pathway, which increases the rate of diffusion [1 mark]. The number of alveoli provide a large surface area for gas exchange, which also increases the rate of diffusion [1 mark]. There's a steep concentration gradient between the alveoli and the capillaries surrounding them, which increases the rate of diffusion [1 mark]. This is maintained by the flow of blood and ventilation [1 mark].

2 Maximum of 10 marks available.
Goblet cells [1 mark] secrete mucus, which traps bacteria and dust so they don't reach the alveoli [1 mark]. Other cells have cilia [1 mark] which move the mucus towards the throat to be removed [1 mark]. Elastic fibres [1 mark] stretch when we breathe in, then recoil to help us breathe out [1 mark]. Smooth muscle tissue [1 mark] relaxes to make air passages wider and make breathing easier when exercising [1 mark]. Cartilage [1 mark] provides support and keeps the air passages open [1 mark].

Page 109 — Breathing

1 Maximum of 5 marks available.
The intercostal muscles contract [1 mark], making the ribs move up and out [1 mark], and the diaphragm contracts/flattens [1 mark]. This increases the volume of the thorax [1 mark], so the pressure inside decreases, drawing air into the lungs [1 mark].

Page 111 — How Lung Disease Affects Function

1 Maximum of 7 marks available.
Emphysema is where foreign particles (e.g. from cigarette smoke) become trapped in the alveoli [1 mark]. This causes inflammation, which encourages phagocytes to the area [1 mark]. The phagocytes produce an enzyme that breaks down elastin in the walls of the alveoli [1 mark]. The alveolar walls are destroyed and the elasticity of the lungs is lost [1 mark]. This reduces the surface area of the alveoli [1 mark], so the rate of gas exchange decreases [1 mark]. Sufferers will breathe quicker to compensate for the reduction in the rate of gaseous exchange [1 mark].

Page 113 — Interpreting Lung Disease Data

1 a) Maximum of 3 marks available.
   The daily death rate increased rapidly after 4th December [1 mark], peaking around the 7th then decreasing afterwards [1 mark]. Both pollutants followed the same pattern [1 mark].
   You could also get the marks by saying it the other way round — the pollutants rose and peaked around the 7th then decreased, with the death rates following the same pattern.
  b) Maximum of 1 mark available.
   There is a link/correlation between the increase in sulfur dioxide and smoke concentration and the increase in death rate [1 mark].
   Don't go saying that the increase in sulfur dioxide and smoke <u>caused</u> the increase in death rate — there could have been another reason for the trend, e.g. there could have been other pollutants responsible for the deaths.

Section 11 — The Circulatory System

Page 115 — The Heart

1 Maximum of 10 marks.
After entering the right atrium from the vena cava, blood flows through the right atrioventricular valve [1 mark] and into the right ventricle [1 mark]. It then flows past a semi-lunar valve [1 mark] and out of the heart via the pulmonary artery to the lungs [1 mark]. Blood re-enters the heart at the left atrium [1 mark] via the pulmonary vein [1 mark]. It then moves through the left atrioventricular valve [1 mark] and into the left ventricle [1 mark]. It then passes through another semi-lunar valve [1 mark], into the aorta and out of the heart [1 mark].

2 Maximum of 6 marks available.
The valves only open one way [1 mark]. Whether they open or close depends on the relative pressure of the heart chambers [1 mark]. If the pressure is greater behind a valve (i.e. there's lots of blood in the chamber behind it) [1 mark], it's forced open, to let the blood travel in the right direction [1 mark]. Once the blood's gone through the valve, the pressure is greater in front of the valve [1 mark], which forces it shut, preventing blood from flowing back into the chamber [1 mark].
Here you need to explain how valves function in relation to blood flow, rather than just in relation to relative pressures.

3 a) Maximum of 1 mark available.
   The sino-atrial node acts as a pacemaker/initiates heartbeats [1 mark].
  b) Maximum of 1 mark available.
   The Purkyne fibres conduct electrical impulses through the ventricle walls [1 mark].

Page 117 — The Cardiac Cycle

1 Maximum of 8 marks available.
When the heart muscles are relaxed, blood enters the atria from the veins [1 mark]. The semi-lunar valves prevent blood coming back into the ventricles from the arteries [1 mark]. Next, the atria contract [1 mark]. This pushes blood from the atria into the ventricles [1 mark] through the atrioventricular valves [1 mark]. Then the ventricles contract [1 mark]. This pushes blood out from the ventricles into the arteries [1 mark]. The atrioventricular valves shut to prevent blood going back into the atria [1 mark].

2 a) Maximum of 1 mark available.
   0.2 - 0.4 seconds [1 mark].
   The AV valves are shut when the pressure is higher in the ventricles than in the atria.
  b) Maximum of 1 mark available.
   0.3 - 0.4 seconds [1 mark].
   When the ventricles relax the volume of the chamber increases and the pressure falls. The pressure in the left ventricle was 16.5 kPa at 0.3 seconds and it decreased to 7.0 kPa at 0.4 seconds, so it must have started to relax somewhere between these two times.

Answers

Page 119 — ECGs and Heart Rate

1   Maximum of 2 marks available.
The ventricle is not contracting properly *[1 mark]*. This could be because of muscle damage / because the AVN is not conducting impulses to the ventricles properly *[1 mark]*.

2   Maximum of 2 marks available, from any of the 3 points below.
Invertebrates are considered to be simpler than vertebrates *[1 mark]*.
They're more distantly related to humans than other vertebrates *[1 mark]*.
They have less sophisticated nervous systems than vertebrates, so may feel less/no pain *[1 mark]*.

Page 121 — Blood Vessels

1   Maximum of 6 marks available.
They have thick, muscular walls *[1 mark]* to cope with the high pressure produced by the heartbeat *[1 mark]*. They have elastic tissue in the walls *[1 mark]* so they can expand to cope with the high pressure produced by the heartbeat *[1 mark]*. The inner lining (endothelium) is folded *[1 mark]* so that the artery can expand when the heartbeat causes a surge of blood *[1 mark]*.

2   Maximum of 4 marks available.
Their walls are only one cell thick *[1 mark]*, which shortens the diffusion pathway *[1 mark]*. Capillaries form networks called capillary beds *[1 mark]*, which provide a large surface area for exchange *[1 mark]*.
The question asks how the <u>structure</u> of capillaries relates to their function. If you'd written about how their location in the body related to their function (i.e. they're found very near cells, so there's a short diffusion pathway) you wouldn't get a mark.

3   Maximum of 4 marks available.
At the start of the capillary bed, the pressure in the capillaries is greater than the pressure in the tissue fluid outside the capillaries *[1 mark]*. This means fluid from the blood is forced out of the capillaries *[1 mark]*. Fluid loss causes the water potential in the blood capillaries to become lower than that of the tissue fluid *[1 mark]*. So fluid moves back into the capillaries at the vein end of the capillary bed by osmosis *[1 mark]*.

Page 123 — Haemoglobin

1   Maximum of 3 marks available.
The fetus relies on oxygen from the mother's blood *[1 mark]*. By the time it reaches the fetus, the mother's blood is not fully oxygenated *[1 mark]*. Fetal haemoglobin must therefore have a higher affinity for oxygen than its mother's blood in order to take up enough oxygen *[1 mark]*.

2   Maximum of 2 marks available.

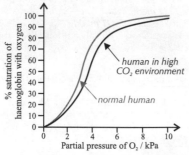

The curve should be the same basic shape as a normal human dissociation curve, but should be shifted down *[1 mark]*. High concentrations of carbon dioxide increase the rate of oxygen unloading, so the saturation of blood with oxygen is lower for a given pO_2 *[1 mark]*.

3   Maximum of 6 marks available.
Most of the CO_2 from respiring cells is converted to carbonic acid by the enzyme carbonic anhydrase *[1 mark]*. The carbonic acid splits up to form hydrogen ions and hydrogencarbonate ions *[1 mark]*. The hydrogencarbonate ions are transported in the blood plasma *[1 mark]*. Oxyhaemoglobin unloads some of its oxygen and binds to the hydrogen ions, forming haemoglobinic acid *[1 mark]*. At the lungs, the haemoglobin releases its hydrogen ions *[1 mark]*, which recombine with the hydrogencarbonate ions to be breathed out as carbon dioxide *[1 mark]*.

Page 125 — Cardiovascular Disease

1   Maximum of 3 marks available.
Their blood clotting mechanism will be impaired/Their blood won't clot as fast as a non-sufferer's blood *[1 mark]* because less prothrombin is available to be converted to thrombin *[1 mark]*. This means that less fibrinogen will be converted to fibrin *[1 mark]*, which reduces blood clot formation.

2   Maximum of 5 marks available.
An atheroma plaque may break through the endothelium (inner lining) of the artery, leaving a rough surface *[1 mark]*. This damage could cause a blood clot (thrombus) to form over the area *[1 mark]*. If the blood clot completely blocks a coronary artery, it will restrict blood flow to part of the heart muscle *[1 mark]*, cutting off its oxygen supply *[1 mark]* and causing a heart attack *[1 mark]*.

3   Maximum of 3 marks available.
Atheroma plaques damage and weaken arteries *[1 mark]* and can lead to increased blood pressure *[1 mark]*. When blood at high pressure travels through a weakened artery, the pressure can push the inner layers of the artery through the outer layer to form an aneurysm *[1 mark]*.
This question is not asking about the consequences of an aneurysm, so no extra marks will be given if you write about it.

Page 127 — Risk Factors for Cardiovascular Disease

1   Maximum of 11 marks available.
Carbon monoxide in cigarette smoke combines with haemoglobin *[1 mark]*, which reduces the amount of oxygen transported in the blood *[1 mark]*. This reduces the amount of oxygen available to body tissues *[1 mark]*. If the heart muscle/brain doesn't receive enough oxygen it can cause a heart attack/stroke *[1 mark]*. Nicotine in cigarette smoke makes platelets sticky *[1 mark]*. This increases the chance of blood clots forming *[1 mark]*, which increases the risk of CVD *[1 mark]*. Smoking also decreases the amount of antioxidants in the blood *[1 mark]*. Fewer antioxidants means cell damage in the artery walls is more likely *[1 mark]*, and this can lead to atheroma formation *[1 mark]*, which increases the risk of CVD *[1 mark]*.

2   Maximum of 6 marks available.
HDLs are mainly protein *[1 mark]*. They transport cholesterol from body tissues to the liver *[1 mark]*, to reduce the total blood cholesterol level when it's too high *[1 mark]*. LDLs are mainly lipid *[1 mark]*. They transport cholesterol from the liver to the blood *[1 mark]*, to increase the total blood cholesterol level when it's too low *[1 mark]*.
Make sure you don't get HDLs mixed up with LDLs. <u>High</u> density lipoproteins reduce cholesterol when the level is too <u>high</u>. <u>Low</u> density lipoproteins increase cholesterol when the level is too <u>low</u>.

Page 129 — Prevention and Treatment of CVD

1 a)   Maximum of 4 marks available.
The GP could prescribe antihypertensive drugs to reduce his patient's blood pressure *[1 mark]*. Lower blood pressure would reduce the risk of damage occurring to the artery walls *[1 mark]*, reducing the risk of atheroma/clot formation and CHD *[1 mark]*. One disadvantage of taking antihypertensives is they can cause side effects, e.g. palpitations/ abnormal heart rhythms/fainting/headaches/drowsiness/allergic reactions/depression *[1 mark]*.

     b)   Maximum of 2 marks available.
He could go on a diet *[1 mark]*. He could exercise more frequently *[1 mark]*.
We know that this patient is obese, so the GP would advise lifestyle changes to reduce his weight.

Section 12 — Variation, Evolution and Classification

Page 131 — Variation

1 a)   Maximum of 3 marks available.
For species A, as the temperature increases the development time decreases *[1 mark]*. For species B the development time also decreases as the temperature increases *[1 mark]*. The development time of species B is less affected by temperature than species A *[1 mark]*.

Answers

b) Maximum of 4 marks available.
The variation between the species is mainly due to their different genes *[1 mark]*. Variation within a species is caused by both genetic and environmental factors *[1 mark]*. Individuals have different forms of the same genes (alleles), which causes genetic differences *[1 mark]* Individuals may have the same genes, but environmental factors affect how they're expressed in their appearance (phenotype) *[1 mark]*.

Page 133 — Variation

1 a) Maximum of 1 mark available.
To provide a control against which the women who smoked could be compared *[1 mark]*.
b) Maximum of 4 marks available.
Environmental factors (smoking) affect birth mass *[1 mark]*. Women who smoked showed a mean reduction in the birth mass of their babies of 377 g *[1 mark]*. Genetic factors also affect birth mass of babies born to women who smoke *[1 mark]*. The reduction in birth mass was as much as 1285 g among women who smoked and had certain genotypes *[1 mark]*.
c) Maximum of 2 marks available, from any of the 5 points below.
E.g. pre-pregnancy mass of the mothers *[1 mark]*, age *[1 mark]*, fitness levels *[1 mark]*, ethnic origin *[1 mark]*, if they'd had a previous pregnancy *[1 mark]*.
Think of all the variables that need to be considered to isolate smoking as the only environmental factor that is influencing the variation.

Page 135 — Investigating Variation

1 a) Maximum of 1 mark available.
It would be too time-consuming/impossible to look at the whole population *[1 mark]*.
b) Maximum of 1 mark available.
To study the effect of environment on mass, height and waist circumference *[1 mark]*.
Identical twins have the same alleles/genes, so any difference between them must be due to the environment.
c) Maximum of 4 marks available.
Genetic factors affect BMI and waist circumference *[1 mark]*. The identical twins (who have identical genes/alleles) had more similar BMIs and waist circumferences than the non-identical twins (who have different genes/alleles) *[1 mark]*.
Environmental factors affect BMI and waist circumference *[1 mark]*. The identical twins have identical genes/alleles, but did not have identical BMIs and waist circumferences, so the environment must affect them *[1 mark]*.

Page 137 — Adaptation and Evolution

1 Maximum of 8 marks available.
Behavioural — It can roll into a ball when alarmed *[1 mark]*, which increases it chance of escaping attack *[1 mark]*.
Physiological — It can hibernate over winter *[1 mark]*, which means it's more likely to survive the winter months when food is scarce *[1 mark]*.
For anatomical you can get any two from the list below, to a maximum of 4 marks — 1 mark for each adaptation and 1 mark for explaining why each adaptation increases survival.
Anatomical — Brown colour *[1 mark]*, camouflages it, so it's harder for predators to spot *[1 mark]*. Spiky fur *[1 mark]*, protects it from predators *[1 mark]*. Long fur *[1 mark]*, provides warmth *[1 mark]*. Small ears *[1 mark]*, help to reduce heat loss *[1 mark]*. Claws *[1 mark]*, are used to catch prey *[1 mark]*.

2 Maximum of 4 marks available.
Individuals within a population show variation in their phenotypes (characteristics) *[1 mark]*. Predation, disease and competition create a struggle for survival *[1 mark]*. Individuals with better adaptations are more likely to survive, reproduce and pass on their advantageous adaptations to their offspring *[1 mark]*. Over time, the number of individuals with the adaptations increases *[1 mark]*.

Page 139 — Evolution

1 a) Maximum of 4 marks available.
Genetic mutations would have resulted in some moths being resistant to DDT *[1 mark]*. When the population was exposed to DDT, only those individuals who were resistant would survive to reproduce *[1 mark]*. The alleles which code for resistance would be passed on to the next generation *[1 mark]*. Over time, the number of individuals with DDT resistance would increase and it would become more common within the population *[1 mark]*.
b) Maximum of 2 marks available, from any of the 3 points below.
Moth infestations would be harder to control *[1 mark]*. Broader pesticides might be used, which could kill beneficial insects *[1 mark]*. New pesticides might need to be developed if the moth develops resistance to all pesticides in use *[1 mark]*.

Page 141 — Principles of Classification

1 a) Maximum of 1 mark available.
The act of arranging organisms into groups based on their similarities and differences *[1 mark]*.
b) Maximum of 1 mark available.
The study of classification *[1 mark]*.
c) Maximum of 1 mark available.
The study of the evolutionary history of groups of organisms *[1 mark]*.

2 Maximum of 3 marks available. 1 mark for every 3 correct answers.

	Kingdom	Phylum	Class	Order	Family	Genus	Species
Humans	Animalia	Chordata	Mammalia	Primates	Hominidae	Homo	sapiens
Bonobos	Animalia	Chordata	Mammalia	Primates	Hominidae	Pan	paniscus

3 Maximum of 3 marks available.
E.g. you can't study the reproductive behaviour of extinct species *[1 mark]*. Some species reproduce asexually *[1 mark]*. There are practical and ethical issues involved in studying some reproductive behaviour *[1 mark]*.

Page 143 — Classification Systems and Dichotomous Keys

1 Maximum of 2 marks available.
A — Trichodesmium *[1 mark]*
B — Anabaena *[1 mark]*

2 a) Maximum of 3 marks available, from any of the 4 points below.
The enzyme RNA polymerase differs between the Bacteria and Archaea *[1 mark]*. Archaea, but not Bacteria, have similar histones to Eukarya *[1 mark]*. The bonds of lipids in the cell membranes of Bacteria and Archaea are different *[1 mark]*. The development and composition of flagellae are different between Bacteria and Archaea *[1 mark]*.
b) Maximum of 2 marks available, from any of the 4 points below.
Prokaryotic cells *[1 mark]*. Single-celled *[1 mark]*. No nucleus *[1 mark]*. Less than 5 μm *[1 mark]*.

Page 145 — Classifying Species

1 Maximum of 5 marks available.
DNA from two species is collected, separated into single strands and mixed together *[1 mark]*. Where the DNA is similar, hydrogen bonds will form between the base pairs *[1 mark]*. The more similar the DNA the more hydrogen bonds will form *[1 mark]*. The strands are heated and the temperature at which they separate is recorded *[1 mark]*. A higher temperature will be needed to separate DNA strands from more similar species because more hydrogen bonds will have formed *[1 mark]*.
You need to use the right terminology here to get the marks, e.g. hydrogen bonds (not just bonds) and base pairs (not just bases).

2 a) Maximum of 1 mark available.
Mouse and rat *[1 mark]*.
b) Maximum of 1 mark available.
Chicken *[1 mark]*.

Section 13 — Biodiversity and Conservation

Page 147 — Studying Biodiversity

1 a) Maximum of 2 marks available.
Species richness is the number of different species in an area *[1 mark]*. Species evenness is a measure of the relative abundance of each species in an area *[1 mark]*.

Answers

b) Maximum of 1 mark available.
An index of diversity/Simpson's index of diversity [**1 mark**].

Page 149 — Factors Affecting Biodiversity

1   Maximum of 3 marks available.
Different scientists use different techniques to make their estimates
[**1 mark**]. Relatively little is known about some groups of organisms
(e.g. bacteria and insects) — there could be many more than we think
[**1 mark**]. Some areas where biodiversity is particularly high are largely
unexplored, e.g. rainforests, so estimates might be too low [**1 mark**].

2   Maximum of 5 marks available.
Woodland clearance reduces biodiversity in the area because the number
of trees is reduced [**1 mark**]. Hedgerow removal decreases biodiversity in
the area because hedge species are removed [**1 mark**]. Monoculture
fields support fewer species so biodiversity is reduced [**1 mark**]. Pesticide
use directly kills pest species [**1 mark**]. Herbicide use kills unwanted
plant species [**1 mark**].
The question asks for practices that <u>directly</u> reduce biodiversity, so you
wouldn't get marks for saying that loss of some species affects the numbers
of other species that feed on them or are their prey.

Page 151 — Interpreting Biodiversity Data

1 a) Maximum of 2 marks available.
Both woodland and farmland populations have declined since 1970
[**1 mark**]. Farmland species have declined more than woodland species
[**1 mark**].
b) Maximum of 3 marks available, from any of the 5 points below.
(or other suitable answers).
Loss of habitat [**1 mark**].
Fewer hedgerows/larger fields [**1 mark**].
Deforestation/clearance of land [**1 mark**].
Farming intensification/changes to farming practice [**1 mark**].
Pesticides causing disruption in the food chain [**1 mark**].
c) Maximum of 8 marks available, from any of the 14 points below.
Maximum of 4 marks available for benefits. Maximum of 4 marks
available for risks.
Agriculture benefits — more food can be produced/there is an increased
yield [**1 mark**]. Food is cheaper to produce, so prices are lower [**1 mark**].
Local areas become more developed by attracting businesses [**1 mark**].
Agriculture risks — natural beauty is lost [**1 mark**]. Diversity is reduced
because of monoculture [**1 mark**]. Diversity is reduced because of land
and hedgerow clearance [**1 mark**]. Diversity is reduced from use of
pesticides/herbicides [**1 mark**].
Deforestation benefits — wood is provided as well as access to other
resources [**1 mark**]. More land is available for homes/agriculture [**1 mark**].
Local areas become more developed by attracting businesses [**1 mark**].
Deforestation risks — less carbon dioxide is stored, which contributes to
climate change [**1 mark**]. Potential medical/scientific discoveries are lost
[**1 mark**]. Natural beauty is lost [**1 mark**]. Diversity is reduced/extinctions
may occur [**1 mark**].
When the question asks you to discuss an issue, you need to make sure you
talk about both sides — the benefits and the risks.

Page 153 — Importance of Biodiversity

1   Maximum of 4 marks available.
If one species is removed from a food chain it can affect all organisms
further up the food chain [**1 mark**]. The loss of certain organisms (such as
decomposers) can affect the nutrient cycle in the area, which will affect
the growth of plants and reduce the amount of food available to animals
[**1 mark**]. The loss of one habitat (such as a hedgerow) would affect other
habitats as they may become isolated, so availability of food/nesting sites
would be reduced [**1 mark**]. The destruction of species and habitats that
store CO_2, like trees and peat bogs, contributes to climate change, which
is reducing biodiversity [**1 mark**].

2   Maximum of 5 marks available.
Biodiversity provides a range of species that are used as food for people
and livestock [**1 mark**]. Many crops are pollinated by a diverse range of
insects [**1 mark**], and other insects are used as natural predators of pest
species [**1 mark**]. Cross-breeding with wild plants can create plants with
new characteristics [**1 mark**]. A greater variety of crops grown means that
food sources are less susceptible to disease or pests [**1 mark**].

Page 155 — Conservation and Biodiversity

1 a) Maximum of 5 marks available.
In situ methods could include protecting the turtles from hunters
[**1 mark**] and protecting their nesting sites [**1 mark**]. A national park/
protected area could also be established to restrict human usage of the
area [**1 mark**]. Ex situ methods could include relocating the turtles or their
eggs to a safer environment [**1 mark**] or to start a captive breeding
programme [**1 mark**].
b) Maximum of 4 marks available.
It's only possible to conserve a limited number of individuals with ex situ
methods [**1 mark**]. They can be very expensive [**1 mark**].
It may be difficult to sustain the environment for the turtle [**1 mark**].
They don't protect the habitat of the turtle [**1 mark**].
c) Maximum of 1 mark available.
International cooperation is important because it means that hunting
endangered species is illegal in all countries — making hunting illegal in
one country would have little use if it was legal in a neighbouring country
[**1 mark**].

Page 157 — Conservation and Biodiversity

1   Maximum of 4 marks available.
It might be difficult to recreate the exact conditions of the lizard's
environment in captivity, so they may have problems breeding [**1 mark**].
Some people think it's cruel to keep animals in captivity, even if it's done
to prevent them becoming extinct [**1 mark**]. The reintroduced lizards
could bring new diseases to the habitat, harming any organisms that are
already there [**1 mark**]. Because they were born in captivity, any
reintroduced lizards may not exhibit all their natural behaviours in the wild
(e.g. they may have problems finding food or communicating with other
members of their species) [**1 mark**].

Section 14 — Transport in Plants

Page 159 — Xylem and Phloem

1   Maximum of 6 marks available.
The distribution can be explained in words or by diagrams —
whichever you find easier. In either case, these are the key points:
In the stem, the xylem and phloem are towards the outside, with the
phloem outside the xylem [**1 mark**]. This provides a scaffold for the stem
to reduce bending [**1 mark**]. In the root, the xylem and phloem are in the
centre, with the phloem outside the xylem [**1 mark**]. This provides
support for the root as it pushes through the soil [**1 mark**]. In the leaves,
the veins run throughout the leaves, with the xylem above the phloem
[**1 mark**]. This provides support for the thin leaves [**1 mark**].

2   Maximum of 8 marks available.
Xylem vessel cells have no end walls [**1 mark**], making an uninterrupted
tube that allows water to pass through easily [**1 mark**]. The vessel cells are
dead and contain no cytoplasm [**1 mark**], which allows water to pass
through [**1 mark**]. Their walls are thickened with a woody substance
called lignin [**1 mark**], which helps support the xylem vessels and stop
them collapsing inwards [**1 mark**]. The vessel walls have small holes
called pits where there's no lignin [**1 mark**]. This allows substances to
pass in and out of the vessels [**1 mark**].

Page 161 — Water Transport

1   Maximum of 4 marks available.
Loss of water from the leaves, due to transpiration, pulls more water into
the leaves from the xylem [**1 mark**]. There are cohesive forces between
water molecules [**1 mark**]. These cause water to be pulled up the xylem
[**1 mark**]. Removing leaves means no transpiration occurs, so no water
is pulled up the xylem [**1 mark**].
It's pretty obvious (because there are 4 marks to get) that it's not enough
just to say removing the leaves stops transpiration. You also need to explain
why transpiration is so important in moving water through the xylem. It's
always worth checking how many marks a question is worth — this gives you a
clue about how much detail you need to include.

2 a) Maximum of 2 marks available.
In the symplast pathway, water moves through the cytoplasm [**1 mark**].
The cytoplasm of neighbouring cells is connected through plasmodesmata
(small gaps in the cell walls) [**1 mark**].

Answers

b) Maximum of 4 marks available.
In the apoplast pathway, water passes through the cell walls [1 mark].
The walls are very absorbent so water simply diffuses through them
[1 mark]. In the endodermis layer of the root the Casparian strip inhibits
the apoplast pathway [1 mark]. From here the water must take the
symplast pathway [1 mark].

Page 163 — Transpiration

1 *Maximum of 8 marks available. 1 mark for each factor, and 1 mark for*
explaining each factor's effect.
Transpiration is increased when it's light [1 mark], as the stomata open
only when it's light [1 mark]. A high temperature increases transpiration
[1 mark] because water evaporates from the cells inside the leaf faster/
water diffuses out of the leaf faster [1 mark]. A low humidity level
increases the rate of transpiration [1 mark] because it increases the water
potential gradient between the leaf and the surrounding air [1 mark].
Transpiration is increased if it's windy [1 mark] because wind blows away
water molecules from around the stomata, increasing the water potential
gradient [1 mark].

2 *Maximum of 4 marks available.*
'Hairs' on the epidermis [1 mark] trap moist air round the stomata,
which reduces the water potential gradient and so reduces transpiration
[1 mark]. Thick cuticle [1 mark] is waterproof so stops water evaporating
[1 mark].

Page 165 — Translocation

1 *Maximum of 4 marks available.*
Sugars are actively loaded into the sieve tubes at the source end [1 mark].
This lowers the water potential of the sieve tubes at the source end
[1 mark], which causes water to enter by osmosis [1 mark]. This causes a
pressure increase inside the sieve tubes at the source end [1 mark].
I think this is a pretty nasty question. If you got it all right first time you're
probably a genius. If you didn't, you're probably not totally clear yet about the
pressure idea. If there's a high concentration of sugar in a cell, this draws
water in by osmosis, and so increases the pressure inside the cell.

Section 15 — Resources from Plants

Page 167 — Plant Cell Structure and Plant Stems

1 a) *Maximum of 2 marks available.*
x — sclerenchyma fibres [1 mark], y — xylem vessels [1 mark]
  b) *Maximum of 9 marks available.*
The function of xylem vessels is to transport water and mineral ions, and
provide support [1 mark]. The function of sclerenchyma fibres is to
provide support [1 mark]. The cells of xylem and sclerenchyma are longer
than they are wide [1 mark], they have no cytoplasm [1 mark] and no end
walls [1 mark]. They are made of dead cells, joined end to end [1 mark].
The cell walls of both are thickened with lignin, which helps to support
the plant [1 mark]. The cell walls of sclerenchyma have more cellulose
than xylem vessels [1 mark]. Water and mineral ions pass into and out of
xylem cells through pits in the walls where there's no lignin [1 mark].

Page 169 — Starch, Cellulose and Fibres

1 a) *Maximum of 4 marks available.*
The cell wall contains cellulose microfibrils in a net-like arrangement
[1 mark]. The strength of the microfibrils [1 mark] and their arrangement
in the cell wall [1 mark] makes plant fibres strong [1 mark].
  b) *Maximum of 4 marks available.*
Secondary thickening is the production of another cell wall between the
normal cell wall and the cell membrane [1 mark]. The secondary cell wall
is thicker [1 mark] and usually has more lignin than the normal cell wall
[1 mark]. This also gives plant fibres lots of strength [1 mark].

2 a) *Maximum of 8 marks available.*
The students could have attached each of the four fibres to a clamp stand
at one end [1 mark] and hung weights from the other end [1 mark].
Weights could then have been added one at a time to each of the fibres,
until they all broke [1 mark]. They would then have recorded the mass
taken to break each fibre [1 mark]. They could have done repeat
experiments for each of the fibres [1 mark]. They should also have
ensured that all the fibres tested were of the same length [1 mark]. They
should have kept all other variables constant, like the temperature and
humidity of the environment [1 mark], and they should have taken safety
precautions, such as wearing protective goggles/making sure the area
where the weights fall was clear [1 mark].

  b) *Maximum of 2 marks available.*
Fibre B would be most suitable [1 mark] because it has the highest tensile
strength/can hold the most weight without breaking [1 mark].

Page 171 — Sustainability and Plant Minerals

1 *Maximum of 6 marks available.*
Take a number of plant seedlings, and plant them in separate pots
[1 mark]. They should all be the same age and height [1 mark]. Make up
nutrient broths that contain different concentrations of nitrate ions
[1 mark]. Split the plants into equal sized groups and give each group
one of the broths you have made up [1 mark]. After several weeks,
measure the height of the plants, to see how the growth has been affected
[1 mark]. During the investigation, you need to keep all other variables
constant, such as the amount of light and water the plants receive
[1 mark].

Page 173 — Drug Testing and Drugs from Plants

1 *Maximum of 5 marks available.*
William Withering made a chance observation — a patient suffering from
dropsy made a good recovery after being treated with a traditional
remedy containing foxgloves [1 mark]. Digitalis is found in foxgloves
[1 mark]. He tested different versions of the remedy containing different
concentrations of digitalis [1 mark]. He found that too much digitalis
poisoned his patients, while too little had no effect [1 mark]. Through this
trial and error method, he discovered the right amount to give to his
patients [1 mark].

2 a) *Maximum of 10 marks available.*
Take an extract from the plant you want to test by drying and grinding the
plant [1 mark], then soaking it in ethanol [1 mark]. Filter off the liquid bit
[1 mark]. Evenly spread a sample of bacteria on an agar/nutrient plate
[1 mark]. Dip a disc of absorbent paper in the plant extract [1 mark].
Soak a disc in ethanol to act as a control [1 mark]. Place the discs on the
plate, widely spaced apart [1 mark]. Incubate the plate to allow the
bacteria to grow [1 mark]. If the plant has antibacterial properties there'll
be an inhibition zone/clear patch on the lawn of bacteria [1 mark]. There
should be no inhibition zone around the control disc [1 mark].
  b) *Maximum of 7 marks available.*
The first phase involves testing the drug on a small group of healthy
individuals [1 mark]. It's done to identify any side effects, the safe dosage
and how the body reacts to the drug [1 mark]. The second phase involves
testing the drug on a large group of patients [1 mark]. It's done to see
how well the drug works [1 mark]. The third phase involves testing the
drug on a very large group of patients [1 mark]. It's done to compare the
effectiveness of the drug with existing drugs [1 mark]. Patients are
randomly split into two groups, one which receives the new drug, and one
which receives an existing treatment [1 mark].

Index

Index

Index